Rita Cantor·

Probability and Mathematical Statisti·
WILLIAMS • Diffusions, Mar'
Foundations
ZACKS • Theory of Statistical

Applied Probability and Statistics
ANDERSON, AUQUIER, HAUCK, OAKES,
WEISBERG • Statistical Methods for Comparative Studies
ARTHANARI and DODGE • Mathematical Programming in Statistics
BAILEY • The Elements of Stochastic Processes with Applications to the
Natural Sciences
BAILEY • Mathematics, Statistics and Systems for Health
BARNETT • Interpreting Multivariate Data
BARNETT and LEWIS • Outliers in Statistical Data
BARTHOLOMEW • Stochastic Models for Social Processes, *Third
Edition*
BARTHOLOMEW and FORBES • Statistical Techniques for Manpower
Planning
BECK and ARNOLD • Parameter Estimation in Engineering and Science
BELSLEY, KUH, and WELSCH • Regression Diagnostics: Identifying
Influential Data and Sources of Collinearity
BENNETT and FRANKLIN • Statistical Analysis in Chemistry and the
Chemical Industry
BHAT • Elements of Applied Stochastic Processes
BLOOMFIELD • Fourier Analysis of Time Series: An Introduction
BOX • R. A. Fisher, The Life of a Scientist
BOX and DRAPER • Evolutionary Operation: A Statistical Method for
Process Improvement
BOX, HUNTER, and HUNTER • Statistics for Experimenters: An
Introduction to Design, Data Analysis, and Model Building
BROWN and HOLLANDER • Statistics: A Biomedical Introduction
BROWNLEE • Statistical Theory and Methodology in Science and
Engineering, *Second Edition*
BURY • Statistical Models in Applied Science
CHAMBERS • Computational Methods for Data Analysis
CHATTERJEE and PRICE • Regression Analysis by Example
CHERNOFF and MOSES • Elementary Decision Theory
CHOW • Analysis and Control of Dynamic Economic Systems
CHOW • Econometric Analysis by Control Methods
CLELLAND, BROWN, and deCANI • Basic Statistics with Business
Applications, *Second Edition*
COCHRAN • Sampling Techniques, *Third Edition*
COCHRAN and COX • Experimental Designs, *Second Edition*
CONOVER • Practical Nonparametric Statistics, *Second Edition*
CORNELL • Experiments with Mixtures: Designs, Models and The Analysis
of Mixture Data
COX • Planning of Experiments
DANIEL • Biostatistics: A Foundation for Analysis in the Health Sciences,
Second Edition
DANIEL • Applications of Statistics to Industrial Experimentation
DANIEL and WOOD • Fitting Equations to Data: Computer Analysis of
Multifactor Data, *Second Edition*
DAVID • Order Statistics, *Second Edition*
DEMING • Sample Design in Business Research
DODGE and ROMIG • Sampling Inspection Tables, *Second Edition*
DRAPER and SMITH • Applied Regression Analysis, *Second Edition*
DUNN • Basic Statistics: A Primer for the Biomedical Sciences, *Second
Edition*
DUNN and CLARK • Applied Statistics: Analysis of Variance and
Regression
ELANDT-JOHNSON • Probability Models and Statistical Methods in
Genetics
ELANDT-JOHNSON and JOHNSON • Survival Models and Data
Analysis

continued on back

Interpreting
Multivariate Data

Proceedings of the Conference Entitled
"Looking at Multivariate Data" held
in the University of Sheffield, U.K.
from 24–27 March 1980

Interpreting Multivariate Data

Edited by
VIC BARNETT
Professor of Statistics
University of Sheffield

JOHN WILEY & SONS
Chichester · New York · Brisbane · Toronto

British Library Cataloguing in Publication Data:

Looking at Multivariate Data *(1980: University
    of Sheffield)*
    Interpreting multivariate data.—(Wiley
    series in probability and mathematical
    statistics: applied probability and statistics
    section)
    1. Multivariate analysis—Congress
    I. Title   II. Barnett, Vic
    519.5'3   QA278

ISBN 0 471 28039 9

Typeset by Preface Ltd, Salisbury, Wilts.
Printed at the Pitman Press, Bath.

Preface

Over the last 20 years there has been a substantial redirection of emphasis in the processing of multivariate statistical data. The attitude is, in certain respects, one of 'going back to the drawing board'.

The developments of multivariate analysis from the 1930s until recent years have concentrated on statistical methods, and associated distribution theory, tied to well-defined models and based predominantly (and inevitably from the need for tractability) on the multivariate normal distribution to describe error structure. This has produced a vital heritage of specific methodology for such problems as multivariate analysis of variance, principal component analysis, classification, and so on—and some useful, complex and elegant results on sampling distributions for multivariate normal statistics. But it is inevitable, with the present breadth of areas of application of statistical enquiry and the complexity of resulting data, that we must be free to range beyond the traditional methods and distributional assumptions and to ask more fundamental questions such as:

What do the data really show us in the midst of their apparent chaos?
How can we cogently summarize and represent these data?
How can we reduce dimensionality and scale to a level where the message of the data is, at least informally, clear, and sensible models can be developed?

The emphasis is on *exploring the data*, rather than on subjecting them to models and procedures based often more on convenience than relevance. This implies 'going back' in the sense of reestablishing the somewhat discredited ideas of *descriptive statistics* and developing powerful modern equivalents specifically suited to the complexities of multivariate data, with facilities for incisive tabulation, summary and display. It extends the ideas of descriptive statistics, however, in one crucial respect—namely in seeking structure and form either for informal interpretation or as a basis for more sophisticated modelling and analysis. The ubiquity and power of modern computers opens up unprecedented prospects here: graphical display devices and interactive facilities bring the 'drawing board' from the draughtsman's office to the desk of the statistician. On almost immediate demand he can throw the data around: look at them this way or that, transform them, mould them, examine residuals and so on.

Two of our contributors in this volume have elsewhere expressed the ideas rather neatly. David Andrews (1978) remarks:

Exploratory data analysis is the manipulation, summarisation, and display

v

of data to make them more comprehensible to human minds, thus uncovering underlying structure in the data and detecting important departures from that structure.

Comprehensibility is the key. John Tukey limits intuitional comprehension to $2\frac{2}{3}$ dimensions—quite convenient really for the almost flat-earth format of graph paper or video screen! It was, of course, his evangelical call (Tukey, 1962):

Is it not time to seek out novelty in data analysis?

that has been largely responsible for its revitalization over the last two decades, and his own contributions have blazed a trail.

As a modest contribution to this process of revitalization, the Department of Probability and Statistics at Sheffield University has recently organized two major conferences. The first, in 1977, was entitled *Graphical Methods in Statistics* and several of the invited papers were published in 1978 in the journals *Applied Statistics* and *Biometrika*. The second conference in March 1980 under the title

LOOKING AT MULTIVARIATE DATA

broadened the emphasis from graphical display to all aspects of exploratory data analysis for multivariate data. This volume presents the Proceedings of the conference in the form of expanded versions of the invited papers.

The conference attracted an international audience of some 300 participants and there was lively discussion and comment on the material which was presented. In preparing this material for publication authors have taken account of the comments of discussants and the papers have been arranged in groups which broadly reflect different aspects of multivariate data analysis, as described below. The invited speakers and their affiliations were as follows.

Professor D. F. Andrews	University of Toronto, Canada.
Dr. P. J. Diggle	University of Newcastle upon Tyne, U.K.
Mr. B. S. Everitt	University of London, U.K.
Professor S. E. Fienberg	Carnegie-Mellon University, Pittsburgh, U.S.
Professor K. R. Gabriel	University of Rochester, U.S.
Professor, H. Goldstein	University of London, U.K.
Mr. J. C. Gower	Rothamsted Experimental Station, U.K.
Dr. I. Graham	University of London, U.K.
Dr. P. J. Green	University of Durham, U.K.
Dr. M. J. Greenacre	University of South Africa, Johannesburg, S.A.
Professor D. G. Kendall	University of Cambridge, U.K.
Professor R. Sibson	University of Bath, U.K.
Dr. B. W. Silverman	University of Bath, U.K.

Professor A. F. M. Smith   University of Nottingham, U.K.
Professor, J. W. Tukey   Princeton University and Bell Laboratories,
                             U.S.
Dr. P. A. Tukey   Bell Laboratories, U.S.

In the chapters of the book the name of the invited speaker who presented the material appears first, followed by the names of collaborators involved in the work. Apart from individual talks of a research, applications or review nature, a special feature of the conference was the presentation of two sets of three linked lectures—one by P. J. Green, R. Sibson and B. W. Silverman on *Methods of Investigating Bivariate Data*, the other by J. W. Tukey and P. A. Tukey on *Graphical Display of Data Sets in 3 or more Dimensions*. These are presented in *Part I* and in *Part III*, respectively, of these published proceedings.

Part I (Chapters 1 to 5) takes up some novel aspects of the presentation and processing of (predominantly) *bivariate data*. The representation of extreme values as points on the convex hull of a data set, with successive 'peeling' of the convex hulls to yield partially ranked bivariate data, leads to methods for dealing with outliers and robust estimation procedures (P. J. Green). R. Sibson considers problems of spatial interpolation and spatial smoothing of data; existing methods of interpolation are reviewed and a new method, natural neighbour interpolation, is introduced, assessed and illustrated. Estimation of an underlying density function for moderately large data sets aids exploration, modelling and presentation; methods, with particular reference to contouring, are discussed by B. W. Silverman. The special problems of displaying spatial point data are considered (P. J. Diggle) together with the fitting of relevant models and the testing of 'complete spatial randomness'. D. G. Kendall reports some pioneering ideas and methods for the representation of 'shape' in (principally) two dimensions.

Part II is concerned primarily with the manipulation, reduction and processing of data matrices and multiway tables with more emphasis on the nature of the numerical and statistical methods than on direct display of the data. We start (in Chapter 6 by J. C. Gower and P. G. N. Digby) with a review of methods applicable to one-way multivariate data, and to two-way and three-way tables including asymmetric data matrices and hierarchical representations. Subsequent chapters take up specific aspects in more detail. Correspondence analysis (M. J. Greenacre) is explained and illustrated and shown to encompass a variety of individual techniques including unfolding, multidimensional scaling, simultaneous linear regression and canonical correlation analysis. K. R. Gabriel shows how his idea of the biplot can be extended, beyond its original role of providing a two-dimensional summary of higher-dimensional data to aid study of clustering effects, to provide a means of examining the relevance of a variety of underlying models. Graphical methods which reflect simultaneously both the adequacy of form, and the precision, of models for multi-variate data (D. F. Andrews, Chapter 9) are presented for use with multiway tables including the possibility of hierarchical effects.

Part III (Chapters 10 to 12) contains the material of the linked lectures by J. W. Tukey and P. A. Tukey. It presents a catalogue of new ideas in the difficult area of meaningful and interpretable display of data of three- (or higher-) dimensional form. Various issues are considered: the degree of resolution or merging of data points; scaling; curvature reduction; pre-chosen sequences of display viewpoints; data-dependent view-selection; agglomeration of data clouds; summarization; smoothing; choice of symbols, characters and backgrounds, to facilitate interpretation of displays; and many other relevant matters.

Part IV presents a variety of practical applications of data-analytic methods. In Chapter 13 (B. S. Everitt and J. C. Gower) we see the method of non-linear mapping and the generalized Procrustes method applied to the construction of maps of the positions of neural responses to electrical stimuli in vision substitution therapy for blind people. Multivariate directed graphs and corresponding stochastic log-linear models are examined by S. E. Fienberg, M. M. Meyer and S. S. Wasserman and applied to the analysis of a network of U.S. companies and organizations linked by factors reflecting finance, service support and information need. Child development (specifically physical growth) is the topic for study in the application by H. Goldstein of methods for fitting growth curves to longitudinal data where, as so often happens, there are missing data and observations may not have been taken at precisely the target ages. I. Graham illustrates the use of spectral analysis for archaeological data with particular reference to the spatial relationships between objects found in graves in an iron age cemetery. In the closing chapter (A. F. M. Smith and D. J. Spiegelhalter, Chapter 17), Bayesian methods are applied to the study of multivariate data-structure and illustrated briefly for examples in the fields of medicine and of education.

The material presented in the book reviews existing methods in multivariate exploratory data analysis, illustrates their application in many fields and contains a wealth of new ideas and methods. In publishing this material we hope to provide the practical statistician and statistical research worker with a cross-section of useful techniques and much food for thought in a vital rapidly developing area of statistical enquiry. An important special feature of the book is the large proportion of diagrammatic material which is designed to firmly motivate, illustrate and reinforce the basic principles and methods. No set of conference proceedings can claim to constitute a comprehensive research and methods text for its subject area. By its very nature, coverage must be selective, since it represents individual viewpoints and specific personal research contributions. To date there seem to be no books which attempt a homogeneous coverage of the whole field of multivariate data analysis;

perhaps the mould needs first to set a little firmer. In the meantime, it is hoped that these proceedings will provide useful material in some important areas. Access to wider study of the subject area is provided through the extensive sets of references given at the end of each chapter. For convenience these are also presented in augmented form (with further relevant publications from professional journals) as a single *composite reference list* at the end of the book. There is also a (short but comprehensive) *bibliography* which lists books, with various emphases and levels of treatment, containing work on different specific aspects of exploratory data analysis; and a fairly detailed *index* covering the topics contained in the text.

It is a pleasure to express my thanks to all who have contributed to the production of this book. Foremost, my thanks must go to the conference speakers and their co-workers for their confidence in allowing me to act as Editor, for their forebearance in conforming to editorial strictures and, especially, for their prompt and careful preparation of their material. But no conference proceedings would be possible if there were no conference in the first place, and I must express my sincere thanks to members of the Department of Probability and Statistics at Sheffield University who joined together in the planning and organization of the conference. I am particularly grateful to Clive Anderson and Nick Fieller who (with administrative assistance from Audrey Barnett) bore the brunt of the local organization and (aided by Les Underhill) took major parts in reporting the discussion and comment sessions. I have tried accurately to present these conference proceedings but, as Editor, the responsibility for any errors or omissions in the presentation rests with me.

Sheffield, November 1980   VIC BARNETT

Contents

PART 1   METHODS FOR INVESTIGATING BIVARIATE DATA

1. Peeling Bivariate Data   3
P. J. Green

    1.1   Convex hulls   3
    1.2   Peeling generally   8
    1.3   Distribution theory   11
    1.4   Correlation   14
    1.5   Location   15
    1.6   Conclusion   17
    References   18

2. A Brief Description of Natural Neighbour Interpolation   21
R. Sibson

    2.1   The interpolation problem   21
        2.1.1   Comments   22
    2.2   Existing methods   23
        2.2.1   Finite element methods   23
        2.2.2   Kriging   24
        2.2.3   Stiff lamina methods   24
    2.3   Natural neighbour interpolation   25
    2.4   Computing the natural neighbour interpolant in two
        dimensions   31
    2.5   Looking at functions over the plane   33
    2.6   Example   35
    References   35

3. Density Estimation for Univariate and Bivariate Data   37
B. W. Silverman

    3.1   General considerations   37
        3.1.1   Exploratory analysis   38
        3.1.2   Confirmatory analysis   39
        3.1.3   Presentation   40
        3.1.4   Choice of smoothing parameter   41

3.2   Computing kernel estimates   43
      3.2.1   The univariate case   43
      3.2.2   The bivariate case   46
References   51

4. Some Graphical Methods in the Analysis of Spatial Point Patterns   55
P. J. Diggle

4.1   Preliminary testing   57
4.2   Model fitting   60
4.3   Probability surfaces   63
4.4   Sparsely sampled patterns   68
References   72

5. The Statistics of Shape   75
D. G. Kendall

References   80

PART II   REDUCTION, DISPLAY, AND ANALYSIS OF DATA
             MATRICES AND MULTIWAY TABLES

6. Expressing Complex Relationships in Two Dimensions   83
J. C. Gower and P. G. N. Digby

6.1   Data as a two-way table or matrix   84
      6.1.1   Picture displays   84
      6.1.2   Units plotted in two dimensions   85
      6.1.3   Principal components analysis   85
      6.1.4   Putting extra information on a point plot   87
      6.1.5   Displaying goodness-of-fit   88
      6.1.6   Representation of variates   90
      6.1.7   The biplot   90
      6.1.8   Correspondence analysis   93
6.2   Data as a symmetric matrix   95
      6.2.1   Metric scaling   95
      6.2.2   Multidimensional unfolding   99
      6.2.3   Non-metric scaling   100
      6.2.4   Considering a symmetric matrix as a two-way table   101
6.3   Asymmetric square tables   103
6.4   Graphical methods with 3-way data   106
      6.4.1   Individual scaling   107
      6.4.2   Generalized Procrustes analysis   108

6.5 Hierarchical representation 111
   6.5.1 Classification order 111
   6.5.2 Shading 111
   6.5.3 Reordering of the data matrix 115
   6.5.4 Ordination 116
References 117

7. Practical Correspondence Analysis

M. J. Greenacre

7.1 Introduction 119
7.2 Geometric definition of correspondence analysis: a simple example 122
7.3 Applications of correspondence analysis 131
   7.3.1 Display of frequency data in ecology 132
   7.3.2 Display of ratings in psychology 136
   7.3.3 Displays of heterogeneous data in meteorology 140
7.4 Concluding remarks 144
References 145

8. Biplot Display of Multivariate Matrices for Inspection of Data and Diagnosis

119

K. R. Gabriel

8.1 The biplot 147
8.2 Inspection of data 150
8.3 Diagnosis of models 160
8.4 Some general comments 171
References 173

9. Statistical Applications of Real-Time Interactive Graphics

175

D. F. Andrews

9.1 Introduction 175
9.2 Displays of measures of fit 176
   9.2.1 Models with up two terms 176
   9.2.2 Models with more than two terms 177
   9.2.3 An example of measure display 178
9.3 Displays of fits 180
   9.3.1 Examples 182
9.4 Quick rotations 184
References 185

PART III   GRAPHICAL DISPLAY OF DATA SETS IN 3 OR MORE
                                   DIMENSIONS

10. **Preparation; Prechosen Sequences of Views**   189
    P. A. Tukey and J. W. Tukey

    10.1   Introduction   189
           10.1.1   The opportunity and the challenge   189
           10.1.2   Scales for important quantities   194
           10.1.3   General outline of material in Chapters 10–12   195
    10.2   Preparation   195
           10.2.1   Centring and scaling   196
           10.2.2   Sphering   196
           10.2.3   Curvature reduction   197
           10.2.4   Looking at shape   198
    10.3   Prechosen direct views   201
           10.3.1   Prechosen direct views of three-dimensional point
                    clouds   202
           10.3.2   Prechosen direct views of four-dimensional point
                    clouds   206
           10.3.3   Automatic view selection in still higher dimensions   210
    References   212

11. **Data-Driven View Selection; Agglomeration and Sharpening**   215
    P. A. Tukey and J. W. Tukey

    11.1   The need for careful selection   215
           11.1.1   Cap sizes   215
           11.1.2   Ways out   216
    11.2   Selecting direct views   217
           11.2.1   Composites, coordinates, etc.   217
           11.2.2   Judgment composites and residuals   218
           11.2.3   Pursuing a criterion   218
           11.2.4   The Friedman–Tukey projection-pursuit algorithm   219
           11.2.5   Quadratic criterion approaches   226
           11.2.6   Other components   227
    11.3   Agglomeration and sharpening   228
           11.3.1   Agglomerated views and agglomerated clouds   228
           11.3.2   Balloon densities   233
           11.3.3   Sharpening   237
    References   242

12. Summarization; Smoothing; Supplemented Views   245
P. A. Tukey and J. W. Tukey

    12.1   Summarization   245
        12.1.1   Kinds of summarization of back variables   245
        12.1.2   Smoothing, mainly in the view-plane   246
        12.1.3   Traces and delineations in the view   250
    12.2   Supplemented views   253
        12.2.1   Characters and glyphs   253
        12.2.2   Collective characters and other special
                 considerations   260
        12.2.3   Backgrounds   262
        12.2.4   Deployment of tools   266
    12.3   Topics not covered   272
        12.3.1   Some omissions   272
    References   274

PART IV   SPECIFIC METHODS AND PRACTICAL
                APPLICATIONS

**13. Plotting the Optimum Positions of an Array of Cortical Electrical
Phosphenes**   279
B. S. Everitt and J. C. Gower

    13.1   Minimization method   280
    13.2   Weighted generalized Procrustes method   283
    13.3   Conclusions   287
    References   287

**14. Analysing Data from Multivariate Directed Graphs: An Application
to Social Networks**   289
S. E. Fienberg, M. M. Meyer, and S. S. Wasserman

    14.1   Introduction   289
    14.2   A specific network: Towertown, U.S.A.   292
    14.3   Log-linear models for multivariate directed graphs   295
    14.4   Fitting the models to data   298
    14.5   Initial analyses of the Towertown data   301
    14.6   A possible graphical display for multivariate directed graphs 304
    References   305

15. Some Graphical Procedures for the Preliminary Processing of Longitudinal Data   307
  H. Goldstein

    15.1   The adjustment procedure   307
    15.2   Data analysis   308
    15.3   Standardization for variance   309
    15.4   Outlier detection   316
    15.5   Conclusions   319
    References   319

16. Interpreting Archaeological Data   321
  I. Graham

    16.1   Spatial analysis   321
        16.1.1   The definition of 'random'   323
        16.1.2   Spectral analysis   324
        16.1.3   Preliminary results   327
    16.2   Results   329
    References   333

17. Bayesian Approaches to Multivariate Structure   335
  A. F. M. Smith and D. J. Spiegelhalter

    17.1   Vague prior information and imaginary observations   337
    17.2   Hypotheses involving means   338
        17.2.1   One sample: hypothesis of zero mean   338
        17.2.2   Two samples: hypothesis of equality of mean
                 vectors   340
        17.2.3   Several samples: hypothesis of equality of means   341
    17.3   Hypotheses involving covariances   341
        17.3.1   Two samples: hypothesis of equal covariances   341
        17.3.2   Several samples: hypothesis of equal covariances   342
    17.4   A mixture form of classification rule   343
    17.5   Transformation to normality   344
    17.6   Numerical illustrations   347
    References   347

Bibliography   349

Composite Reference List   353

Index   365

PART I

Methods for Investigating Bivariate Data

CHAPTER 1

Peeling Bivariate Data

P. J. Green, *University of Durham, U.K.*

Order statistics play an important role in various contexts for univariate data. In more than one dimension, no unique, complete, ordering of either the data or the sample space exists. However, the statistical methods described in this paper are in many ways analogous to those developed from order statistics: they are examples of partial ordering, one of the sub-ordering principles discussed by Barnett (1976).

Many of the concepts herein apply in any number of dimensions although not all of the details of the methods or of the algorithms involved are yet available. Attention is restricted to the bivariate case, and this chapter is mainly a review of known material, much of which has appeared elsewhere.

1.1 CONVEX HULLS

A convex set in the plane is one with the property that the line segment joining any two points of it lies entirely within the set. The convex hull of an arbitrary set is the smallest convex set containing it, and if the original set consists of a finite number of points, the convex hull is simply a closed convex polygon whose vertices are those points around the periphery of the configuration. Interest in the convex hull of a bivariate sample in data analysis stems from the analogy between the peripheral points forming its vertices and the extremes of a univariate sample. An alternative intuitive definition of the convex hull may be obtained if we envisage the data points as pins in a board: a large elastic band is looped around the pins and released. The band will come to rest forming a polygon: the pins it touches are the extremes.

If the extreme points are deleted from the data set, and the convex hull of the remainder constructed, we discover the 'next-most-extreme' points. This procedure may be repeated until no points are left. The analogy with the univariate situation is preserved—we are successively trimming the data set, a procedure that has attracted some interest, for example, in the construction of robust estimates of location (see Andrews *et al.*, 1972). In the bivariate case, we call the successive shells so formed the *convex hull peels* of the data: they are the *c*-order groups of Barnett (1976), and are illustrated in Figures 1.1 and 1.3.

3

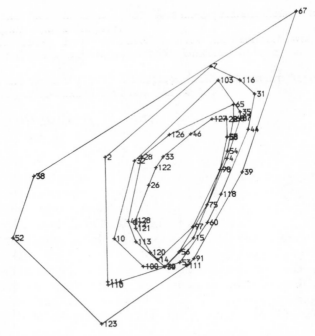

Figure 1.1   Five outermost convex hull peels of a scatter
plot of height (horizontal) versus weight (vertical) for a
sample of 128 4-year-old Nepalese children

Computation of the peels presents no problem in the bivariate case. Various efficient computer algorithms for the convex hull are known, and may be adapted to peeling: see the paper by Green and Silverman (1979), which provides a review, and describes a method whose workload is apparently linear in the sample size for most distributions. Briefly, the method proceeds by pushing lines—*test edges*—out from the centre of the configuration, discarding points from further consideration as they are proved to be inside triangles formed by test edges (see Figure 1.4). In higher dimensions, computation is less straightforward. There have been various approaches, for example Preparata and Hong (1977) give an appropriate algorithm for this process and W. F. Eddy of Carnegie-Mellon, Pa., is also developing a new method.

Statistical uses for the construction of convex hull and peels parallel those for order statistics of univariate data. For example, they can play a natural rôle in the identification and treatment of outliers, as plots of heavy-tailed or contaminated distributions suggest (see Figure 1.3). Seheult, Diggle and Evans (1976) proposed adopting the centroid of the innermost peel as a

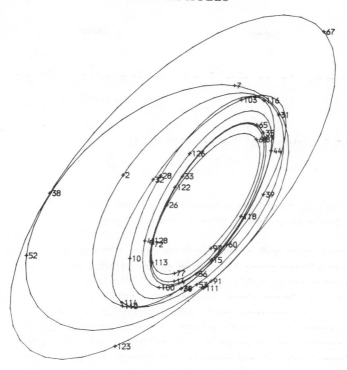

Figure 1.2   Nine outermost elliptical peels for the same data
as Figure 1.1

median for the data, and suitably interpolating between intermediate peels to construct an *interquartile set* containing 50% of the data. This suggestion might be adapted to yield a bivariate analogue of a Tukey box-and-whisker plot, in which, say, the median, inter-quartile set, and a set of extremes including the outer convex hull could be plotted as a summary display of the data (see Figure 1.5). (There are, incidentally, problems of uniqueness of definition in interpolating between peels.) The efficiency of this median as an estimate of location is investigated later in Section 1.5. Alternative notions of median are the vector of marginal medians, which ignores the bivariate structure of the data, and the *mediancentre* which is that point from which the aggregate distance to the data points is minimized (Gower, 1974). This seems less resistant to outlying data values than the peeling defintion above, at least for certain sample configurations. Similar ideas have been exploited in the estimation of probability contours for unimodal bivariate distributions—see Sager (1979), and Eddy and Hartigan (1977) who proposed using the smallest convex set containing a proportion α of the data as an estimate of

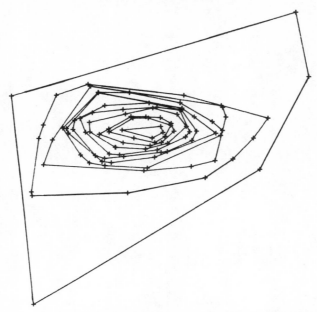

Figure 1.3   Convex-hull peels of a simulated 100-point data set: 91 points from **N** (0, 0, 1, 1, 0), 9 points from **N** (0, 0, 3, 3, 0.5) (unequal scale plot)

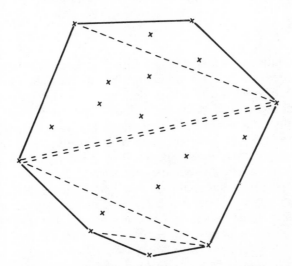

Figure 1.4   Illustrating the Green–Silverman algorithm—broken lines represent test edges, solid lines the convex hull

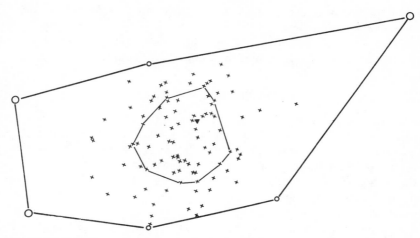

Figure 1.5 The analogue of a box-and-whisker plot for a 100-point bivariate sample: the polygons are the convex hull and the interquartile set, the solid triangle is the median

the probability-density contour containing probability α (see Figure 1.6). Note that this set is *not* necessarily one of the peeled convex hulls.

Convex hull peels can be used to establish significance levels for Monte-Carlo tests with a bivariate test-statistic: again this is exactly analogous with the (two-sided) univariate case. Applications to estimation of parameters of correlation and location will be considered in detail in later sections of this chapter.

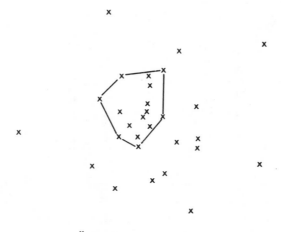

Figure 1.6 The smallest convex set containing a proportion $\alpha = 0.5$ of a 30-point bivariate sample

By implication, most of the applications mentioned above refer to homogeneous random samples—those from a single distribution. Convex hulls have also found many other uses, for example in discrimination problems (Kendall, 1966) and in pattern recognition (Toussaint, 1978).

1.2 PEELING GENERALLY

Convex hulls provide by no means the only method of peeling a multivariate random sample. This section considers various alternative definitions of peel. The common strand is that each provides a way of assigning a positive integer *index* to each data point, measuring the distance of that point from the outside of the data swarm. The collection of points assigned index i form the ith peel, and the intention will be that subsequent analysis of the data will make explicit use of this peel structure.

The principle embodied in the definition of convex-hull peel may be generalized: find the set of given form of smallest area containing all the data points, discard the points on its perimeter, and iterate until no points are left. The points discarded on the ith iteration form the ith peel. Various procedures that have received attention in the literature may be considered here. If the 'given form' is a rectangle, we have *rectangular trimming*, as studied by, for example, Nath (1971) and Dyer (1973) in the context of estimation for a truncated bivariate normal distribution. Such a definition of peel takes no regard of the joint distribution of the sample, and could fail, for example, to identify outliers in strongly correlated data (see Figure 1.7). The same is true of the *minimum covering circle*, and successive peels. The outermost circular

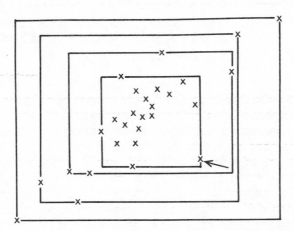

Figure 1.7 Rectangular trimming of a small sample: the indicated point is extreme in the joint distribution sense, yet is not trimmed until the fourth stage

peel and its distribution theory were considered by Daniels (1952), investigating a quick estimate of bivariate dispersion, by analogy with the range.

More recently, Silverman and Titterington (1981), discuss the *minimal covering ellipsoid* problem, and devise an exact terminating algorithm for the bivariate case. As they point out, and this is equally true for circular peeling, the sequence of minimal ellipses need not be nested: this may inhibit interpretation, although of course the *points* peeled at each stage are nested in some sense. Elliptical peeling is compared with convex-hull peeling in Figures 1.1 and 1.2, and also illustrated in Figure 1.8.

Algorithmically (and indeed in view of the current predilection for 'circularizing' multivariate data, perhaps statistically) the minimum covering circle problem is equivalent to the minimum covering ellipse-of-a-given-shape-and-orientation problem. When the given shape and orientation are determined (perhaps resistantly) by the covariance structure of the data, this seems quite appealing, and indeed variants have been implicitly used by, for example, Kudo (1956), Siotani (1959) and Devlin, Gnanadesikan, and Kettenring (1975) in defining degrees of extremity in multivariate data. Such procedures overlap into another of Barnett's sub-ordering principles, reduced ordering.

Occasionally, it may be relevant to require that the 'given form' of peeling set should specify the location (usually the centre) as well as the shape. Thus we might consider the minimum *central* covering ellipsoid, and so on. In the data analysis context this corresponds to considering dispersion about some pre-determined measure of location. Another possibility is that only extremes

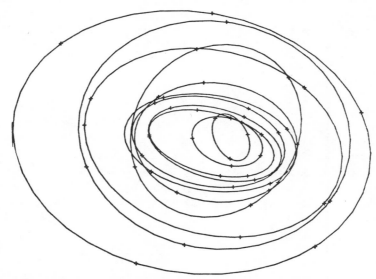

Figure 1.8 Elliptical peels of a 100-point sample from an
uncorrelated Normal distribution

in certain directions are of interest. A case of some practical interest would be 'positive quadrant' convex-hull peeling: in terms of the intuitive definition of Section 1.1 the elastic band must also enclose the 'points' $(-\infty, 0)$ and $(0, -\infty)$. This is illustrated in Figure 1.9.

Tukey's statistically equivalent blocks (1947) may be viewed as a type of peeling. These blocks form a partition of the plane determined by the bivariate data set: their probability contents have a joint distribution that is not dependent on the underlying distribution of the data, providing that it is continuous. Quesenberry and Gessaman (1968) exploit the idea of statistically equivalent blocks in extending Kendall's (1966) proposal for multivariate discrimination.

It seems most natural to define peeling iteratively, as discussed above. But other methods are possible, although not explored here in detail. One interesting suggestion is that by Tukey (1975) who defines the $(i - \frac{1}{2})$-polygon to be the closed figure formed by segments of the directed lines in the plane which have at least i points on them or to their left, but at most $(i - 2)$ strictly to their left. Almost surely in the continuous case all such lines go, of course, through exactly two data points. This construction is illustrated in Figure 1.10: note that the $1\frac{1}{2}$-polygon is the convex hull. Tukey interpolates between the $(i - \frac{1}{2})$- and $(i + \frac{1}{2})$-polygons to construct the i-polygon. Empirical study suggests that these polygons are perhaps more informative and

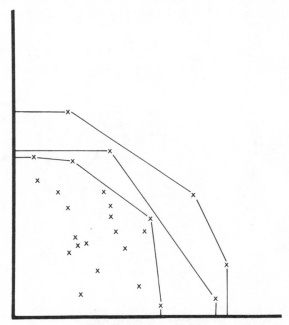

Figure 1.9   Positive quadrant peeling

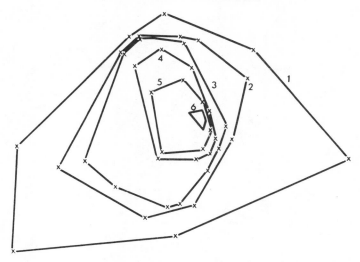

Figure 1.10   Tukey peeling: the $(i + \frac{1}{2})$-polygons of a 40-point
sample for $i = 1, 2, 3, 4, 5, 6$

sensitive in representing the sample structure than are convex-hull peels. No
efficient computer algorithm is yet available—this is a subject of present
investigation—though approximations to the polygons can be readily constructed by simply ordering the projections of the points onto lines of sufficiently close angular separation.

If 'adjacency' between data points can be defined (see, for example, Green
1976), we can measure distance across a data swarm in units of steps between
adjacent points. Then index can be defined as number of steps to the
periphery of the configuration. However, it may be difficult to define adjacency so that the resulting peels respect the correlation structure of the data.
Adjacency peeling making use of the Delaunay triangulation (see Green and
Sibson, 1978) is illustrated in Figure 1.11.

Most modes of peeling are cumulative from the outside of the data—outer
peels are defined independently of inner points. So, instead of trimming off
outer sample points, we can envisage the use of peel-based methods on
centre-truncated data.

At this point, it is instructive to look back at the various concepts discussed
as they apply to the univariate case: note that all are familiar order statistics.

1.3 DISTRIBUTION THEORY

In this section we discuss various invariance and distributional aspects of
convex hulls and other minimal covering sets. The distribution theory proves
fairly difficult.

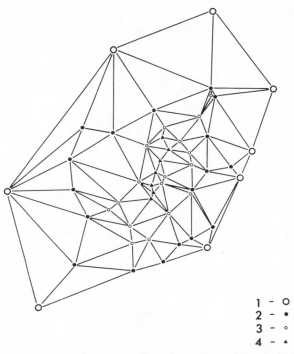

1 - ○
2 - ●
3 - ○
4 - ▲

Figure 1.11   Peeling according to the adjacencies
defined by the Delaunay triangulation: points with
index 1, 2, 3, 4 are coded as indicated

The usual probability model in this context has been an affine transformation of a circularly symmetric distribution, either arbitrary or of prescribed form. Convex hull, minimum ellipse and Tukey peeling are all affine invariant, in that the peels of affinely transformed data are the transformed peels of the original data. Affine invariance is of course quite a strong property: many statistical procedures are not invariant under rotations, or under different scale changes for different margins. In some situations, for example with anisotropic spatial models, too much invariance may inhibit the application of these peeling techniques; indeed before using any procedure for data analysis it should surely be decided under precisely what transformations of the data are the conclusions to be invariant.

Various properties of the convex hull of a sample from a circularly symmetric distribution are known—expected number of vertices, area, probability content—usually as asymptotic results depending on tail behaviour. See Renyi and Sulanke (1963/4), Carnal (1970) and Raynaud (1970); Efron (1965) gives some useful integrals for finite sample size. Simulations suggest

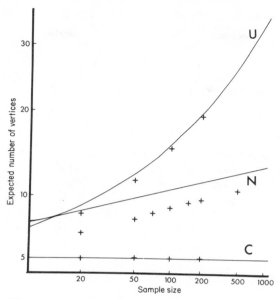

Figure 1.12 Expected number of convex-hull
vertices for samples of various sizes from circularly
symmetric distributions: Uniform on disc, Normal
and Cauchy. Continuous curves show asymptotic
formulae, crosses the actual values obtained from
simulations

that for some distributions the rates of convergence to asymptotic results for
number of vertices are too slow for them to be of direct use with realistic-
sized samples (see Figure 1.12).

Recently Eddy (1980) has shown how to treat the whole asymptotic distribution of size and shape of the convex hull by representing it as an
extreme-value process in an appropriate space.

By relating the minimum covering ellipse to the solution of a dual problem
from the theory of optimal design of experiments Titterington (1975) shows
that for continuous distributions the number of points peeled at each stage is
almost surely 3, 4 or 5. This is in stark contrast to the convex hull case, where
for example in a sample of size n from a normal distribution, the number of
points in the first peel has expectation of order $\sqrt{(\log n)}$. Elliptical peeling is
thus considerably less coarse than convex-hull peeling, or equivalently, leads
to a greater 'depth' of peel. As pointed out by Silverman and Titterington
(1981), this effect is even stronger in a higher number of dimensions, where a
large proportion of a sample may be determined as extreme by the convex
hull. Tukey peeling is also less coarse than convex-hull peeling; although

again the maximum depth of peel cannot be pre-determined, it lies between one-quarter and one-half of the sample size.

When evaluating applications of peeling to robust statistical procedures, it would be desirable to know their influence curves (see for example Andrews *et al.*, 1972): but their derivation for peel-based statistics seems too difficult, and robustness must therefore be assessed qualitatively.

1.4 CORRELATION

We turn now to the first of two specific applications of peeling to be considered in more detail—that of estimation of correlation.

Barnett (1976) proposed basing a simple estimator on the numbers of positive and negative slopes among the line segments forming the peels. He does not investigate this in detail, but it is not difficult to show that if n_i^+, n_i^- are the number of positive and negative slopes on the ith peel, then for each i,

$$E\left(\frac{n_i^+ - n_i^-}{n_i^+ + n_i^-}\right) = \frac{2}{\pi}\sin^{-1}\rho$$

for any circularly symmetric distribution affinely transformed to have correlation ρ. Thus any weighted average of these slope-count ratios may be used as an estimator. It is perhaps surprising to discover that the slope-count ratio is related to a rather well-known statistic—namely Kendall's rank-correlation coefficient τ (see Kendall, 1948). If the signs of the slopes of the line segments connecting *all* pairs of points in the sample are counted, giving n^+ and n^-, then τ is defined in the same fashion:

$$\tau = \frac{n^+ - n^-}{n^+ + n^-},$$

and of course the expectation equality still holds.

Two recent papers, Bebbington (1978) and Titterington (1978), treat the conventional product-moment correlation coefficient for data trimmed by removing the outer convex hull or elliptical peel respectively. Distributional behaviour is obtained by simulation for the normal case, with or without contamination; results suggest that little efficiency is lost, while much protection against the bias caused by contamination is gained. Both authors also try their methods on Fisher's well-known *Iris setosa* data (1936). The shape of the trimmed ellipse itself provides an estimate of correlation, which might be used when the central part of the data is not available. Despite the limited information used, efficiency is at least 25% or so for sample sizes up to 200. Finally, Titterington demonstrates four-dimensional elliptical trimming on the full *Iris setosa* data set in comparison with the six two-dimensional marginal versions.

1.5 LOCATION

Several of the robust estimates of univariate location considered in the Princeton study (Andrews *et al.*, 1972) involve trimming: a natural bivariate analogue seems to be to use a weighted average of convex-hull peel sample means to estimate location.

Thus, equivalently, if the data consist of the n bivariate points $x_1, x_2, \ldots, x_n$, and if $i(j)$ is the index of the point numbered j, we will consider the estimator

$$M = \sum_j c_{i(j)} x_j \bigg/ \sum_j c_{i(j)}$$

for some appropriate weights $c_1, c_2, c_3, \ldots$. (Here the denominator is determined naturally by translation invariance.) The ordinary sample mean arises when $c_i \equiv 1$. A degree of robustness against heavy-tailed distributions is obtained by setting $c_i = 0$ for small i, 1 otherwise; these are trimmed means. The median suggested by Seheult, Diggle, and Evans (1976) corresponds to $c_i = 0$ for all but the innermost i.

Others among the Princeton estimators involve weights $\{c_i\}$ chosen adaptively according to the spacing of the data. Let us consider for the bivariate case certain partially adaptive weights $\{c_i\}$. Empirical study suggests that the manner of distribution of the sample points between the convex-hull peels—the *index distribution*—is a reliable indicator to how heavy- or light-tailed is the pattern of the data. For the sake of smoothness, as a partial answer to objections concerning the discontinuity of these statistics as functions of the data values, and because peeling itself is cumulative, we use the *cumulative* index distribution. To simplify interpretation this is then normalized by dividing by the expected cumulative index distribution for a normal random sample of the same size. Thus if there are n_i points on the ith peel, the *signature* of the data set is the sequence $\{s_i\}$, where

$$s_i = \left(\sum_{r=1}^{i} n_r \right) \bigg/ E_N\left(\sum_{r=1}^{i} n_r \right)$$

(where $E_N(\ )$ denotes expectation for an assumed normal distribution). For a 'typical' sample from a bivariate normal distribution, $s_i \equiv 1$. A heavier-tailed distribution gives $s_i < 1$, a lighter-tailed one $s_i > 1$, and in any case s_i approaches 1 as i increases: see Figure 1.13 for some specimen signatures.

This notion of signature could probably be usefully extended for other applications. For example a signature obtained by suitably normalizing the area or perimeter of the polygons formed by successive peels may provide sensitive detection of outliers.

The weights used here in the estimator M depend on the data only through the index-distribution signature, and not otherwise on the shape or size of the

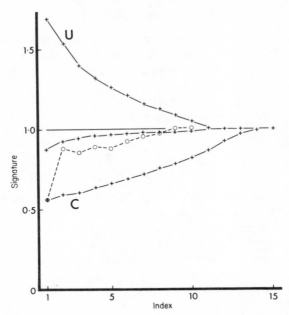

Figure 1.13   Signatures for 100-point data sets obtained from simulations. Crosses (from the top): uniform distribution on disc; **N** (0, 0, 1, 1, 0) contaminated with 2% **N** (0, 0, 3, 3, 0.5); Cauchy. Circles: the single sample from Figure 1.3

peels. In addition to evidence from simulated distributions with various tail behaviours, it seems intuitively reasonable that a convex-hull peel with more members should tend to be more centrally located. Thus the weight c_i is an increasing function of the corresponding s_i. It does not seem possible to proceed formally and make an optimal choice of this function but, empirically, simulations suggest that weights of the form

$$c_i = [\max (0, s_i - 0.75)]^2$$

perform well, sacrificing little precision in the normal case, and yield enormous improvements for heavy-tailed alternatives like the Cauchy. The distributions we use as examples have circular symmetry, so the performance of any estimator of location that preserves this symmetry can be judged solely on the resulting distribution of radial error. Figure 1.14 illustrates this error distribution for two models (normal, Cauchy) and two estimators (sample mean, weighted mean using the weights above). The important feature of these weights is that they vanish for outer peels if 'too few' points of the sample are

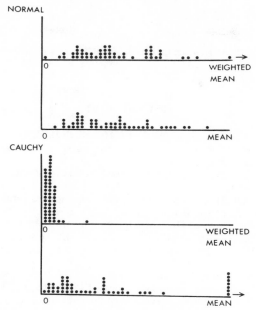

Figure 1.14 Histograms of radial error, comparing two estimators applied to two models

located here. Such weighted means will automatically compensate for various types of rogue behaviour in the tails of the data.

Considering the well-known problem of estimating parameters from a univariate rectangular distribution, it might also be hoped that similar weight functions should give estimators that perform better than the sample mean for *light*-tailed distributions.

1.6 CONCLUSION

Peeling methods seem attractive ways of introducing some order to multivariate data. Although their calculation by hand is tedious, efficient computer programs are available, and plots of the peels can aid the interpretation of scatter diagrams. There are objections to their use, stimulated in part by their discontinuous behaviour which is not found in the univariate case; this suggests some caution in their application.

Further work is needed in investigating the performance of peeling in the presence of marked asymmetry, bimodality or non-linear dependency, its potential for detecting these features, and its sensitivity to coarse rounding of the data.

Acknowledgements

The author is grateful to Professor John Tukey, Professor Ruben Gabriel and Dr. Bernard Silverman for helpful discussions, suggestions and correspondence.

REFERENCES

Andrews, D. F., Bickel, P. J., Hample, F. R., Huber, P. J., Rogers, W. F., and Tukey, J. W. (1972) *Robust estimates of location: survey and advances*. Princeton: Princeton University Press.

Barnett, V. (1976) The ordering of multivariate data (with discussion). *J. Roy. Statist. Soc. A*, **139**, 318–54.

Bebbington, A. C. (1978) A method of bivariate trimming for robust estimation of the correlation coefficient. *Applied Statistics*, **27**, 221–6.

Carnal, H. (1970) Dir konvexe Hülle von *n* rotations-symmetrisch verteilten Punkten. *Z. Wahrscheinlichskeitstheorie und Verw. Gebiete*, **15**, 168–76.

Daniels, H. E. (1952) The covering circle of a sample from a circular normal distribution. *Biometrika*, **39**, 137–43.

Devlin, S. J., Gnanadesikan, R., and Kettenring, J. R. (1975) Robust estimation and outlier detection with correlation coefficients. *Biometrika*, **62**, 531–46.

Dyer, D. D. (1973) On moments estimation of the parameters of a truncated bivariate normal distribution. *Applied Statistics*, **22**, 287–91.

Eddy, W. F. (1980) The distribution of the convex hull of a Gaussian sample. *J. Appl. Prob.*, **17**, 686–95.

Eddy, W. F. and Hartigan, J. A. (1977) Uniform convergence of the empirical distribution function over convex sets. *Ann. Statist.*, **5**, 370–4.

Efron, B. (1965) The convex hull of a random set of points. *Biometrika*, **52**, 331–43.

Fisher, R. A. (1936) The use of multiple measurements in taxonomic problems. *Annals of Eugenics*, **7**, 179–88.

Gower, J. C. (1974) The mediancentre (Algorithm AS78). *Applied Statistics*, **23**, 466–70.

Green, P. J. (1976) Contribution to the discussion of Barnett (1976).

Green, P. J. and Sibson, R. (1978) Computing Dirichlet tessellations in the plane. *The Computer Journal*, **21**, 168–73.

Green, P. J. and Silverman, B. W. (1979) Constructing the convex hull of a set of points in the plane. *The Computer Journal*, **22**, 262–6.

Kendall, M. G. (1948) *Rank correlation methods*. London: Griffin.

Kendall, M. G. (1966) Discrimination and classification, in Krishnaiah, P. R. (ed.) (1966) *Multivariate Analysis, Vol. I*. New York: Academic Press.

Kudo, A. (1956) On the testing of outlying observations. *Sankhya A*, **17**, 67–76.

Nath, G. B. (1971) Estimation in truncated bivariate normal distributions. *Applied Statistics*, **20**, 313–9.

Preparata, F. P. and Hong, S. J. (1977) Convex hulls of finite sets of points in two and three dimensions. *Comm. A.C.M.*, **20**, 87–93.

Quesenberry, C. P. and Gessaman, M. P. (1968) Nonparametric discrimination using tolerance regions. *Ann. Math. Statist.*, **39**, 664–73.

Raynaud, H. (1970) Sur l'enveloppe convexe des nuages de points aléatoires dans $\mathbb{R}^n$. I. *J. Appl. Prob.*, **7**, 35–48.

Renyi, A. and Sulanke, R. (1963/4) Über die konvexe Hülle von n zufällig gewählten Punkten I and II. *Z. Wahrscheinlichskeitstheorie und Verw. Gebiete*, **2**, 75–84 and **3**, 138–47.

Sager, T. W. (1979) An iterative method for estimating a multivariate mode and isopleth. *J. Amer. Statist. Assn.*, **74**, 329–39.

Seheult, A. H., Diggle, P. J., and Evans, D. A. (1976) Contribution to the discussion of Barnett (1976).

Silverman, B. W. and Titterington, D. M. (1981) Minimum covering ellipses. *SIAM J. on Scientific and Statistical Computing* (to appear).

Siotani, M. (1959) The extreme value of the generalized distances of the individual points in the multivariate normal sample. *Ann. Inst. Statist. Math., Tokyo*, **10**, 183–208.

Titterington, D. M. (1975) Optimal design: some geometrical aspects of D-optimality. *Biometrika*, **62**, 313–20.

Titterington, D. M. (1978) Estimation of correlation coefficients by ellipsoidal trimming. *Applied Statistics*, **27**, 227–34.

Toussaint, G. T. (1978) The convex hull as a tool in pattern recognition, in *Proc. AFOSR Workshop in Communication Theory and Applications*, Provincetown, Mass.

Tukey, J. W. (1947) Non-parametric estimation II. Statistically equivalent blocks and tolerance regions in the continuous case. *Ann. Math. Statist.*, **18**, 529–39.

Tukey, J. W. (1975) Mathematics and the picturing of data, in *Proc. International Congress of Mathematicians*. Vancouver, 1974, Vol. 2, pp. 523–31.

CHAPTER 2

A Brief Description of Natural Neighbour Interpolation

R. Sibson, *University of Bath, U.K.*

Natural neighbour interpolation offers a new approach to spatial interpolation which has good mathematical properties and is computationally efficient.

2.1 THE INTERPOLATION PROBLEM

A common form of spatial data comprises the following elements:

a region E of euclidean space in K dimensions (usually $K = 1, 2, 3$) of some fairly simple kind, probably bounded, possibly convex, possibly polyhedral, which we call a *window*;

a finite number N of distinct points, P_n at vector position $\mathbf{u}_n$, which we call *data sites*;

at each data site a numerical observation, z_n at P_n, which we call a *data value*.

Conventional height surveying can be thought of as producing data of this kind; rainfall and other meteorological data provide another example.

It is very difficult to appreciate the pattern followed by such data in their raw form. Consider briefly an example to be considered in more detail later (Section 2.6). The data shown in Figure 2.5 are taken from the function shown in Figure 2.4, but it would be very difficult to appreciate the behaviour of the function directly from these data. To see the behaviour, we want to reconstruct as far as possible the appearance of the function from the isolated data, making sensible assumptions as we do so about how to 'fill in the gaps'. Thus, in technical language, we want to find an exact interpolant, a function f: $E \to$ the reals, such that

$$f(\mathbf{u}_n) = z_n \quad \text{for } n = 1, \ldots, N;$$

that is, the function must achieve the observed value at each data site. One such function is defined by

$$f(\mathbf{u}) = \begin{cases} 0 & \text{if } \mathbf{u} \neq \text{any } \mathbf{u}_n \\ z_n & \text{if } \mathbf{u} = \mathbf{u}_n \quad (n = 1, \ldots, N) \end{cases}$$

21

but this is obviously quite arbitrary and has nothing to do with the data in between the data sites. Our interpolant must satisfy a number of conditions which among other things make it relate naturally to the data and make it reasonably smooth, so that there is a good chance that it looks and behaves very much like the original function from which the data were drawn. The following comments are not to be interpreted as offering axioms or necessary conditions for an interpolation method, but we believe that they do, broadly speaking, outline desirable properties of any method; at the very least, the user of an interpolation technique is entitled to be warned if the method fails to meet any of these points.

2.1.1 Comments

A C^1 (continuously differentiable) function is visually smooth and (implicit function theorem) has smooth 'contour lines' (an important application area). Functions which are not continuously differentiable definitely do not look smooth. Higher-order smoothness properties than C^1 do not appear to be detectable by eye except in special cases.

In many, perhaps most, applications there is no convincing way of modelling the quantity being observed. The interpolant is an aid to the assimilation and comprehension of the pattern of variation. The interpolant should accordingly run as little risk as possible of provoking misinterpretation of the data.

We are not trying to do extrapolation. The data sites should occupy most of the window. They may be regularly or irregularly placed, or a mixture; this should not matter.

The method should not depend on either concealed (e.g. choice of coordinate system) or explicit (e.g. choice of a superimposed grid of 'panels') *arbitrary* choices unrelated to the data.

The dependence of the interpolant function on the data values should be very well-behaved and simple; it is best if it can actually be linear, so that if the system of data values is multiplied throughout by a scalar, the interpolant is also multiplied by that scalar, and if two systems of data values at the same data sites are added, the interpolant for the sum should be the sum of the interpolants.

The dependence of the interpolant function on the data sites should be reasonably well-behaved; at least continuity is desirable, so that the interpolant does not jump from one state to another in response to a small change in data-site position.

The interpolant should be localized, in that in some suitable sense only data sites which are reasonably near neighbours should influence the interpolated value at a point.

The method should be directly computationally feasible on a reasonably large scale, say, 10 000 data sites and interpolation to 10 000 points without undue difficulty. Localization can allow very large problems to be broken down and the results fitted together.

Obviously interpolation in two dimensions is of great interest. Interpolation in one dimension is such a special problem that it is not hard to devise reasonable satisfactory methods; these may guide us in higher-dimensional cases. Interpolation in three dimensions is also very much of interest, but as in all multivariate analysis the edge effects quickly predominate with a fixed number of data sites as the dimension increases. However, it is attractive if the theory behind a method is not tied to any specific dimensionality.

It is helpful in applications if the gradient, as well as the value, of the interpolant is calculable.

Often the problem encountered is one of exact interpolation, but *smoothing* problems are also common, when the requirement is that $f(\mathbf{u}_n)$ should be 'near' z_n rather than equal to it, and a tradeoff between goodness-of-fit and smoothness is allowed. Solving the problem of exact interpolation is a major step towards the solution of smoothing problems.

We would expect the interpolation method to recover exactly (apart perhaps from some edge effects) functions from some simple class:

constants	$z = \alpha$
first-degree functions	$z = \alpha + \boldsymbol{\beta}^T\mathbf{u}$
spherical quadratics	$z = \alpha + \boldsymbol{\beta}^T\mathbf{u} + \gamma\mathbf{u}^T\mathbf{u}$
general quadratics	$z = \alpha + \boldsymbol{\beta}^T\mathbf{u} + \mathbf{u}^T\boldsymbol{\Gamma}\mathbf{u}$

and so on. (Throughout this book the superscript ^{T} will be used to denote the transpose of a vector.) The less ambitious we are, the worse the errors we make internally; the more ambitious we are, the less localized the interpolant can be and the worse and more far-reaching the edge effects become. But we would be most unlikely to accept a method which did not at least recover first-degree functions.

2.2 EXISTING METHODS

There are many methods which are so defective that they scarcely merit detailed discussion. An example is the method of bicubic splines in two dimensions. Three classes of method appear to merit serious consideration.

2.2.1 Finite element methods

These methods depend on splitting up the window into polyhedral (usually simplex) panels in a data-determined manner, and fitting together standard smooth functions (finite elements) across the panels. The technique is a standard tool of numerical analysis. An excellent detailed account of a two-dimensional interpolation method of this kind is given by Lawson (1977). The Delaunay triangulation (see below) provides a systematic method of constructing the panels. Given the availability of an efficient Dirichlet tessellation/Delaunay triangulation algorithm, a finite-element type method can be *very* efficient. Some of the unresolved arbitrariness pointed out by Lawson in his own method can be sorted out by techniques similar to those discussed below for the natural-neighbour method. The major disadvantage of *all* such methods is their discontinuous response to data-site position, and it is particularly awkward that a discontinuity occurs, and has to be resolved artificially, when the data sites are partly or wholly on a regular rectangular grid. A minor disadvantage is the artificiality of the finite elements themselves, and the lack of any systematic family of such elements running through the dimensions.

2.2.2 Kriging

Methods based on spatial moving averages (cf. time-series analysis) have been elaborated by the French school of geostatisticians in the context of an elaborate stochastic model for random functions with stationary generalized increments. Interpolation is seen as a process of statistical estimation within the model. The methods are named after D. Krige, who was influential in developing the early use in geology of spatial moving average techniques. A detailed mathematical account is given by Matheron (1973) and there is a very readable less formal account by Delfiner and Delhomme (1975). It is very much open to question whether the stochastic model on which these methods are based is well related to the phenomena it purports to describe, and little or no attention to this matter seems to have been given in the literature. Viewed purely as a procedure for generating data-analytic interpolation methods it is undoubtedly attractive. It is necessary to consider the level of generalization known as 'universal kriging' to obtain methods of interpolation comparable with the other methods discussed here. There are still many unresolved questions connected with this, particularly to do with the degree of smoothness of the interpolant functions and the behaviour of their gradients, and the computational position appears to be highly unsatisfactory.

2.2.3 Stiff lamina methods

The idea of interpolating in one dimension by using the curve followed by a constrained stiff wire is an old one, and leads to the familiar idea of the cubic smoothing spline. It has been exploited elegantly by Wahba and Wold (1975), to produce a one-dimensional smoothing method of an appropriate kind for data analysis. More recently Wahba (1979) has extended this work to two dimensions and to higher degrees of smoothness. At the lowest degree of smoothness the physical model is a uniform stiff lamina constrained to take the data values as (infinitesimal) displacements at the data sites. The extension to any number of dimensions is physically straightforward, but its practical realization depends on finding appropriate solutions of the biharmonic equation. Like Kriging, the method is not a localized one, and this makes for major computational difficulty. The linear system which has to be solved rapidly becomes ill-conditioned as well as large as the number of points increases, and although Wahba is able to report successful results on 120 data sites she concludes her account with a warning about the difficulty of attacking substantially larger problems.

It is undoubtedly the case that these three classes of method have much to offer, and also have considerable scope for further development and computational improvement. Awareness of their limitations is an important element in applying them successfully, and it is clear that no one existing method is universally satisfactory, nor indeed is any one method ever likely to be so. The natural neighbour method introduced below is not a replacement for these methods, but a further alternative. It has its own limitations which must be recognized, but it also has a distinctive pattern of mathematically and computationally attractive features not found in other methods.

2.3 NATURAL NEIGHBOUR INTERPOLATION

All interpolation methods involve to some extent the idea that the value of the interpolant at a point should depend more on data values at nearby data sites than at distant ones. In natural-neighbour interpolation the idea of 'neighbour' in a spatial configuration is formalized in a natural way and made quantitative, and the properties of the method depend on an apparently new geometrical identity relating this quantitative measure of 'neighbourliness' to position.

Consider just the data sites, $P_1, \ldots, P_N$ at $\mathbf{u}_1, \ldots, \mathbf{u}_N$. For convenience at this stage, take the window E to be open, convex, and polyhedral. Let T_n be the subset of E of points with P_n as nearest neighbour among $P_1, \ldots, P_N$; T_n is the *tile*, or *Voronoi* or *Thiessen polyhedron* of P_n with respect to $P_1, \ldots, P_N$ in E. The tiles are themselves open, convex and polyhedral, and are delimited by perpendicular-bisector hyperplanes of line segments joining pairs of data sites, together with, at the periphery of the configuration, the boundary of E. The subdivide E, covering all but their own boundaries. The construction as a whole, the *Dirichlet tessellation*, is shown in Figure 2.1 in two dimensions for 100 arbitrarily scattered points in a square. When two tiles share a common facet, they, and their generating data sites, are *contiguous*, or are *neighbours*. Joining neighbouring data sites generates a triangulation of (most of) E,

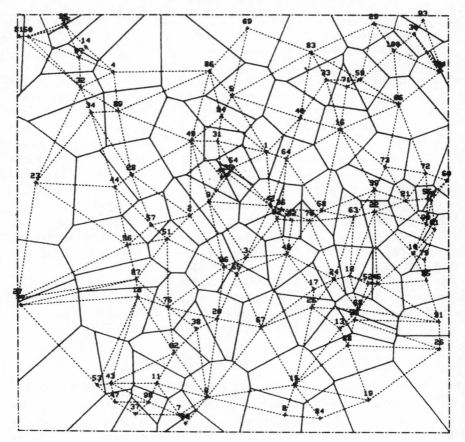

Figure 2.1   The tessellation and triangulation on 100 points

called the *Delaunay triangulation*. It is also shown on Figure 2.1. This concept of 'neighbour' is completely data-determined and is the one we shall use. In one dimension a data site not contiguous to the boundary of E has two neighbours. In K dimensions it has at least $K + 1$; it may have more, but the lower bound is attainable.

To make the neighbour relation quantitative, we subdivide T_n into *subtiles* T_{nm}; T_{nm} is the part of T_n with P_m as second-nearest neighbour, so that if P_n were removed, T_m would be enlarged by adding T_{nm} to it (plus a bit of common boundary). The T_{nm} subdivide T_n, and are open, convex, and polyhedral. T_{nm} is nonempty if and only if m and n are neighbours. Write $\kappa(n)$ for the Lebesgue measure (length, area, volume . . .) of T_n, $\kappa_m(n)$ for that of T_{nm}. We regard $\kappa_m(n)$ (or the normalized form $\lambda_m(n) = \kappa_m(n)/\kappa(n)$) as measuring the strength of the 'neighbourliness' of P_m as a neighbour of P_n.

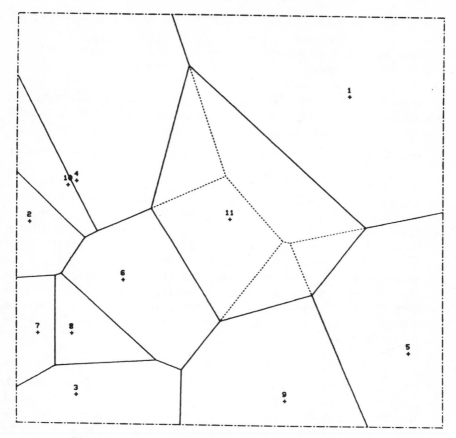

Figure 2.2   A tile divided into subtiles in two dimensions

The values $\kappa_m(n)$ and $\kappa_n(m)$ are zero or positive together, but when positive they are not necessarily equal, neither are the normalized values $\lambda_m(n)$, $\lambda_n(m)$. Figure 2.2 shows a tile divided into subtiles, in two dimensions.

In addition to measuring the neighbour relationship between the data sites, we also want to measure the relationship between an arbitrary point P in coordinate position $\mathbf{u}$, and the data sites. To do this, just add P to the tessellation. Nothing new is involved except a slight extension of the notion: $\kappa(\mathbf{u})$ for the measure of the tile of P, $\kappa_m(\mathbf{u})$ for the measure of the P_m subtile, $\lambda_m(\mathbf{u})$ for $\kappa_m(\mathbf{u})/\kappa(\mathbf{u})$.

The $\lambda_m(\mathbf{u})$ are called *local coordinates*. They have two fundamental properties:

$\lambda_m(\mathbf{u})$ is a continuous function of $\mathbf{u}$, and is continuously differentiable except at the data sites. This follows from properties of $\kappa_m(\mathbf{u})$ (note that

$\kappa(\mathbf{u}) = \Sigma \kappa_m(\mathbf{u}))$ which can actually be established by writing down $\nabla \kappa_m(\mathbf{u})$.

The $\lambda_m(\mathbf{u})$ satisfy an identity called the *local coordinates property (LCP)*, namely that (provided the tile of P does not meet the boundary of E)

$$\Sigma \lambda_m(\mathbf{u})\mathbf{u}_m = \mathbf{u}.$$

That is, the $\lambda_m(\mathbf{u})$ express $\mathbf{u}$ as a convex combination of its neighbours (provided $\mathbf{u}$ is not 'at the edge'). The *LCP* is vital to what follows. It holds in any number of dimensions. The proof is nontrivial; see Sibson (1980).

A simple interpolant can be constructed directly from the local coordinates:

$$Z^{(0)}(\mathbf{u}) = \Sigma \lambda_m(\mathbf{u})z_m.$$

This is the *natural neighbour C^0 interpolant*. It is not what we want because it is only C^0—the derivative is discontinuous at the data sites—but it may be useful for other purposes. In one dimension $Z^{(0)}$ gives piecewise-linear interpolation, and in any number of dimensions it reproduces a first-degree function ($z = \alpha + \boldsymbol{\beta}^{\mathrm{T}}\mathbf{u}$) correctly, because of the *LCP*.

A procedure which has been suggested in the literature, as for example in the documentation for what is known as *General Purpose Contouring Package (GPCP)*, is to determine a suitable gradient, say $\mathbf{b}_n$, for the interpolant at each data site P_n and then instead of mixing constants, as in $Z^{(0)}$, to mix first-degree functions

$$z = z_n + \mathbf{b}_n^{\mathrm{T}}(\mathbf{u} - \mathbf{u}_n)$$

with an inverse distance factor in the weighting, that is, a factor $1/d_n(\mathbf{u})$, where $d_n(\mathbf{u}) = + \sqrt{[(\mathbf{u} - \mathbf{u}_n)^{\mathrm{T}}(\mathbf{u} - \mathbf{u}_n)]}$. This has the effect (we hope) of matching the interpolant gradient to $\mathbf{b}_n$ at $\mathbf{u}_n$ as well as matching the interpolant value to z_n. Its defect has not been pointed out in the literature: a one-dimensional example shows it clearly. With $\mathbf{u}_n, z_n, \mathbf{b}_n$ as shown in Figure 2.3, the interpolant, as a mixture of two first-degree functions, must pass through

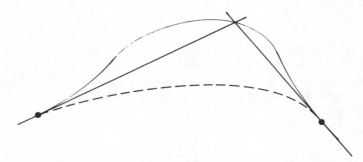

Figure 2.3   The 'Prussian helmet' effect produced by mixing
first-degree functions

their common point, and must thus look something like the solid curve. We would like it to look like the broken curve. This approach, of mixing functions, although defective as it stands, contains the germ of the idea we use.

We first obtain a value $\mathbf{b}_n$ for the gradient at P_n. This is done very simply, by fitting a first-degree function

$$z = z_n + \mathbf{b}^{\mathrm{T}}(\mathbf{u} - \mathbf{u}_n)$$

through $(\mathbf{u}_n, z_n)$ and *as closely as possible* to other $(\mathbf{u}_m, z_m)$ by choosing $\mathbf{b}_n$ to be the $\mathbf{b}$ minimizing

$$\Sigma w_m(n)\{z_m - [z_n + \mathbf{b}^{\mathrm{T}}(\mathbf{u}_m - \mathbf{u}_n)]\}^2$$

where the $w_m(n)$ are weights. We want $w_m(n)$ to be zero if P_m is not a neighbour of P_n—so as to get a localization property—and we can do this by putting in a factor $\lambda_m(n)$ as part of $w_m(n)$. Clearly if $(\mathbf{u}_n, z_n)$ and all neighbouring $(\mathbf{u}_m, z_m)$ lie on a first-degree function, this gives the slope correctly. But first-degree functions are a $(K + 1)$ parameter family: we have data at a point P_n and at least $(K + 1)$ neighbouring points—$(K + 2)$ items of data in all—so we can be a little more ambitious. Using the *LCP*, it is easy to show that if we take $w_m(n)$ to be $\lambda_m(n)/d^2_m(n)$ (where $d^2_m(n) = (\mathbf{u}_m - \mathbf{u}_n)^{\mathrm{T}}(\mathbf{u}_m - \mathbf{u}_n)$) then $\mathbf{b}_n$ is the correct slope if $(\mathbf{u}_n, z_n)$ and the neighbouring $(\mathbf{u}_m, z_m)$ lie on a spherical quadratic. Note that we cannot guarantee to go to even a general quadratic (with $\frac{1}{2}(K + 1)(K + 2)$ parameters) without considering more remote data sites. $\mathbf{b}_n$ is given explicitly by

$$\mathbf{b}_n = \mathbf{H}_n^{-1}\mathbf{p}_n,$$

where

$$\mathbf{H}_n = \sum_m \lambda_m(n) \frac{(\mathbf{u}_m - \mathbf{u}_n)(\mathbf{u}_m - \mathbf{u}_n)^{\mathrm{T}}}{(\mathbf{u}_m - \mathbf{u}_n)^{\mathrm{T}}(\mathbf{u}_m - \mathbf{u}_n)},$$

$$\mathbf{p}_n = \sum \lambda_m(n) \frac{(\mathbf{u}_m - \mathbf{u}_n)(z_m - z_n)}{(\mathbf{u}_m - \mathbf{u}_n)^{\mathrm{T}}(\mathbf{u}_m - \mathbf{u}_n)}.$$

(2.1)

This shows us how to calculate gradients at data sites in a manner which takes full advantage of all the local information we can guarantee to have, and it also suggests the appropriateness of spherical quadratics as a class of functions to aim at for exact reproduction.

To see how to construct the interpolant itself, we first consider what happens if we follow the *GPCP* 'recipe'. Write

$$\zeta_n(\mathbf{u}) = z_n + \mathbf{b}_n^{\mathrm{T}}(\mathbf{u} - \mathbf{u}_n)$$

so $\zeta_n(\mathbf{u})$ is the first-degree function through $(\mathbf{u}_n, z_n)$ with slope $\mathbf{b}_n$. Mix these with weights $\lambda_n(\mathbf{u})/d_n(\mathbf{u})$, the $\lambda_n(\mathbf{u})$ factor, our contribution, guaranteeing localization, and with the hope that the $1/d_n(\mathbf{u})$ factor, *GPCP*'s contribution, produces correct slopes at the $\mathbf{u}_n$.

Then define

$$\zeta(\mathbf{u}) = \quad z_n \qquad\qquad\qquad \text{if } \mathbf{u} = \mathbf{u}_n$$

$$\zeta(\mathbf{u}) = \frac{\sum\left[\lambda_m(\mathbf{u})\dfrac{\zeta_m(\mathbf{u})}{d_m(\mathbf{u})}\right]}{\sum\dfrac{\lambda_m(\mathbf{u})}{d_m(\mathbf{u})}} \qquad \text{if } \mathbf{u} \neq \text{ any } \mathbf{u}_n.$$

What happens if the data values actually lie on a spherical quadratic? If

$$z_n = \alpha + \boldsymbol{\beta}^T\mathbf{u}_n + \gamma\mathbf{u}_n^T\mathbf{u}_n)$$

at least at the neighbours of $\mathbf{u}$ and at their neighbours, then already we know that

$$\mathbf{b}_n = \boldsymbol{\beta} + 2\gamma\mathbf{u}_n;$$

so

$$\zeta_n(\mathbf{u}) = \alpha + \boldsymbol{\beta}^T\mathbf{u} + \gamma\mathbf{u}^T\mathbf{u} - \gamma d_n^2(\mathbf{u})$$

and

$$\zeta(\mathbf{u}) = \alpha + \boldsymbol{\beta}^T\mathbf{u} + \gamma\mathbf{u}^T\mathbf{u} - \gamma\frac{\sum \lambda_n(\mathbf{u})d_n(\mathbf{u})}{\sum[\lambda_n(\mathbf{u})/d_n(\mathbf{u})]}.$$

This differs only in the last term from the spherical quadratic we would like to recover; it is this last term which gives rise to the defect pointed out above. If under the same assumptions we calculate $Z^{(0)}$, we obtain

$$Z^{(0)}(\mathbf{u}) = \alpha + \boldsymbol{\beta}^T\mathbf{u} + \gamma\mathbf{u}^T\mathbf{u} + \gamma\sum\lambda_n(\mathbf{u})d_n^2(\mathbf{u})$$

(this depends on using the *LCP*). So we can use $Z^{(0)}$ to knock out the unwanted term, and define

$$Z^{(1)}(\mathbf{u}) = \frac{\dfrac{\sum \lambda_n(\mathbf{u})d_n(\mathbf{u})}{\sum[\lambda_n(\mathbf{u})/d_n(\mathbf{u})]} Z^{(0)}(\mathbf{u}) + \sum[\lambda_n(\mathbf{u})d_n^2(\mathbf{u})]\zeta(\mathbf{u})}{\dfrac{\sum \lambda_n(\mathbf{u})d_n(\mathbf{u})}{\sum[\lambda_n(\mathbf{u})/d_n(\mathbf{u})]} + \sum \lambda_n(\mathbf{u})d_n^2(\mathbf{u})} \tag{2.2}$$

which takes the correct value $\alpha + \boldsymbol{\beta}^T\mathbf{u} + \gamma\mathbf{u}^T\mathbf{u}$ on a spherical quadratic. $Z^{(1)}$ is the *natural neighbour C^1 interpolant*, and in the course of setting it up we have established that it reproduces spherical quadratics—indeed, it was set up to do just that. Despite its repellent appearance, it has other good properties of a theoretical nature.

It is indeed C^1, with gradient $\mathbf{b}_n$ at P_n. Although the weighting factor

$1/d_n(\mathbf{u})$ was put in in an attempt to achieve this, it is not at all obvious that it succeeds; the proof requires many pages of tedious detailed analysis.

In one dimension it reduces to a Hermite cubic. This is easy to establish. Note that it is *not* the smoothing spline, which has different gradients at the data sites, determined in a non-localized way to make the function C^2 rather than just C^1.

All the above theory depends on the *LCP*, and consequently leaves open the question of edge effects. Inevitably these have to be dealt with in a somewhat *ad hoc* manner, but it is not hard to find an appropriate treatment which extends $Z^{(1)}$ as a C^1 function over the whole of E and maintains other good properties over virtually the whole window. We shall not consider the details here. Apart from a few edge anomalies, $Z^{(1)}$ depends continuously differentiably, not just continuously, on the positions of the data sites.

2.4 COMPUTING THE NATURAL NEIGHBOUR INTERPOLANT IN TWO DIMENSIONS

The computation follows the mathematics in that first a gradient value $\mathbf{b}_n$ is computed at P_n, and then the interpolant is computed at all points of interest.

The first step in computing the $\mathbf{b}_n$ is to compute the Dirichlet tessellation of $P_1, \ldots, P_N$ in E. In one dimension this is trivial. In two dimensions it can be carried out very efficiently by the TILE algorithm (Green and Sibson, 1978). In three or more dimensions an algorithm due to Bowyer (1981) looks very promising.

The second step in computing the $\mathbf{b}_n$ is the calculation of subtile areas for each P_n. Given the tessellation in two dimensions, which is the case we now primarily discuss, this is a complicated but reasonably efficient geometrical computation. Depending on the nature of the application, the computed areas can either be used immediately and discarded, or saved in parallel with the 'neighbour' information for repeated calculation using different systems of data values at the same data sites.

The third and final step in computing the $\mathbf{b}_n$ is actually to work them out from the formula (2.1) above. This is quick and easy.

The first step in computing the interpolant at an arbitrary point P is to determine how P would fit into the tessellation and to calculate its subtile areas. The computation can be set out in various ways; roughly speaking, it is equivalent to the main iterative step in the TILE algorithm followed by an area calculation. It is quite efficient, much more so if the points at which the interpolant value is wanted are accessed in a geometrically fairly systematic way.

The second and final step in computing the interpolant is to work it out from the formula (2.2). Despite the complicated appearance of the formula, there is no difficulty over the calculation.

The storage required is as follows. If we denote by NPTS the number of data sites then for the computation of the original tessellation, we need (following the FORTRAN convention)

a   REAL array PT(2,NPTS) to hold data site coordinates
an INTEGER array NADDR(NPTS) used as an address vector
an INTEGER array L(LTOP) used as a heap to store the contiguities, with (usually) LTOP the larger of 9 * NPTS and 1000

plus a small amount of other working space not dependent on NPTS. For computing the $\mathbf{b}_n$, we need

a   REAL array VAL(NPTS) to hold data values
a   REAL array GRAD(2,NPTS) to hold gradients.

If it is desired to save subareas, an additional real array A(LTOP) is needed for this, and there is also a small amount of working space needed, of a size not dependent on NPTS. In some applications where knowledge of the extent of edge effects is important, an INTEGER array ICS(NPTS) may be needed to hold edge-effect indicator flags. Finally, for computing interpolant values, only a small amount of working space independent of NPTS is needed in addition to the storage already described; of course, space will be needed if it is desired to store these values.

The basic Green–Sibson algorithm has a computation time of the form

$$T = AN^{3/2} + BN + o(N)$$

on N data sites. It is possible to modify the algorithm (at a cost in storage) to make the leading term $N \log N$ rather than $N^{3/2}$, but A is so small in relation to B that there is little point in this up to, say, $N = 10\,000$. Other steps in the computation of $\mathbf{b}_n$ lead to nothing worse than an additional contribution to B. The computation of the interpolant value is normally carried out in a geometrically systematic manner at a spacing fairly close in relation to the typical spacing of data sites, and in this case the time per interpolated value is virtually independent of the number of data sites.

The program has been implemented in ISO FORTRAN; although efficient it is very complex, amounting to about 4000 lines of code including copious comments. Some of the programming intricacies of the tessellation calculation are discussed in the Green–Sibson paper. On a Honeywell Multics system, the time taken to interpolate from 400 data sites to 625 interpolated values is about 12 s, and there is still some scope for further program optimization. The '10 000 to 10 000' scale of operation mentioned in Section 2.1.1 appears to be well within reach.

2.5 LOOKING AT FUNCTIONS OVER THE PLANE

The usual graph representing the behaviour of a real function of one real variable has as its two-variable analogue a surface, lying in three-dimensional space. There are two familiar ways of presenting such a surface in two dimensions:

(a) by a contour plot;
(b) by a perspective view.

There are also various combinations of these, and additional techniques such as shading; there is much of interest on this topic in Davis and McCullagh (1975). We confine ourselves to the two basic techniques.

Contour plotting is usually appropriate when other data have to be related to the function being displayed—cartographic applications come immediately to mind, and have trained us to 'read' diagrams conventionalized in this way. Natural-neighbour interpolation allows us to determine, from arbitrarily spaced and positioned data sites, the value (and, if desired, gradient) of the interpolant on a regular grid of points, and from this a variety of standard methods are available for contouring. A method based on the use of piecewise quadratic functions has been developed (Sibson and Thomson, 1981).

Perspective views are appropriate for the qualitative appreciation of the surface. The usual way to present them is to plot a perspective view of a network (usually square) of lines on the surface. Many programs for this exist, but almost invariably they either use an artificial draughtsman's perspective,

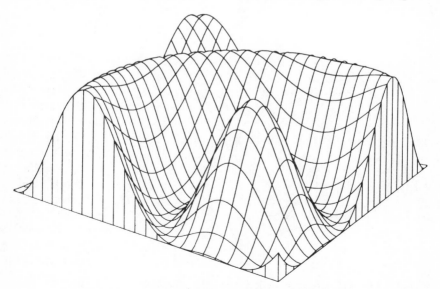

Figure 2.4   The function (2.3) on the unit square

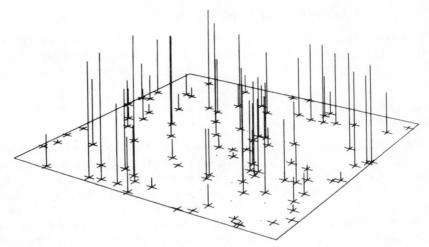

Figure 2.5   Values of the function (2.3) at data sites in the unit square

such as isometric projection, often from a predetermined viewpoint, or they use an unsatisfactory technique for hidden line removal. An elegant solution to the problem has been devised by A. Bowyer of the University of Bath, and is used in the examples in the final section.

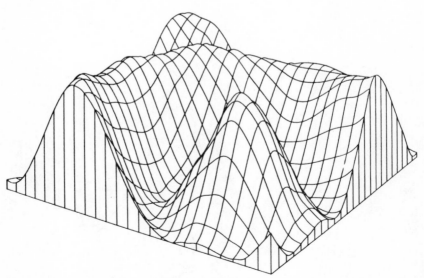

Figure   2.6   The   reconstruction   of   the   function   (2.3)   by   the C^1
natural-neighbour method

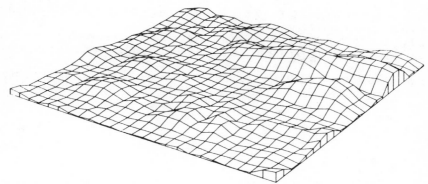

Figure 2.7   The absolute error of interpolation for the function (2.3)

2.6 EXAMPLE

We use a battery of standard functions to check the behaviour of the method. As an example, we illustrate the results on one of the most complicated of these,

$$f(x, y) = \cos\{4\pi\sqrt{[(x - \tfrac{1}{4})^2 + (y - \tfrac{1}{4})^2]}\} \qquad (2.3)$$

which is a system of circular ripples centred at $(\tfrac{1}{4}, \tfrac{1}{4})$. Figure 2.4 is a perspective view of this function on the unit square. In order to remove edge effects from the illustrative example we have taken data sites in a larger region. Figure 2.5 shows the data sites which fall in the unit square, and the values at them; there are about 100 of them. Figure 2.6 shows the reconstruction produced by the C^1 natural neighbour method, and Figure 2.7 shows the absolute error.

REFERENCES

Bowyer, A. (1981) Computing Dirichlet tessellations. *The Computer Journal,* **24**, 162–6.

Davis, J. C. and McCullagh, M. J. (eds.) (1975) *Display and Analysis of Spatial Data*. New York: Wiley.

Delfiner, P. and Delhomme, J. P. (1975) Optimum interpolation by kriging. In Davis, J. C. and McCullagh, M. J. (eds.) (1975) *Display and Analysis of Spatial Data*. London: Wiley, pp. 96–114.

Green, P. J. and Sibson, R. (1978) Computing Dirichlet tessellations in the plane. *The Computer Journal,* **21**, 168–73.

Lawson, C. L. (1977) Software for C^1 surface interpolation. In Rice, J. (ed.) (1977) *Mathematical Software III*. New York: Academic Press, pp. 161–94.

Matheron, G. (1973) The intrinsic random functions and their applications. *Adv. Appl. Prob.,* **5**, 439–68.

Sibson, R. (1980) A vector identity for the Dirichlet tessellation. *Math. Proc. Camb. Phil. Soc.,* **87**, 151–5.

Sibson, R. and Thomson, G. D. (1981) A seamed quadratic element for contouring. *The Computer Journal* (in press).

Wahba, G. (1979) How to smooth curves and surfaces with splines and cross-validation. *Technical Report No. 555*. University of Wisconsin, Department of Statistics.

Wahba, G. and Wold, S. (1975) A completely automatic French curve; fitting spline functions by cross-validation. *Comm. Stat.*, **4**, 1–17.

CHAPTER 3

Density Estimation for Univariate and Bivariate Data

B. W. Silverman, *University of Bath, U.K.*

The problem of probability density estimation is easily stated: given observations $X_1, \ldots, X_n$ from some unknown density f, we are required to reconstruct an estimate of the density f.

This chapter falls into two main sections. In the first part, some general remarks about density estimation are made, and some specific examples of applications are given. It should be stressed that although the examples given happen to be univariate, all the remarks made apply equally to the bivariate case, and to the general multivariate case where appropriate.

The second part consists of some remarks about the computation of the estimates. The section on computing the estimates in the univariate case is intended to correct the very common misconception that the formula for the kernel estimate should be used directly for its calculation.

The final section shows how the inherent smoothness properties of the estimate can be used to facilitate its calculation in the bivariate case.

3.1 GENERAL CONSIDERATIONS

The modern study of fully non-parametric density estimates began with Rosenblatt (1956) who first explicitly introduced the kernel estimate, defined subsequently for d-variate data by

$$f_n(\mathbf{t}) = \frac{1}{nh^d} \sum_{i=1}^{n} K\left[\frac{1}{h}(\mathbf{t} - \mathbf{X}_i)\right], \qquad (3.1)$$

where the function K is (usually) a d-variate probability density function called the *kernel function*, and h is the *smoothing parameter* or *window width*.

There is a considerable literature on density estimation, mostly of a theoretical nature. A recent bibliography is given by Wertz and Schneider (1979); useful papers which give the flavour of the subject from various points of view are Boneva, Kendall and Stefanov (1971), Wegman (1972), Rosenblatt (1971) and Fryer (1977).

Before making specific remarks about particular methods of density estimation, it is worth pausing to consider our reasons for estimating densities. To do this, we can think of the process of the statistical treatment of data as, broadly speaking, consisting of three main stages: exploratory, confirmatory and presentational; we shall consider these three stages successively. The various examples given are intended throughout both to illustrate particular points and also to give a general feel for the subject.

3.1.1 Exploratory analysis

The rôle of density estimation in the exploratory analysis of data has been widely discussed. Density estimates give valuable indication of such features as skewness, weight of tails and multimodality in the data; these features can be investigated further at the confirmatory stage.

For an example see Figure 3.1. The data presented here concern the unfortunate phenomenon of sudden infant death or 'cot death'. The figure is reproduced from Emery and Carpenter (1974). The density estimates were obtained using the spline transform of Boneva, Kendall and Stefanov (1971). For fuller details of the measurements made the reader is referred to the original paper. The curve A is constructed from the observations made on the cot-death cases, while the cases used to construct curve B are a control sample consisting of infants who died in hospital of known causes. The density estimates suggest that the density underlying the cot-death population may be a mixture of the control density with a smaller proportion of a contaminating

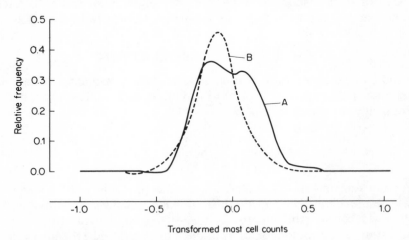

Figure 3.1   Spline transforms of degranulated mast cell counts. A—Cot deaths; B—Hospital deaths. (From Emery and Carpenter (1974). Reproduced by permission of the Canadian Foundation for the Study of Infant Deaths)

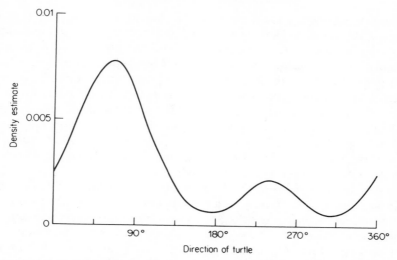

Figure 3.2   Directions of turtles. (Adapted from Silverman (1978).
Reproduced by permission of the Biometrika Trustees)

density of higher mean, and hence that in a minority, perhaps a third, of the
unexpected deaths, the degranulated mast-cell count is abnormally high.
Obviously these remarks cannot be regarded as any more than tentative
conclusions pointing the way to further analysis and/or data collection.

Another example is given in Figure 3.2. The data presented, a standard
directional data set, consist of the directions in which each of 76 turtles were
observed to swim when released. For other analyses of these data, see
Stephens (1969), Mardia (1975) and Boneva, Kendall and Stefanov (1971).
The graph in Figure 3.2 was obtained by Silverman (1978) using the kernel
method adapted for directional data. The density estimate makes it very clear
that most of the turtles show a preference for swimming approximately in the
60° direction, while a small proportion prefer exactly the opposite direction.

Further examples, both univariate and bivariate, where density estimation
is useful as an exploratory technique will be given below.

3.1.2 Confirmatory analysis

Confirmatory analysis is, of course, often unnessary or inappropriate. In
many cases either the conclusions are obvious from exploratory examination
of the data or else, on the other hand, the data set is so small, or unreliable, or
untypical for known reasons, that it is dangerous or misleading to attempt to
draw any firm conclusions of a classical statistical kind.

An example of the first possibility is perhaps given by the turtle data
estimate of Figure 3.2. Here, all the conclusions to be drawn are clear from

the density estimate, and, while it is possible to set up formal tests and models, if this is the only information we have there is little point in doing so. Of course it is an entirely different matter if this is only part of a larger set of data, or if there are important concomitant observations available.

Turning away from these (intentionally provocative) remarks, there is indeed a limited range of applications where density estimates are useful directly in formal statistical analysis. The first of these is in non-parametric discriminant analysis; density estimates have been used where the classical parametric assumptions of discriminant analysis are felt to be inappropriate. Much of the work in this area has been done by the Dutch school; see for example Habbema, Hermans and van der Broek (1974).

Another application is in the field of Monte Carlo testing; see, for example, Besag and Diggle (1977), for a wider discussion of Monte Carlo testing. One possible object is, given a data set, to construct numerous independent replications which have broadly the same characteristics as the original data but which differ from it in fine detail. A possible method is to construct a density estimate from the data and then to simulate from this estimate, either by using a rejection technique, or, if a kernel estimate is being used, by using the method proposed by Efron (1979) for his closely related smoothed bootstrap approach. Here, members of the original data set are sampled uniformly with replacement and then perturbed by a quantity drawn from the density obtained by scaling the kernel appropriately.

A problem of this kind is also considered by Kendall and Kendall (1980); they propose a more sophisticated, but somewhat related approach.

Good and Gaskins (1980) have applied ideas of density estimation to a problem in high-energy physics. Their method makes it possible to assess the posterior odds on a particular bump in the density, thus giving information relevant to the discovery of new elementary particles.

3.1.3 Presentation

Statisticians are often so concerned with talking to each other that they forget that their ultimate aim is to convince their clients of the conclusions they have obtained by possibly sophisticated means. Density estimates are ideally suited to this purpose for the simple reason that people, as opposed to mathematicians, understand them! Even those statisticians who are sceptical about *estimating* densities would, I am sure, explain a normal distribution to a layman by drawing a bell-shaped curve rather than drawing an S-shaped curve or writing down the moment-generating function! This perspective alone would amply justify the study of probability density estimation.

Figures 3.1 and 3.2 above both give examples where density estimates provide an excellent presentation of the data, intelligible to the layman. Another example, which we shall return to later, arises from the study of the frictional properties of machined metal surfaces. The data set discussed here

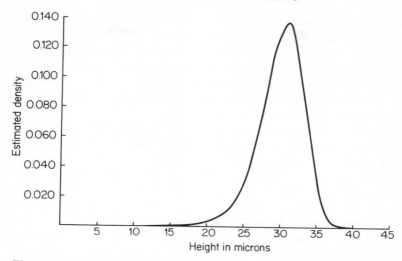

Figure 3.3 Steel surface data. (Adapted from Silverman (1980). Reproduced by permission of Academic Press, Inc.)

was obtained and kindly provided by Dr. A. Bowyer of Bath University; for further details see Bowyer (1978 and 1980).

The data consist of about 15 000 observations of the height of a nominally flat stainless steel surface above an arbitrary datum level. Gaussian processes are often used to model such surfaces and it is obviously of interest to investigate the validity of such models. A possible check is to examine the marginal distribution of height at a point. Figure 3.3 gives an estimate of the density of this distribution, constructed from the 15 000 heights, using the Fourier-transform technique described below. This graph is reproduced from Bowyer (1980) and Silverman (1980).

From an engineering point of view, the tails of this distribution are interesting for different reasons. The upper tail represents the part of the surface which might come into contact with other surfaces. The lower tail represents the hollows in which lubricant might gather, and also the possible starting points of fatigue cracks. Figure 3.3 shows that the distribution is obviously not Gaussian. The long lower tail is heavier than that predicted by a Gaussian model, while the upper tail is short. This skewness accords with the notion that the machining process removes the peaks of the surface but leaves the valleys largely unaffected.

3.1.4 Choice of smoothing parameter

So far, little has been said about specific methods for density estimation. Indeed, various general principles appear to hold whatever method is being used. Most, if not all, methods involve, implicitly or explicitly, the choice of a parameter which controls the amount by which the data are smoothed to obtain the estimate. The character of the estimate depends mainly on this choice. There are often other choices to be made, such as the choice of kernel in the kernel method, but, broadly speaking, these choices are of secondary importance; even the choice between methods is somewhat less serious than the choice of smoothing since it appears that a similar range of estimates is obtained whatever method is being used.

When using density estimates as exploratory aids, there is in any case no need to concentrate on one particular amount of smoothing. Indeed it may be of great interest to examine features which appear at some degrees of smoothing but are absent at others. For an example, see Figure 3.4. The data analysed here are the figures for annual snowfall precipitation in Buffalo from 1910 until 1972. The graphs presented are due to Parzen (1979). They are not in fact estimates of the density but of the related function fF^{-1}, where f is the density and F the distribution function underlying the data; for further details see Parzen's paper. The two curves are constructed using different amounts of smoothing, and it can be seen that the data are either unimodal or trimodal. Considering the relatively small size of the data set it may in any case be impossible to reliably resolve this dichotomy on the basis of the data alone; Parzen shows a preference for the unimodal explanation while others have preferred the trimodal. Whatever one's preference is, the two curves together demonstrate an interesting feature of the data.

The idea of looking at several different estimates can be summed up by saying that density estimates give a summary of the data, and that estimates with different amounts of smoothing give summaries emphasizing different features; the summaries have different emphasis again from, for example, probability plots.

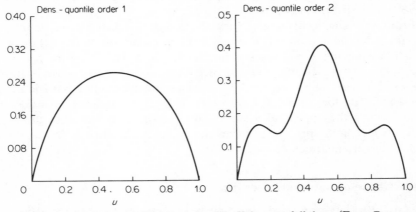

Figure 3.4   Density quantile estimates of Buffalo snowfall data. (From Parzen (1979). Reproduced by permission of the American Statistical Association)

In many contexts it is indeed important to have a single choice of smoothing parameter. The problem of objective smoothing-parameter choice is one of current research interest, and several objective and partially objective methods have been suggested; see, for example, Woodroofe (1970), Habbema, Hermans and van der Broek (1974), Fryer (1977), Silverman (1978 and 1980), and Parzen (1979). It is probably fair to say that there is as yet no universally accepted method and that at present the choice is very often made subjectively.

Finally it should be mentioned that the value of the smoothing parameter at which a particular feature *just* disappears may itself be used as a statistic; see Silverman (1981a).

3.2 COMPUTING KERNEL ESTIMATES

The second part of this chapter consists mainly of remarks on the computation of kernel estimates. While it is not crucial for all applications to be able to compute the estimates very quickly, the use of efficient computational methods makes it possible, for example, to compute density estimates on an interactive graphics system without great expense. The cases of univariate and bivariate estimation will be considered separately.

3.2.1 The univariate case

It will be convenient to restrict attention to estimates constructed with normal kernel. Theoretical considerations (Epanechnikov, 1969) and practical experience suggest that this choice of kernel is sensible, and in addition we shall see that it has considerable computational advantages. The estimate f_n based on real observations $X_1, \ldots, X_n$ will then be given by

$$f_n(t) = \sum_{j=1}^{n} \frac{1}{nh} \phi\left(\frac{t - X_j}{h}\right) \tag{3.2}$$

where the function ϕ is the standard normal density and h is the window width.

For most purposes, it is necessary to calculate $f_n(t)$ at a fairly large number of points t, for example in order to plot the estimate. It is highly inefficient to use (3.2) directly for this purpose; if $f_n(t)$ is to be calculated at m points t, then the kernel has to be evaluated mn times. Some amelioration is available if a kernel of bounded support is used, but the calculations are still likely to be fairly slow for large samples.

Considerable savings may be made by using a method based on Fourier transforms. The estimate (3.2) is precisely a convolution of the data with a scaled version of the kernel, and therefore its Fourier transform may be obtained very easily as a multiple of the product of the Fourier transforms of the data and the kernel. Letting $\sim$ denote Fourier transformation, we have, by standard Fourier-transform theory,

$$\tilde{f}_n(s) = u(s) \exp(-\tfrac{1}{2} h^2 s^2). \qquad (3.3)$$

where $u(s)$ is the Fourier transform of the data

$$u(s) = \frac{1}{\sqrt{2\pi}} \frac{1}{n} \sum_{j=1}^{n} \exp(isX_j).$$

The fact that the kernel is normal has allowed its Fourier transform to be inserted explicitly in (3.3).

The fast Fourier transform (Cooley and Tukey, 1965) makes it possible to find u and f_n very quickly, using the algorithm set out below. Since all the transforms handled are those of real functions, the approach of Gentleman and Sande (1966), implemented by Monro (1976), can be used to save storage and time.

Step 1   Choose an interval $[a, b]$ which is somewhat larger than the interval on which f_n is to be calculated, to avoid edge effects.

Step 2   Putting $m = 2^k$($k = 8$ or 10 is amply large enough) bin the data into a histogram v on (a, b) with 2^k cells; multiply v by $2^k n^{-1}(b - a)^{-1}$ to make the total area equal to one. Obtain the fast Fourier transform u of v.

Step 3   (repeat for each window width of interest). Use (3.3) above to find $\tilde{f}_n$ for each s for which $u(s)$ has been calculated. Use the fast Fourier transform to invert $\tilde{f}_n$ and obtain f_n.

Note that if estimates for several window widths are required, then only the last step need be repeated. If derivatives of the estimates are required (for example for the test graph method of Silverman, 1978) they are easily obtained by using the fact that the Fourier transform of $f_n^{(r)}$ is given by $i^{-r}s^{-r}\tilde{f}_n(s)$.

An assessment of the saving in computer time available by using this algorithm is given in Table 3.1. Here NFT is the number of points at which the estimate is calculated and NDATA is the sample size. The figures tabulated are the ratio of the time required by the algorithm just described to that required for direct calculation from (3.2). For each value of NFT and NDATA, the upper figure given refers to the first estimate evaluated, where all the steps of the algorithm are executed, while the lower figure refers to subsequent invocations where only Step 3 is involved. It is clear that the algorithm is particularly advantageous for reasonably large data sets and where several estimates are required.

There is obviously some error arising in the discretization used in the algorithm. An assessment of this is given in Table 3.2. The estimates were

Table 3.1 Relative timings for Fourier transform algorithm

NDATA	20	100	1000
NFT			
64	0.22	0.05	0.010
	0.10	0.02	0.002
256	0.20	0.04	0.006
	0.09	0.02	0.002
1024	0.20	0.04	0.005
	0.10	0.02	0.002

Table 3.2 Maximum calculation errors for estimates of a standard normal density based on 100 independent observations

NFT	Window	Error
64	0.2	2.5×10^{-2}
	0.6	3.8×10^{-3}
	1.2	1.4×10^{-3}
128	0.2	8.6×10^{-3}
	0.6	1.8×10^{-3}
	1.2	5.3×10^{-4}
256	0.2	6.7×10^{-3}
	0.6	7.8×10^{-4}
	1.2	2.5×10^{-4}
512	0.2	3.8×10^{-3}
	0.6	1.2×10^{-4}
	1.2	2.3×10^{-5}

calculated on the interval $[-8, 8]$ from 100 observations from a standard normal distribution. The errors tabulated are the maximum over the interval $[-4, 4]$ of the difference between the values yielded by the algorithm and the exact values of the estimate obtained by direct evaluation of (3.2). They do *not* refer to the difference between the estimated and true densities, which is much larger in all cases. For most practical purposes choosing NFT to be 256 gives excellent results.

For an implementation and further details, see Silverman (1981b). The algorithm was used to compute Figure 3.3. Apart from the time taken to read in the 15 000 data values, the algorithm took only 0.9 s to compute the estimate on a Honeywell twin processor Level 68 DPS machine.

3.2.2 The bivariate case

The range of feasible methods available for density estimation in the multivariate case is by no means as large as that available for univariate data. Probably the only easily used methods at present are the kernel method and the nearest-neighbour method (Loftsgaarden and Quesenberry, 1965). Mention should also be made of the hybrid method of Breiman, Meisel and Purcell (1977).

In this section attention will be concentrated on the kernel method, though some of the remarks can in fact be generalized to other methods as well. In the multivariate case, the window width h can of course be generalized to a vector or even a matrix of shrinking coefficients. To avoid this complication it is probably best to rescale the data if the marginal variances differ substantially. In certain cases it may be appropriate to refer to principal components.

When the estimates are being used for exploratory or presentational purposes it is necessary to produce some representation of the density surface such as a perspective view or a contour plot. Examples of both of these techniques will be given below; while the perspective view gives a very good general impression of the surface, the contour plot may be clearer on certain occasions.

Most methods for constructing views or contours of surfaces require information about the height of the surface at each point on a reasonably fine grid. If the formula (3.1) for the kernel estimate is used, then even for a 30×30 grid of points nearly a thousand evaluations of the estimate are required, and so for a large data set the computation time is likely to be excessive. However a considerable saving can be made by noticing that it is extremely easy, provided a differentiable kernel is used, to calculate not only the height but also the gradients of the density estimate at any particular point. This is in contrast to most surface plotting problems, where gradient information is often unavailable or else expensive to obtain.

The gradient of the density estimate is given in the d-variate case by

$$\nabla f_n(\mathbf{t}) = n^{-1} h^{-d-1} \sum_j \nabla K[h^{-1}(\mathbf{t} - \mathbf{X}_j)]$$

and so, for suitable kernels K, is available at trivial additional cost once the estimate itself is being calculated.

Another useful feature of the kernel density estimate is that all the continuity and differentiability properties of the estimate are inherited from those of the kernel, and therefore can be prescribed by the user. This fact is particularly useful if we wish to interpolate to intermediate points from a grid of values and gradients.

Suppose we are interpolating a function on a square, given its value and gradients at each corner of the square. Suppose our interpolation method has the property that it is linear in the given values and gradients and that it reproduces quadratic surfaces exactly. Then some elementary manipulation using Taylor's theorem shows that, if the square has side l, then the maximum interpolation error is $O(l^3)$, as l tends to zero, provided the function has bounded third derivatives. It follows that interpolation even from a fairly large square is still quite accurate.

Just such a method of interpolation can be obtained by using the seamed quadratic element designed for contouring by Sibson and Thomson (1980). This produces a continuously differentiable surface whose value and gradients can be prescribed at each point of a rectangular grid. Each grid cell is divided into sixteen panels (see Figure 3.5); the surface is quadratic on each panel.

An advantage of the Sibson–Thomson method is that, using the method of Marlow and Powell (1976), it is possible exactly to calculate the contours of the piecewise-quadratic surface to produce high-quality contour maps.

The remarks made above suggest that good plots of bivariate density estimates can be obtained, provided the kernel has bounded third derivatives, by calculating the values and gradients of the estimate at each point of a coarse grid and then using the Sibson–Thomson method to produce a perspective view or contour plot. A suitable kernel, whose value and derivatives are easily evaluated, is given by

$$K(x, y) = \begin{cases} 4\pi^{-1}(1 - x^2 - y^2)^3 & x^2 + y^2 \leqslant 1 \\ 0 & \text{otherwise.} \end{cases}$$

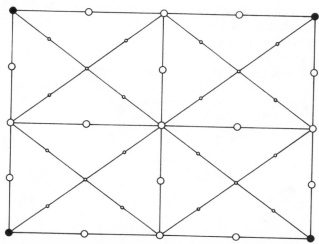

Figure 3.5   Panels for contouring method. (Adapted from Sibson and Thomson (1980). Reproduced by permission of the authors)

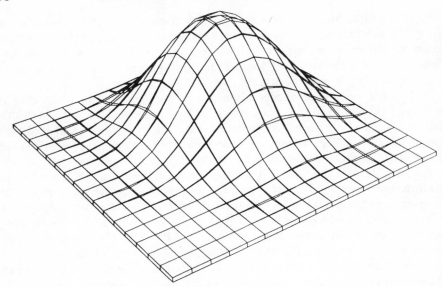

Figure 3.6   Kernel function, true and interpolated

This kernel was used to calculate all the examples in the remainder of this section. Figure 3.6 gives superimposed perspective views of the kernel calculated exactly and interpolated from a grid of size half the window width. It can be seen that even for one data point, as is effectively the case here, interpolation from a coarse grid introduces very little error!

Experiments with moderate data sets of size around 100 show that excellent results can be obtained for grid sizes up to about three-quarters the window width, while for large data sets using grids as large as the window width introduces no appreciable error. As an illustration, one hundred points were simulated from an equal mixture of unit normal distributions with means $(-1, 1)$ and $(1, 1)$ as shown in Figure 3.7; here and in the subsequent figures the display is on the square with corners $(\pm 3, \pm 3)$. Figures 3.8 and 3.9 give

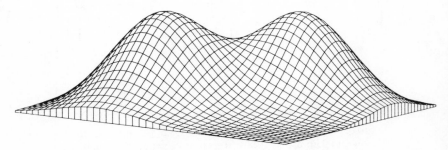

Figure 3.7   Bivariate normal mixture

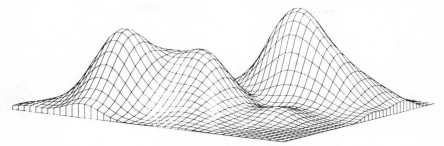

Figure 3.8   Density estimate, window width 1.2, grid size 0.6

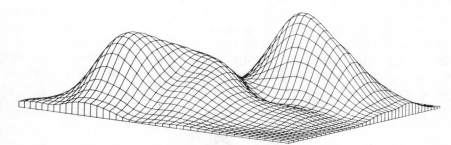

Figure 3.9   Density estimate, window width 1.2, grid size 1.2

estimates with window width 1.2 interpolated from grids of size 0.6 and 1.2 respectively. Though the difference is visible, it is very slight and would cause no difficulty in practice. Figures 3.10 and 3.11, both calculated with grid size 1.2, show how the estimate changes as the window width is varied.

For the final example, we return to the steel surface data described above. Another check whether the surface is Gaussian is given by examining a bivariate marginal distribution of height. For this purpose, the pair (height at **x**, height at **x** + **u**) was found for about 15 000 points **x** on the surface, with **u**

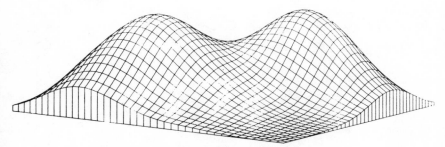

Figure 3.10   Density estimate, window width 2.2

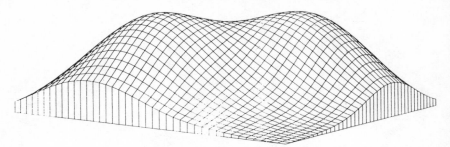

Figure 3.11   Density estimate, window width 2.8

a vector of fixed direction and fixed length 20 μm. A contour plot of the density estimate constructed from these points with window width 3.0 is given in Figure 3.12; the data have been adjusted to have mean (0, 0). The non-Gaussian nature of the data is clear from the fact that the mode does not correspond to the mean, while the approximate symmetry of the figure about its leading diagonal shows that any effects of abrasion of the surface appear to be invariant under rotation of the surface through 180°. Figure 3.13 is an

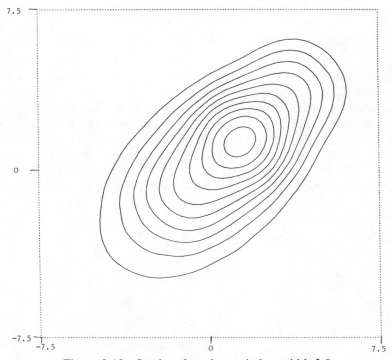

Figure 3.12   Steel surface data, window width 3.0

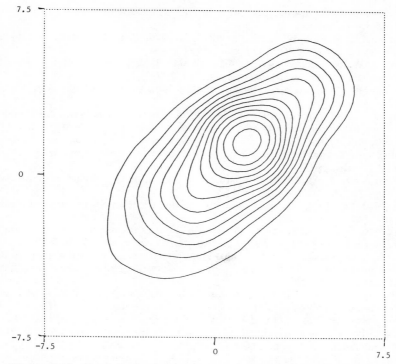

7.5

0

-7.5

-7.5   0   7.5

Figure 3.13   Steel surface data, window width 1.5. (Adapted from Sibson and Thomson (1980). Reproduced by permission of the authors)

estimate constructed with window width 1.5. Because of the large sample size, this reduction does not substantially affect the estimate.

Acknowledgements

The author is grateful to the Social Science Research Council for research assistance and facilities; to the authors of those papers from which figures have been reproduced; and to A. Bowyer and G. D. Thomson for assistance with the computing.

REFERENCES

Besag, J. E. and Diggle, P. J. (1977) Monte Carlo tests for spatial pattern. *Applied Statistics*, **26**, 327–33.

Boneva, L. I., Kendall, D. G., and Stefanov, I. (1971) Spline transformations. *J. Roy. Statist. Soc. B.*, **33**, 1–70.

Bowyer, A. (1978) A computer model of sliding friction. *Proc. 4th Leeds–Lyon symposium on surface roughness*. I. Mech. E. pubs.

Bowyer, A. (1980) Experiments and Computer Modelling in Stick-slip. *Ph.D. Thesis,* University of London.

Breiman, L., Meisel, W., and Purcell, E. (1977) Variable kernel estimates of multivariate densities. *Technometrics,* **19**, 135–44.

Cooley, J. W. and Tukey, J. W. (1965) An algorithm for the machine calculation of complex Fourier series. *Math. Comput.,* **19**, 297–301.

Efron, B. (1979) Bootstrap methods—another look at the jackknife. *Ann. Statist.,* **7**, 1–26.

Emery, J. L. and Carpenter, R. G. (1974) Pulmonary mast cells in infants and their relation to unexpected death in infancy. In Robinson, R. R. (ed.) (1974) *Proceedings of the Francis E. Camps International Symposium on Sudden and Unexpected Deaths in Infancy.* Toronto: Canadian Foundation for the Study of Infant Deaths, pp. 7–19.

Epanechnikov, V. A. (1969) Nonparametric estimation of a multivariate probability density. *Theor. Prob. Appl.,* **14**, 153–8.

Fryer, M. J. (1977) A review of some non-parametric methods of density estimation. *J. Inst. Maths. Appl.,* **20**, 335–54.

Gentleman, W. M. and Sande, G. (1966) Fast Fourier transforms—for fun and profit. *AFIPS Proceedings of the Fall Joint Computer Conference,* **19**, 563–78.

Good, I. J. and Gaskins, R. A. (1980) Density estimation and bump-hunting by the penalized likelihood method exemplified by scattering and meteorite data. *J. Amer. Stat. Assn.,* **75**, 42–56.

Habbema, J. D. F., Hermans, J., and van der Broek, K. (1974) A stepwise discriminant analysis program using density estimation. *COMPSTAT 1974, Proceedings in Computational Statistics.* Wien: Physica Verlag, pp. 101–10.

Kendall, D. G. and Kendall, W. S. (1980) Internal alignments in random two-dimensional sets of points. *Adv. Appl. Prob.,* **12**, 384–424.

Loftsgaarden, P. and Quesenberry, C. P. (1965) A non-parametric estimate of a multivariate probability density function. *Ann. Math. Statist.,* **36**, 1049–51.

Mardia, K. V. (1975) Statistics of directional data. *J. Roy. Statist. Soc. B,* **37**, 349–93.

Marlow, S. and Powell, M. J. D. (1976) A Fortran subroutine for plotting the part of a conic that is inside a given triangle. *UKAEA Harwell Paper AERE-R 8336.* London: HMSO.

Monro, D. M. (1976) Algorithm AS 97. Real discrete fast Fourier transform. *Applied Statistics,* **25**, 166–72.

Parzen, E. (1979) Non-parametric statistical data modeling. *J. Amer. Stat. Assn.,* **74**, 105–21.

Rosenblatt, M. (1956) Remarks on some non-parametric estimates of a density function. *Ann. Math. Statist.,* **27**, 832–7.

Rosenblatt, M. (1971) Curve estimates. *Ann. Math. Statist.,* **42**, 1815–42.

Sibson, R. and Thomson, G. D. (1980) A seamed quadratic element for contouring. *Internal Report,* School of Mathematics, University of Bath, U.K.

Silverman, B. W. (1978) Choosing a window width when estimating a density. *Biometrika,* **65**, 1–11.

Silverman, B. W. (1980) Density estimation: Are theoretical results useful in practice? In Chakravarti, I. M. (ed.) (1980) *Asymptotic Theory of Statistical Tests and Estimation.* New York: Academic Press, pp. 179–203.

Silverman, B. W. (1981a) Using kernel density estimates to investigate multimodality. *J. Roy. Statist. Soc. B,* **43**, 97–9.

Silverman, B. W. (1981b) Kernel density estimation using the fast Fourier transform. *Internal Report,* School of Mathematics, University of Bath, U.K.

Stephens, M. A. (1969) Techniques for directional data. *Technical Report 150*, Dept. of Statistics, Stanford, Calif.

Wegman, E. J. (1972) Non-parametric probability density estimation. I: *Technometrics*, **14**, 533–46; II: *J. Statist. Comp & Sim.*, **1**, 225–46.

Wertz, W. and Schneider, B. (1979) Statistical Density Estimation: a bibliography. *Int. Stat. Rev.*, **47**, 155–75.

Woodroofe, M. (1970) On choosing a Delta-sequence. *Ann. Math. Statist.*, **41**, 1665–71.

CHAPTER 4

Some Graphical Methods in the Analysis of Spatial Point Patterns

P. J. Diggle, *University of Newcastle upon Tyne, U.K.*

We shall be concerned in this chapter with data in the form of a set of point locations or *events* $\{\mathbf{x}_i: i = 1, \ldots, n\}$ in some essentially planar region A. Figure 4.1 gives four examples. A modest objective for a statistical analysis of such data would be to provide a qualitative description of the *pattern* presented by the events in question. Pattern can be described with reference to an idealized standard of *complete spatial randomness* (henceforth *CSR*): that is to say, a homogeneous planar Poisson process, for which

(1) the number $N(A)$ of events in any region A follows a Poisson distribution with mean $\lambda | A |$.
(2) given $N(A) = n$, the events in A form an independent random sample from the uniform distribution on A.

In (1) above, $| A |$ denotes the area of A, and λ is the *intensity*, or mean number of events per unit area.

Many tests of *CSR* are available. Most aim to distinguish between 'regular' and 'aggregated' departures from *CSR* and would classify the patterns in Figures 4.1(a)–(c) as 'regular', 'random' and 'aggregated', respectively. Figure 4.1(d) might also be classified as 'aggregated', although it appears qualitatively different from Figure 4.1(c). The apparent distinction between patterns generated on the one hand by a clustering mechanism and on the other by heterogeneity, or fluctuations in local intensity, is difficult to preserve in any formal statistical sense (Bartlett, 1964). Analyses of these four data-sets can be found in Bartlett (1964), Besag and Diggle (1977), Ripley (1977) and Diggle (1978, 1979a, b).

Evidently, a test of *CSR* can convey only very limited information about a set of data. A more ambitious analysis might involve fitting a model within some parametric class of spatial point processes. This gives a quantitative description of pattern and may provide some insight into possible generating mechanisms, if the necessary additional assumptions are tenable. For example, a model-fitting exercise typically assumes that the underlying phenomenon is both stationary and isotropic, and this immediately raises

55

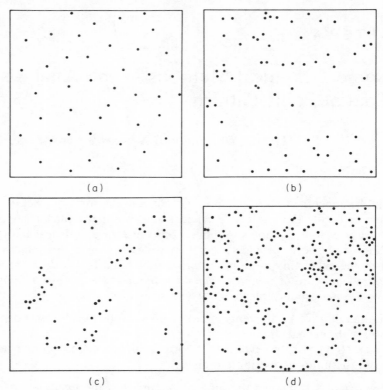

Figure 4.1 Examples of spatial point patterns: (a) 42 biological cell-centres (from Ripley, 1977); (b) 65 Japanese black pine saplings (from Numata, 1961); (c) 62 redwood seedlings (from Ripley, 1977, extracted from Strauss, 1975); (d) 250 balsam fir seedlings (from Ghent, 1963). (Parts (a) and (c) are reproduced by permission of the Royal Statistical Society. Part (d) is reproduced by permission of the Society of American Foresters)

practical difficulties. Spatial point patterns often relate to observational studies in, for example, ecology or geography and are rarely extendable at will, in the manner that some physical time series are, without violation of these basic assumptions. Model-fitting may therefore be confined in practice to relatively sparse data-sets, with the obvious adverse implications for precision of estimation and discrimination between models.

When a large data-set is available, containing of the order of 1000 events, say, it may well have a very heterogeneous structure and restrictive parametric assumptions would be inappropriate. Analysis may then consist in the first instance of presenting the pattern in a more digestible form, possibly to assist in the combined interpretation of multi-type patterns. This problem arises, for example, in ecology when several species are present in the region of interest.

Finally, the pattern may exist only *in situ*, a complete mapping being prohibitively expensive. Data must then be extracted from the pattern in the form of either counts in small sampling areas or distances from sampling points to neighbouring events. For such sparsely sampled patterns, the analysis is properly confined to preliminary testing, and estimation of easily interpretable parameters such as mean number of events per unit area; the available data provide no means of checking, even informally, the assumptions required for a more sophisticated model-fitting exercise.

In the following sections we will illustrate the use of graphical methods in the context of preliminary testing, model-fitting, presentation of large data-sets and analysis of sparsely sampled patterns. Throughout, we take the view that when a map of the data is available this is the most useful single graphical display; our methods are intended to supplement, rather than to replace, inspection of the data. The underlying statistical methodology is generally well established, and we shall include only sufficient methodological commentary to make the material readable in isolation. For further details see Ripley (1977) and Diggle (1979a, b).

4.1 PRELIMINARY TESTING

Rejection of *CSR* is seldom an end in itself, but should be seen as an aid to the formulation of hypotheses for subsequent investigation. For this reason, we advocate tests based on some functional summary description of the data which can elucidate the nature of any observed departure from *CSR*.

A nearest-neighbour analysis is one possibility. Let $\{y_i : i = 1, \ldots, n\}$ be the distances from each of the events in question to its nearest neighbour and consider their empirical distribution function $\hat{F}_1(y) = n^{-1}\#(y_i \leq y).$* Under *CSR*, the corresponding marginal distribution function is approximately $F(y) = 1 - \exp(-\pi\lambda y^2)$ and a plot of $\hat{F}_1(y)$ against $F(y)$ should be approximately linear. The intensity, λ, is estimated by $\hat{\lambda} = n|A|^{-1}$. Note that the observed distances y_i are not independent and will typically include identical measurements between reciprocal nearest-neighbour pairs.

To assess the sampling fluctuations in $\hat{F}_1(y)$ we can calculate empirical distribution functions $\{\hat{F}_j(y): j = 2, \ldots, m\}$ from $m - 1$ simulations, each consisting of n events generated as an independent random sample from the uniform distribution on A, and define *upper* and *lower simulation envelopes* as

$$U(y) = \max_{j=2,\ldots,m} \{\hat{F}_j(y)\}; \qquad L(y) = \min_{j=2,\ldots,m} \{\hat{F}_j(y)\}.$$

---

*The symbol # is a counting operator, meaning 'the number of occasions on which'.

These envelopes can then also be plotted against $F(y)$. In addition the stimulations can provide a test of *CSR*, using Barnard's (1963) notion of a Monte Carlo test. Let u_j be any convenient measure of the discrepancy between $\hat{F}_j(\ )$ and $F(\ )$, for example the Kolmogorov–Smirnov statistic $u_j = \sup|\hat{F}_j(y) - F(y)|$, and denote the ordered u_j-values by $u_{(1)} < u_{(2)} < \ldots \overset{y}{<} u_{(m)}$. Under *CSR*, $P\{u_1 = u_{(j)}\} = m^{-1}$: $j = 1, \ldots, m$ and the rank of u_1 provides an exact test of *CSR*. The power loss for the Monte Carlo test relative to a classical test based on the statistic u_1 is surprisingly small; for tests at conventional significance levels, $m = 100$ is adequate (Hope, 1968; Marriott, 1979).

Note that in this type of analysis, any shape of region A is permissible and no correction for edge effects is required. If edge-effects are severe, as for example when A is a long, thin rectangle, it would nevertheless be preferable not to use the distribution function $F(y)$ in the specification of the u_j, but rather to measure the discrepancy between $\hat{F}_j(\ )$ and $\bar{F}(\ )$, defined by $\bar{F}(y) = m^{-1}\Sigma_{j=1}^{m}\hat{F}_j(y)$. Although the u_j are no longer independent, they are exchangeable under *CSR* and the required property of equiprobable rankings still holds. Alternatively, the unbiased estimator for $F(y)$ implicit in Ripley (1977) could be used. For this, let $\{d_i: i = 1, \ldots, n\}$ be the distances from each of the events to the nearest point on the boundary of A and define

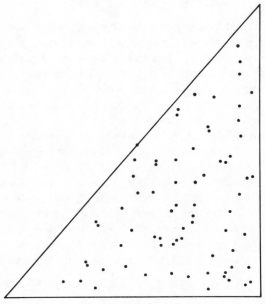

Figure 4.2   72 redwood seedlings in a triangular plot. (From Strauss, 1975. Reproduced by permission of Biometrika Trustees)

$\hat{F}_1(y) = \#(y_i \le y, d_i > y)/\#(d_i > y)$, and similarly for $\hat{F}_j(y)$ from the simulations. The property of unbiasedness is important in any subsequent model-fitting exercise, but for preliminary testing the effective neglect of information from events near the boundary of A is undesirable.

As an illustration, we re-analyse data in Strauss (1975) consisting of a map of 199 redwood seedlings in an experimental plot, divided into two regions by a known discontinuity in soil structure. In Strauss' region II there is clear evidence of clustering which is attributable to the presence of redwood stumps in the plot, and no test of *CSR* is required (see Figure 4.1(c), extracted by Ripley, 1977, from Strauss' data). The pattern in the triangular region I, here reproduced as Figure 4.2, appears more nearly random and Strauss accepts *CSR* against a clustering alternative. The results of our nearest-neighbour analysis are summarized in Figure 4.3. The formal test based on the Kolmogorov–Smirnov statistic with 99 simulations ($m = 100$) rejects *CSR* at the 3% level of significance. The probability plot also suggests what form of alternative to *CSR* might be appropriate. An aggregated, or clustered, pattern would lead to an excess of small distances y, so that at least for sufficiently small y, $\hat{F}_1(y) > U(y)$. Conversely, $\hat{F}_1(y) < L(y)$ would suggest a regular pattern. In Figure 4.3, the relative flatness of $\hat{F}_1(y)$ in the range

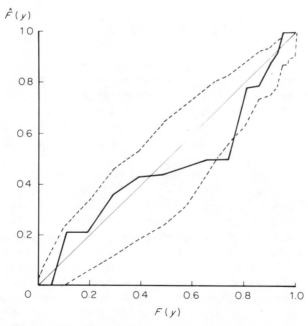

Figure 4.3 Nearest-neighbour analysis of redwood data. ____ data; _ _ _ envelope from 99 simulations of *CSR*

$0.4 \leq F(y) \leq 0.75$ (5–9 feet approximately) suggests a tendency towards regular spacing, rather than the clustering alternative tested by Strauss, although there is clearly no sharply defined inhibition effect in the sense of a minimum permissible distance between seedlings.

The point of this example is not to make any particular claims on behalf of either nearest-neighbour analysis or the Kolmogorov–Smirnov statistic, but rather to suggest that in preliminary testing an open-minded approach based on plotting functional summary descriptions of the data can sometimes yield unexpected results. Whether or not the conclusion in this particular case has interesting implications for the biologist is left as an open question.

4.2 MODEL FITTING

The usual strategy for fitting a model to a point pattern is to match some functional summary description of the model to the corresponding empirical description of the data in what is an intuitively reasonable, if ultimately *ad hoc*, manner. One useful description is the function $K(t)$ introduced by Ripley (1977), which can be interpreted as an integrated version of the covariance density. Explicitly,

$$K(t) = 2\pi\lambda^{-2} \int_0^t \lambda_2(u)u \, du,$$

where λ is the intensity and $\lambda_2(u)$ a joint density for the occurrence of two events at locations a distance u apart (Bartlett, 1978, Ch. 6). Note that $K(t)$ is scale-invariant. In particular, for *CSR* we have that $\lambda_2(u) \equiv \lambda^2$ and $K(t) = \pi t^2$, for all λ. Plots of $\hat{K}(t)$ estimated from a set of data can be used to indicate departures from *CSR* (see Section 4.1), to suggest plausible classes of model, to provide initial estimates of parameters and as a diagnostic check on the fitted model.

We illustrate these ideas using data from Hutchings (1978) on the spatial pattern of bramble canes. Figure 4.4 shows 359 newly emergent canes in a square plot of side 9 m, subsequently taken as the unit of measurement. The visual impression of clustering is confirmed by Figure 4.5, in which $\sqrt{[\hat{K}(t)]}$ for the data lies above the upper envelope from 19 simulations of *CSR*, throughout the plotted range of t. The square-root transformation, suggested by Besag (1977), linearizes the plot and acts as a variance stabilizer.

The simplest mechanism which might describe the pattern in the data is a Poisson cluster process. Specifically, suppose that 'parents' form a Poisson process of intensity ρ, that the numbers of 'offspring' per parent are independent Poisson variates with common mean μ and that the positions of the offspring relative to their parents are independent, radially symmetric Gaussian variates with common dispersion parameter σ. The final pattern consists

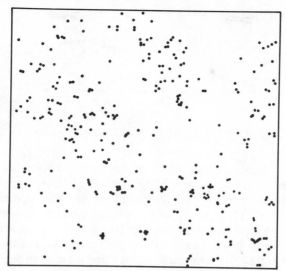

Figure 4.4   359 newly emergent bramble canes.
(See Hutchings, 1978)

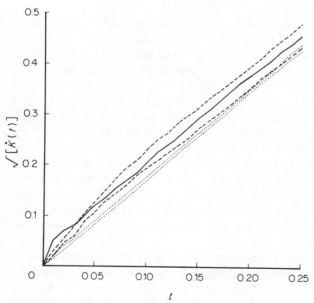

Figure 4.5   Second-order analysis of brambles data.
_____ data; . . . . . envelope from 19 simulations of *CSR*;
- - - - - envelope from 19 simulations of fitted Poisson
cluster process

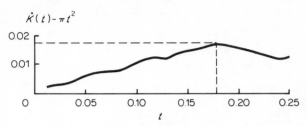

Figure 4.6 $\hat{K}(t) - \pi t^2$ for brambles data

of the totality of offspring so that the intensity of the process is $\lambda = \rho\mu$. Straightforward calculations give $K(t) = \pi t^2 + \rho^{-1}\{1 - \exp[-t^2/(4\sigma^2)]\}$, the parameter μ disappearing as a consequence of the scale invariance.

The form of $K(t)$ for the Poisson cluster process suggests looking at $\hat{K}(t) - \pi t^2$, which is plotted in Figure 4.6. By equating the observed maximum on the plot to the point $(4\sigma, \rho^{-1})$ we obtain initial parameter estimates $(\tilde{\rho}, \tilde{\sigma}) = (56.7, 0.0442)$. Point estimates of ρ and σ are then derived by numerical minimization of

$$u(\rho, \sigma) = \int_0^{0.5} \{[\hat{K}(t)]^{0.25} - [K(t)]^{0.25}\}\, dt. \tag{4.1}$$

The range of integration in (4.1) is somewhat arbitrary, but its effect is greatly diminished by the fourth-root transformation. This effectively weights the estimation procedure in favour of small values of t, where the sampling fluctuations in $\hat{K}(t)$ are relatively small. For further comments, see Diggle (1978).

Equation (4.1) leads to point estimates $(\hat{\rho}, \hat{\sigma}) = (86.0, 0.0276)$. Figure 4.7 shows the empirical sampling distribution of $(-\log \hat{\rho}, \log \hat{\sigma})$ obtained by repeating the estimation procedure with 100 sets of artificial data generated as simulations of the model with $(\rho, \sigma) = (86.0, 0.0276)$. The logtransformation was applied in the first instance because the parameters are necessarily positive. Note that even after transformation both marginal distributions exhibit skewness, and that $-\log \hat{\rho}$ and $\log \hat{\sigma}$ are positively correlated. By way of explanation, we remark that if σ^2 is large relative to t^2, then $K(t) \simeq \pi t^2 + t^2/(4\rho\sigma^2)$, and only the product $\rho\sigma^2$ can be estimated with reasonable precision.

For an informal assessment of fit, Figure 4.5 includes the upper and lower envelopes from 19 simulations of the fitted model. The fit is adequate, except near the origin. A smaller value of σ improves the fit near the origin but introduces discrepancies for larger values of t. The fit is, therefore, not entirely satisfactory, although it does describe the apparent clustering of the bramble canes in a way which could be used in comparisons with other, ostensibly similar, data-sets. Also, any attempt to infer from the fitted model

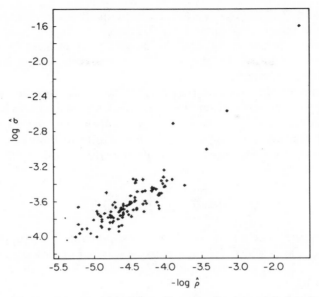

Figure 4.7 Empirical sampling distribution of ($-\log \hat{\rho}$, $\log \hat{\sigma}$) for a Poisson cluster process

a unique underlying biological mechanism is thwarted by the now well-known duality between Poisson cluster and doubly stochastic Poisson processes established by Bartlett (1964).

4.3 PROBABILITY SURFACES

The class of processes introduced by Cox (1955) provides a means of modelling environmental heterogeneity in spatial point patterns. A Cox process, also called a doubly stochastic Poisson process, is an inhomogeneous Poisson process with random intensity function $\Lambda(\mathbf{x})$. Thus, a partial realization of a Cox process, conditioned by the number of events in a region A and by the realized values $\lambda(\mathbf{x})$ of $\Lambda(\mathbf{x})$ for all $\mathbf{x}$ in A, is an independent random sample from the distribution on A with probability density function (pdf) $f(\mathbf{x})$ proportional to $\lambda(\mathbf{x})$. A non-parametric estimate of $f(\mathbf{x})$ (see below) should help to elucidate the nature of the underlying random function $\Lambda(\mathbf{x})$, particularly when the data include events of different types whose spatial inter-relationships are of interest. When the Cox formulation is strictly inappropriate, as for example with data which exhibit inhibitory effects between neighbouring events, these effects may nevertheless be superimposed on a pattern of variation in local intensity whose separate estimation would still be useful.

We recall that *CSR* corresponds to a uniform distribution on A. In order to interpret the estimate $\hat{f}(\mathbf{x})$ relative to this natural working hypothesis we suggest a transformation to a *probability surface* $p(\mathbf{x})$, defined for each $\mathbf{x}$ as the probability under *CSR* that the estimator $\hat{f}(\mathbf{x})$ assumes a value less than or equal to its observed value.

In the remainder of this section we take A to be the unit square; this is both operationally the simplest case and the one which is most common in practice. We use the kernel method (as described by Silverman in Chapter 3) to estimate $f(\mathbf{x})$, incorporating reflections in the boundaries of the unit square (cf. Boneva, Kendall and Stefanov, 1971). Formally, we define the reflected kernel estimator as

$$\hat{f}(\mathbf{x}) = (nh^2)^{-1} \sum_{i=1}^{9n} \delta[(\mathbf{x} - \mathbf{x}_i)/h]. \tag{4.2}$$

In (4.2), the kernel function $\delta(\ \ )$ is a bivariate pdf with finite support, h is a smoothing parameter which depends on n, the number of data points, and the data $\{\mathbf{x}_i : i = 1, \ldots, n\}$ are augmented by $\{\mathbf{x}_i : i = n + 1, \ldots, 9n\}$ defined, for $j = 1, \ldots, n$, by

$$\mathbf{x}_{n+j} = (x_{1j}, -x_{2j}); \qquad \mathbf{x}_{2n+j} = (x_{1j}, 2 - x_{2j});$$
$$\mathbf{x}_{3n+j} = (-x_{1j}, x_{2j}); \qquad \mathbf{x}_{4n+j} = (2 - x_{1j}, x_{2j});$$
$$\mathbf{x}_{5n+j} = (-x_{1j}, -x_{2j}); \qquad \mathbf{x}_{6n+j} = (-x_{1j}, 2 - x_{2j});$$
$$\mathbf{x}_{7n+j} = (2 - x_{1j}, -x_{2j}); \qquad \mathbf{x}_{8n+j} = (2 - x_{1j}, 2 - x_{2j}).$$

We use a simple product kernel $\delta(\mathbf{u}) = \delta_1(u_1)\delta_1(u_2)$, since there is usually no reason *a priori* to specify any directional effects in the data, and choose

$$\delta_1(u) = \begin{cases} 0.75(1 - u^2): & -1 \leqslant u \leqslant 1 \\ 0 & : \quad \text{otherwise.} \end{cases}$$

This kernel was shown by Epanechnikov (1969) to have certain optimality properties, although the precise choice of kernel is not critical (see Section 3.2.1). Equation (4.2) can now be written as

$$\hat{f}(\mathbf{x}) \equiv \hat{f}(x_1, x_2) = (nh^2)^{-1} \sum_{i=1}^{n} \prod_{p=1}^{2} \{\delta_1[(x_p - x_{pi})/h] + \delta_1[(x_p + x_{pi})/h]$$
$$+ \delta_1[(x_p + x_{pi} - 2)/h]\}. \tag{4.3}$$

The purpose of the reflection is to ensure that $\hat{f}(\mathbf{x})$ itself defines a pdf on the unit square; this requires $h < 1$, which is not a severe restriction in practice. A secondary effect is to impose boundary conditions of the form

$$\frac{\partial \hat{f}}{\partial x_1}(\mathbf{x}) = 0: x_1 = 0, 1; \qquad \frac{\partial \hat{f}}{\partial x_2}(\mathbf{x}) = 0: x_2 = 0, 1.$$

Whilst these conditions are a potential source of distortion, they are generally not too severe in view of the natural role played by the uniform distribution in the present context.

The character of the estimator (4.3) is critically dependent on h, larger values of which give a smoother surface. In practice we would recommend some experimentation with a range of values, starting from a data-independent specification for the baseline. We cannot establish a sensible baseline for the uniform distribution itself, since the optimum policy in this case is to take h as large as possible; the estimator (4.3) is exactly unbiased for the uniform distribution and its variance is a monotone decreasing function of h (Gratton, 1981).

The standard theory of kernel estimators (which, *inter alia*, assumes that the underlying density $f(\ )$ has unbounded support) can provide some guidance in the choice of h. We adopt as our baseline value $h_n = 0.68 n^{-0.2}$, which is asymptotically optimal with respect to integrated mean-square error for Epanechnikov's kernel applied to a univariate normal distribution with variance $1/12$, equal to that of a uniform distribution on the unit interval.

Because of the edge-effects, the variance $V_0(\mathbf{x})$ of the estimator (4.3) is a complicated function of $\mathbf{x}$. Details are given in Gratton (1981). The asymptotic normality of the estimator (4.3) follows from a result of Parzen (1963) and, in view of the large sample sizes which we envisage, we calculate the probability surface of $\hat{f}(\mathbf{x})$ as

$$p(\mathbf{x}) = \Phi\{[\hat{f}(\mathbf{x}) - 1]/\sqrt{V_0(\mathbf{x})}\} \qquad (4.4)$$

where $\Phi\{\ \}$ denotes the standard normal integral.

Figure 4.8 shows a set of data due to Gerrard (1969). Tree locations in a 19.6 acre square region are shown as four separate patterns corresponding to the three major species groupings present and as a single pattern of 2251 trees, these including 105 'miscellaneous' individuals. Figures 4.8(a) and 4.8(b) suggest a strong negative relationship between the local intensities of hickories and maples, but there is no obvious pattern in Figures 4.8(c) or 4.8(d). Figures 4.9(a)–(d) show probability surfaces (4.4) corresponding to Figures 4.8(a)–(d), respectively. The results are quite striking, particularly with regard to the hickories and maples whose surfaces are almost exactly complementary. A similar, if less clear-cut, effect is apparent for the oaks, which tend to fill any gaps left by both the hickories and the maples. This explains the very uniform appearance of the surface obtained when all the trees are considered as a single pattern.

This type of analysis is particularly suitable for extensive data whose high 'numerosity' (in the sense employed by Tukey and Tukey in Chapter 10) hinders direct interpretation. The smoothing parameter used in Figure 4.9 was $h_n = 1.36 n^{-0.2}$, twice the baseline value. One reason for inclining towards a high degree of smoothing is to reduce the incidence of spurious 'highs' and

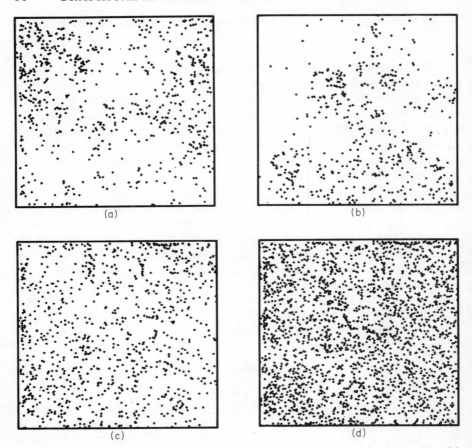

Figure 4.8   Tree locations in Lansing woods: (a) 703 hickories; (b) 514 maples; (c) 929 oaks; (d) 2251 trees. (See Gerrard, 1969)

'lows'. On the other hand, in contrast to conventional probability density estimation, there seems no reason in general to expect the structure of the underlying surface to be particularly simple; ideas of what constitutes a 'reasonable' topographical surface in physical geography may be more relevant. For comparison, Figure 4.10 corresponds to Figure 4.9, but using the baseline smoothing value, $h_n = 0.68n^{-0.2}$. The conclusions are substantially the same although, inevitably, each surface displays a more complex structure and the composite map shows a greater incidence of local highs and lows. With regard to presentation, Figures 4.9 and 4.10 were originally prepared in colour for overhead projection. Here, we have used intensity of hatching to indicate the extent of any departure from uniformity and direction of hatching

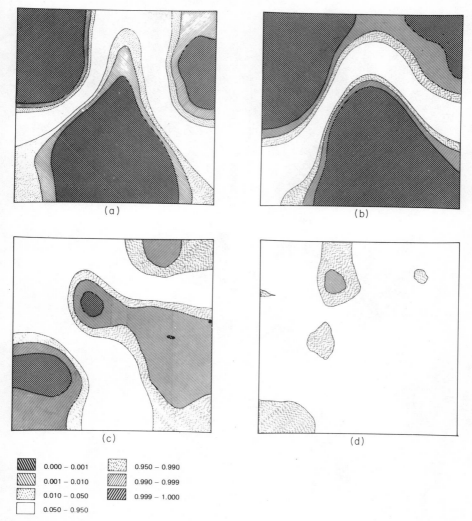

Figure 4.9 Probability surfaces for Lansing woods ($h_n = 1.36n^{-0.2}$): (a) hickories; (b) maples; (c) oaks; (d) all trees

to distinguish between highs and lows. If colour were available, a more effective technique would be to use varying shades of two contrasting colour tones, as in many atlases of physical geography.

Cox (1979) obtains qualitatively similar results for these data using a distance-based method which is related to the k-nearest neighbour estimator of Loftsgaarden and Quesenberry (1965). Cox chooses not to construct a

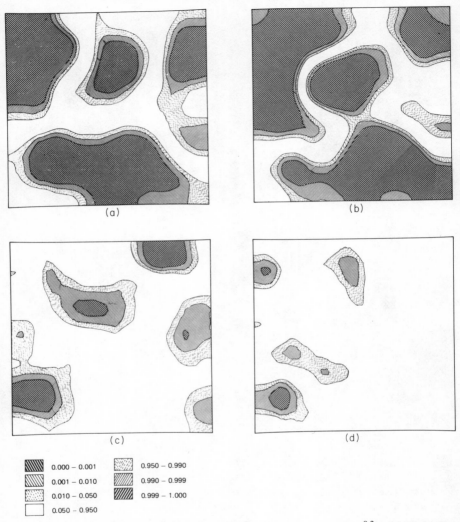

Figure 4.10   Probability surfaces for Lansing woods ($h_n = 0.68_n^{-0.2}$): (a) hickories; (b) maples; (c) oaks; (d) all trees

complete surface, but rather gives contours corresponding to upper and lower 5% critical values relative to *CSR*, for a range of values of his smoothing parameter.

4.4   SPARSELY SAMPLED PATTERNS

References in Diggle (1979a) provide one point of entry to what has become an extensive literature on statistical methods for sparsely sampled patterns.

To illustrate the use of graphical methods in this context we discuss the T-square sampling procedure of Besag and Gleaves (1973). This is one of the more successful distance-based techniques in that it is simple to apply in the field and can give both powerful tests of CSR and robust estimators of the mean number of events per unit area. In addition, the tractability of its associated distribution theory in the case of CSR gives some scope for the derivation of test statistics to detect particular types of departure from CSR (Diggle, Besag and Gleaves, 1976).

In T-square sampling, we record the distance X from a sample point, P say, to the nearest event, at E, and the distance Y from E to the nearest event, at F, such that the angle PEF is at least 90°. This restriction ensures that, under CSR, X and Y are independent with $2\pi\lambda X^2$ and $\pi\lambda Y^2$ each distributed as χ_2^2. Further, m sample points give observations $(x_i, y_i): i = 1, \ldots, m$ which can be assumed to be mutually independent provided m is small relative to the number n of events in the region being investigated. Byth and Ripley (1980) discuss this point and suggest that systematic sampling permits a value of m as large as $0.25n$. In practice, n is unknown but can be estimated retrospectively or from a pilot study, using the data generated by the T-square sampling procedure (Diggle, 1975; Diggle, 1977a).

One 'general purpose' statistic to test CSR is $t_N = m^{-1}\sum_{i=1}^{m} u_i$, where $u_i = x_i^2/(x_i^2 + \frac{1}{2}y_i^2)$. Under CSR, the u_i are uniformly distributed and t_N has a normal distribution with mean $\frac{1}{2}$ and variance $(12m)^{-1}$. This gives a test which is powerful against both aggregated and regular alternatives to CSR, but insensitive to fluctuations in 'local intensity'. Specifically, if CSR applies locally but with possibly different intensities λ_i in the neighbourhood of the ith sample point, the null distribution of t_N prevails. For this alternative to CSR, Diggle (1977b) suggests a likelihood ratio statistic,

$$M = [48m/(13m + 1)][\sum \log v_i - m \log(m^{-1}\sum v_i)],$$

where $v_i = x_i^2 + \frac{1}{2}y_i^2$. This is a version of Bartlett's (1937) test for homogeneity of variances in normal sampling and the null distribution of M is χ_{m-1}^2.

To check the uniformity of the u_i, a cumulative probability plot is a useful graphical supplement to the t_N-test. To check the independence of x_i and y_i a scatterplot is the obvious graphical device. For ease of interpretation we recommend a transformation of the axes to the appropriate distribution function under CSR,[*] i.e. plot $\eta_i = 1 - \exp(-\pi\hat{\lambda}y_i^2/2)$ against $\zeta_i = 1 - \exp(-\pi\hat{\lambda}x_i^2)$, where $\hat{\lambda} = 2m/[\pi(\sum x_i^2 + \frac{1}{2}\sum y_i^2)]$ is the maximum likelihood estimator for λ. This produces a plot of points (ξ_i, η_i) in the unit square. A concentration of points along the diagonal, $\eta = \xi$, suggests local randomness but variation in local intensity. Concentrations in the lower triangle $\eta < \xi$ or the upper triangle $\eta > \xi$ suggest aggregation or regularity, respectively. If each point is labelled so as to identify the location of the corresponding sample

---

[*]Such a transformation has been used in the same context by W. G. S. and R. J. O. Hines of Guelph University, Ontario.

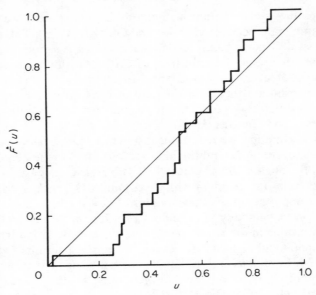

Figure 4.11   Cumulative plot of u_i from T-square sampling of hickories data

point, any gross changes in pattern or intensity over the study region can be identified.

We now apply these techniques to the hickories data given in Figure 4.9(a), sampling the pattern by 25 points in a 5×5 square lattice. Figure 4.11 shows the cumulative probability plot of the u_i. The departure from uniformity is not significant when tested by the Kolmogorov–Smirnov statistic $(0.1 < p < 0.2)$. The plot does suggest an S-shaped distribution function, but this is difficult to interpret in terms of a single underlying spatial point process.

Figure 4.12 shows the scatterplot of η versus ξ. The positive correlation between ξ and η is consistent with a heterogeneous process of varying local intensity although, as noted earlier, the convenient distinction between aggregation and heterogeneity cannot be sustained formally, and there is an unavoidable element of indeterminacy between the two descriptions. The labelling of the points proves not very informative in this instance, as the smooth gradations in local intensity already identified for these data in Section 4.3 are largely swamped by the sampling fluctuations in the individual (x, y)-values.

For completeness, Table 4.1 gives the results of tests of CSR based on t_N and on M applied to each of the four patterns in Figure 4.8, using a 5×5 square lattice of sample points in each case. The conclusions are generally sensible in that the hickories and maples are classified as heterogeneous,

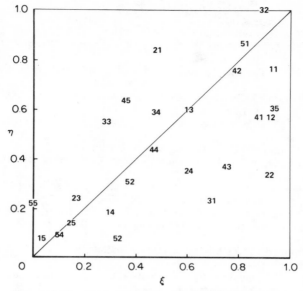

Figure 4.12   Scatterplot of n_i versus ξ_i from T-square sampling of hickories data (label ij indicates observation from sample point in ith row and jth column of 5×5 square lattice)

whilst *CSR* is accepted for the oaks and for the complete population of 2251 trees. However, we emphasize that when a complete map is available, methods based on sparse sampling are potentially wasteful and are therefore not recommended.

Table 4.1   T-square tests of *CSR* applied to the Lansing Woods data (figures in brackets are p-values for two-sided tests based on t_N, one-sided tests based on M)

	Number of trees	t_N	M	Description of pattern
Hickories	703	0.54 (0.53)	41.26 (0.02)	heterogeneous
Maples	514	0.60 (0.08)	38.28 (0.03)	heterogeneous
Oaks	929	0.42 (0.17)	32.18 (0.12)	random
Trees	2251	0.53 (0.23)	18.71 (0.77)	random

REFERENCES

Barnard, G. A. (1963) Contribution to the discussion of Bartlett (1963).

Bartlett, M. S. (1937) Properties of sufficiency and statistical tests. *Proc. Roy. Soc. A*, **168**, 268–82.

Bartlett, M. S. (1963) The spectral analysis of point processes. *J. Roy. Statist. Soc. B*, **25**, 264–96.

Bartlett, M. S. (1964) Spectral analysis of two-dimensional point processes. *Biometrika*, **51**, 299–311.

Bartlett, M. S. (1978) *Stochastic Processes* (3rd edn). Cambridge: Cambridge University Press.

Besag, J. (1977) Contribution to the discussion of Ripley (1977)

Besag, J. and Diggle, P. J. (1977) Simple Monte Carlo tests for spatial pattern. *Applied Statistics*, **26**, 327–33.

Besag, J. and Gleaves, J. T. (1973) On the detection of spatial pattern in plant communities. *Bull. Int. Statist. Inst.*, **45**(1), 153–8.

Boneva, L. I., Kendall, D. G., and Stefanov, I. (1971) Spline transformations: three new diagnostic aids for the statistical data-analyst (with discussion). *J. Roy. Statist. Soc. B*, **33**, 1–71.

Byth, K. and Ripley, B. D. (1980) On sampling spatial patterns by distance methods. *Biometrics*, **36**, 279–84.

Cox, D. R. (1955) Some statistical methods related with series of events (with discussion). *J. Roy. Statist. Soc. B*, **17**, 129–64.

Cox, T. F. (1979) A method for mapping the dense and sparse regions of a forest stand. *Applied Statistics*, **28**, 14–19.

Diggle, P. J. (1975) Robust density estimation using distance methods. *Biometrika*, **62**, 39–48.

Diggle, P. J. (1977a) A note on robust density estimation for spatial point patterns. *Biometrika*, **64**, 91–5.

Diggle, P. J. (1977b) The detection of random heterogeneity in plant populations. *Biometrics*, **33**, 390–4.

Diggle, P. J. (1978) On parameter estimation for spatial point processes. *J. Roy. Statist. Soc. B*, **40**, 178–81.

Diggle, P. J. (1979a) Statistical methods for spatial point patterns in ecology. In R. M. Cormack and J. K. Ord (eds.) (1979). *Spatial and Temporal Analysis in Ecology*, Fairland: International Co-operative Publishing House, pp. 95–150.

Diggle, P. J. (1979b) On parameter estimation and goodness-of-fit testing for spatial point patterns. *Biometrics*, **35**, 87–101.

Diggle, P. J., Besag, J., and Gleaves, J. T. (1976) Statistical analysis of spatial point patterns by means of distance methods. *Biometrics*, **32**, 659–67.

Epanechnikov, V. A. (1969) Non-parametric estimation of a multivariate probability density. *Theor. Prob. Appl.*, **14**, 153–8.

Gerrard, D. J. (1969) Competition quotient: a new measure of the competition affecting individual forest trees. *Res. Bull. No. 20*, Agricultural Experiment Station, Michigan State University.

Ghent, A. W. (1963) Studies of regeneration of forest stands devastated by spruce budworm. *For. Sci.*, **9**, 295–310.

Gratton, R. J. (1981) Density estimation and likelihood inference for implicit statistical models. *Ph.D. thesis*, University of Newcastle upon Tyne.

Hope, A. C. A. (1968) A simplified Monte Carlo significance test procedure. *J. Roy. Statist. Soc. B*, **30**, 582–98.

Hutchings, M. J. (1978) Standing crop and pattern in pure strands of *Mercurialis perennis* and *Rubus fruticosus* in mixed deciduous woodland. *Oikos,* **31**, 351–7.

Loftsgaarden, D. O. and Quesenberry, C. P. (1965) A non-parametric estimate of a multivariate density function. *Ann. Math. Statist.,* **36**, 1049–51.

Marriott, F. H. C. (1979) Monte Carlo tests: how many simulations? *Applied Statistics,* **28**, 75–7.

Numata, M. (1961) Forest vegetation in the vicinity of Choshi. Coastal flora and vegetation at Choshi, Chiba Prefecture IV (in Japanese). *Bull. Choshi Marine Lab. Chiba Univ.,* **3**, 28–48.

Parzen, E. (1963) On estimation of a probability density function and mode. *Ann. Math. Statist.,* **34**, 1065–76.

Ripley, B. D. (1977) Modelling spatial patterns (with discussion). *J. Roy. Statist. Soc. B,* **39**, 172–212.

Strauss, D. J. (1975) A model for clustering. *Biometrika,* **62**, 467–75.

CHAPTER 5

The Statistics of Shape

D. G. Kendall, *University of Cambridge, U.K.*

This is a brief report of work in progress, or in preparation for publication elsewhere. In this investigation 'shape' always means the shape of a (possibly random) configuration of points in euclidean space. The basic idea is to think of k points in m dimensions labelled as $P_1, P_2, \ldots, P_k$ and to identify the shape of that k-ad with the equivalence class of k-ads similar to it relative to changes of location, scale, and orientation, but not normally of handedness. When $m = 1$ (the simplest case) there turns out to be a representation for the quotient space (in which such shapes are points) as the sphere S^{k-2}, while when $m = 2$ the corresponding quotient space is the complex projective space CP^{k-2}, which can be thought of as the sphere S^2 when $k = 3$, so that 'shapes of triangles live on a sphere' (see Figure 5.1).

For larger values of m the most interesting case is that in which $k = m + 1$, and it turns out that what I call the *shape-manifold* is actually endowed with a smooth structure, a group, an invariant riemannian metric, and an invariant measure. Part of the group accounts for the transformations associated with re-labelling points, and it is often convenient to use this fact in the construction of a sub-region of the manifold on which unlabelled shapes can be plotted; Figure 5.1 gives an example of this. The metric can be derived from procrustean considerations concerning the best way of matching two labelled figures when translations, scale changes and rotations are permitted; asymptotic analysis of this then leads to the riemannian metric. This natural metric of itself induces a probability distribution on the shape-manifold which turns out to have connections with a statistical example in which the $m + 1$ points are independent, identically distributed, and have a gaussian distribution. It should be mentioned that the homogeneity of the shape-manifold when $k = 3$ and $m = 2$ is exceptional; for larger values of m the intrinsic geometry of the manifold depends on where one is on it, and the analysis of this is very interesting.

Returning to the general situation, suppose that the k points are generated by an arbitrary random mechanism (not necessarily independently). This will automatically induce a probability distribution on the shape-manifold itself, which I call the *shape-measure*. Moreover, in most cases of interest it turns out

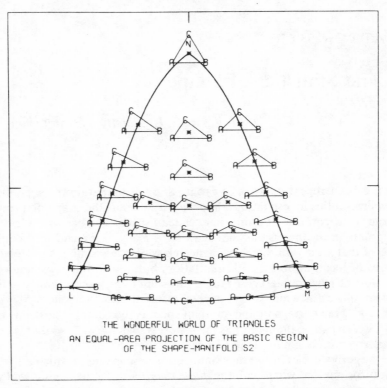

THE WONDERFUL WORLD OF TRIANGLES
AN EQUAL-AREA PROJECTION OF THE BASIC REGION
OF THE SHAPE-MANIFOLD S2

Figure 5.1   The spherical blackboard, showing 32 triangles located
according to their shapes

that this shape-measure possesses a density relative to the invariant measure
mentioned above, and this density is therefore more conveniently taken as a
representation of the way in which the shapes are distributed on the shape-
manifold. It has now been computed in one or two cases. For example, I have
found the shape-density in the general multivariate gaussian case, and when
$m = 2$ this distribution (which is closely related to work by W. S. Kendall,
1981) has proved to be important in the analysis of alignments (whether
3-point or k-point) in empirical sets of points. When $m = 3$ or more, these
results generalize in the obvious way and it becomes particularly interesting to
see how non-isotropy in the generating gaussian distribution is reflected in the
form of the induced density on the shape-manifold. Alternatively, instead of
considering gaussian distributions, one can consider the case in which the
k-points are independently and identically distributed, and lie uniformly
inside some given compact convex region. This problem has been investigated
by C. G. Small of the University of Cambridge for the case $m = 2$, and he has

also done very interesting work on the associated questions of unicity and stability which naturally arise, both in this case and in more general cases.

Now let us forget about statistics for a moment, and think of the k points as given. Then each shape-function (e.g. the maximum angle of the triangle when $k = 3$ and $m = 2$) can be discussed in terms of the real function which it determines over the shape-manifold. In the case just mentioned I have written computer programs to draw contour lines for that particular shape-function, and these have proved useful in the interpretation of observed alignments. Going back to the statistical problem, it will be seen that the theoretical distribution of values of that shape-function (e.g. the distribution of the maximum angle of a random gaussian triangle, originally determined by other methods by W. S. Kendall, 1981) can be obtained by fitting together two components. The first of these is the shape-density determined by the stochastic mechanism generating the points, while the second is the shape-function viewed as a real-valued function over the shape-manifold. The distribution to be found is obtained from these components by an appropriate integration, and a computer program has been constructed to perform it. Examples of the output of that program will be found in Kendall and Kendall (1980).

In the context of the present volume these ideas are relevant because they demand a solution to the problem of visually presenting such data, and this problem is studied in detail in a forthcoming paper (D. G. Kendall, 1981a) in the important case where $m = 2$ and $k = 3$. Here, as mentioned above, the shape-manifold is the sphere, which can be thought of as the union of six regions equivalent under the re-labelling group. If we are also indifferent to reflection (as sometimes in practice we are) then each such region is halved and we have twelve in all. Choosing any one of these as representative of all the others, this basic region is a spherical triangle on which the invariant measure is just Lebesgue, and we can preserve that by a radial projection from any axis through the centre of the sphere onto an enveloping right circular cylinder having that axis. Cutting and opening out the cylinder then gives a measure-preserving map from the shape-manifold to the plane and on this we can display statistical distributions, whether empirical or theoretical, in a manner which is very easy to assimilate once one has learnt by heart the information contained in Figure 5.1.

What might be called the 'bell-shaped region' in that figure is in fact one of the twelve regions derived from relabelling plus reflection, and the situation is that the equilateral shapes are represented by a point at the top of the bell, while collinear shapes are represented by points lying along the curve at the foot of the bell. The isosceles shapes appear on the two sides of the bell and it is interesting that they have to be segregated into two groups; those where the vertical angle is greater than either of the two equal angles—and here the shape-points occur on the right—and those where the vertical angle is less than each of the two equal angles—and here the shape-point occurs on the left. Once this has been explained, the way in which the shape of the triangle changes as one moves about inside the bell can be seen from the diagram. Thus the reader will notice that collinear triplets in which two members of the the triplet coincide or nearly coincide will determine shapes represented by points near the corner of the bell marked by the letter L.

These procedures have been exploited in various ways. The study of nearly collinear (blunt) triangles initiated by Broadbent (1980) with its archaeological and other applications provides one with suitable data, and I have constructed a computer program which accepts such data, calculates the shapes of all the triangles contained in it, and plots the shape-points on the bell. Actually with data of the size of Broadbent's there are too many points to plot (22 100); in order to avoid an output which would be merely an inky mess, the program is therefore directed to draw contour lines on the bell indicating the form of the empirical density function. This can be compared with the output of the same program in another mode when a theoretical stochastic generator for the points is proposed and supplied via a sub-routine, and either the shape-density is theoretically calculated and contour lines drawn on the bell, or alternatively samples derived from that stochastic mechanism are generated by simulation and analysed as if they were data.

It may be interesting to mention that Broadbent's data, when analysed in this way, show an unexpected concentration in the neighbourhood of the point L. This is easily explained because in fact there are one or two cases in the Broadbent data when two sites are very close together. Each such pair of sites can be associated with any one of the fifty remaining sites (there were 52 sites altogether), and therefore one obtains fifty isosceles triangles with a very small vertical angle; this automatically produces a lot of points, and therefore a high empirical density, near the corner marked L. In this way, and in other ways too complicated for summary here, one learns by looking at the bell-plot of the Broadbent data to recognize many intrinsic features of the data-set which were not immediately obvious from earlier visual presentation. Because of its very flexible use, I like to call the bell diagram 'the spherical blackboard'; the main function of the various computer programs I am writing and testing at the moment is to enable one to put onto the spherical blackboard as many different objects of interest as one can.

To take another example, recent work by Mardia, Edwards and Puri (1977) has suggested that one might use the Delaunay triangles associated with an empirical plane point process to investigate whether in fact there is any evidence for the influence of what is called by geographers 'central place theory'. The reason for using the Delaunay triangles in this rôle is that if central place theory is indeed dominant in the true model generating the data then one would expect more nearly equilateral triangles than would be predicted by the Delaunay distribution calculated by R. E. Miles (see the paper by Mardia *et al.* for an appropriate reference) for data coming from a Poisson source. However it is not immediately obvious how one should compare the distribution of the shapes of the observed Delaunay triangles with the distribution of the shapes of theoretical Miles–Delaunay triangles; one way of doing this is to plot the two groups of shapes on the spherical blackboard and see how they differ. This experiment has not yet been completed and will be reported on elsewhere.

So far we have been concerned with static problems, but the theory also has kinematic aspects which did in fact play a determining rôle at the outset of the investigation (reported in summary form in D. G. Kendall, 1977). Suppose in fact that the k-points $P_1, P_2, \ldots, P_k$ are executing some kind of random diffusion in m dimensions; then the shape-point will describe a continuous random motion on the corresponding shape-manifold Σ_m^k, and this random continuous motion is itself seen to be a diffusion if it is watched with the aid of an appropriate (and essentially unique) random clock. We now have a mechanism which translates diffusions into diffusions, instead of the earlier simpler mechanism which translated probability distributions into probability distributions. Many interesting questions then arise; some are discussed in Kendall (1981b).

Coming back to the matter of visual presentation, it is obvious that when the dimension of the shape-manifold exceeds 2 there will be problems to overcome. To some extent one may receive aid and comfort from some of the devices being presented elsewhere in this book to enable one to appreciate many-dimensional distributions. It seems more likely, however, that progress will come through appreciating just which two (or three-) dimensional submersions of the shape-manifold are of interest. For example, it has already become clear how one ought to portray near-coplanarity of tetrads in three dimensions in a two-dimensional diagram resulting from work on Σ_3^4, and it seems that this is going to produce another sort of 'black-board' which will have data-analytic uses. Only the other day an archaeologist (Stephen Cogbill) consulted me about a problem of detecting 'nearly circular' tetrads; that is, sets of four points which lie approximately on a circle. This is important in the context with which he is concerned because, of a large number of points observed in an excavation, some groups of four or more may be associated with the outline of a hut structure but these may be overlaid by many other points not so related. Again there are closely analogous problems in the analysis of bubble-chamber photographs, and so one expects applications in atomic physics.

One feature of the more complicated situation when $m = 3$ or greater is that the manifold (unlike the sphere S^2) now contains singularities. These have a real geometrical meaning, and they also occupy a special position in relation to the differentiable structure and particularly the riemannian metric, and the analysis of this situation raises many interesting questions (D. G. Kendall, 1981b).

REFERENCES

Broadbent, S. R. (1980) Simulating the ley hunter. *J. Roy. Statist. Soc. A*, **143**, 109–40.

Kendall, D. G. (1977) The diffusion of shape. *Adv. Appl. Prob.*, **9**, 428–30.

Kendall, D. G. (1981a) Shape-manifolds, Procrustean metrics and complex projective spaces (in preparation).

Kendall, D. G. (1981b) Foundations of a theory of random shape. *Bull. London Math. Soc.* (to appear).

Kendall, D. G. and Kendall, W. S. (1980) Alignments in two-dimensional random sets of points. *Adv. Appl. Prob.*, **12**, 380–424.

Kendall, W. S. (1981) Random gaussian triangles and k-point collinearities (in preparation).

Mardia, K. V., Edwards, R., and Puri, M. L. (1977) Analysis of central place theory. *Bull. Int. Statist. Inst.*, **7**, (2), 93–110.

Small, C. G., Random uniform triangles and the alignment problem. *Ph.D. thesis* (in preparation), University of Cambridge.

Small, C. G. Characterization of distributions through shapes of samples. *Ph. D. thesis*, (in preparation), University of Cambridge.

PART II

Reduction, Display, and Analysis of Data Matrices and Multiway Tables

Expressing Complex Relationships in Two Dimensions

J. C. Gower and P. G. N. Digby, *Rothamsted Experimental Station, U.K.*

Not so many years ago it was fashionable to view a statistical analysis as one in which a hypothesis, or some formal model, was stipulated. Parameters were estimated and hypotheses tested. Although this may be the ideal, there has been an increasing acceptance that often much groundwork is required before a model or hypothesis can be formulated. This part of statistics is termed exploratory data-analysis and graphical methods play an important part in its methodology. Univariate and bivariate problems lend themselves naturally to graphical displays that exploit the two-dimensional properties of a sheet of paper or VDU screen, but the multidimensional character of general multivariate data introduces special problems. A consequence is that applied multivariate analysis is rich in informal graphical methods that allow multidimensional spaces to be explored and exhibited in a variety of ingenious ways that are intended to reveal any regular structure or pattern that may be contained in the data—hence the term *pattern analysis* coined by W. T. Williams (see e.g. Williams and Gillard, 1971) for some of the techniques in use. Only when pattern exists can the further steps be taken of setting up models and hypotheses, although it must be recognized that multivariate analysis frequently stops when an informative graphical description of the data has been found.

In this chapter we review methods that use *two-dimensional* graphical displays, although occasionally we permit ourselves a third dimension. Excluded are methods that attempt a three-dimensional perception such as the use of perspective, stereoscopy, holographs, the use of different light intensities on VDUs, or the actual construction of physical models. Such methods are invaluable for true three-dimensional data but we question whether (for example) a series of three-dimensional cross-sections of multidimensional space is less confusing than a series of two-dimensional cross-sections. Certainly a prolonged learning period is necessary before one can safely comprehend and interpret such representations.

Many of the methods discussed are well known (known for more than 20 years), others are quite well known (10–20 years) and others fairly novel (less than 10 years). In this review we have two aims; firstly to give a unified account and secondly to make explicit the mathematical models that underly many of the methods. This second aim may seem to contradict some of the statements made in the opening paragraph but the models used here are descriptive ones of a very general nature rather than attempts to model mechanistic or natural processes. Nevertheless awareness of the relevant descriptive model is important, for the algebraic equivalent of a good graphical representation can be the first step in suggesting the form of a more detailed model amenable to formal statistical analysis.

6.1 DATA AS A TWO-WAY TABLE OR MATRIX

In this section we mention several methods for investigating data that are presented either as a two-way table, or as a matrix. The two are schematically equivalent in that there is one value for each row–column combination. Thus it is quite possible to use a multivariate method such as principal components analysis on, say, a table classified by different foodstuffs and countries; alternatively the standard unit × variate data-matrix could be analysed formally as a two-way table, for example by fitting additive row and column parameters followed by a two-way analysis of variance.

Obviously not all combinations of type of data with form of analysis are acceptable. Different methods relate to different underlying models suitable for different types of data and different interpretive purposes. Nevertheless there is no distinct dividing line between data that should be considered as forming a multivariate data-matrix and data that form a two-way table. There are some sets of data that can profitably be considered as either.

We will work through methods designed primarily for units × variates data to methods for tabular data. We will specify the underlying models to help the user decide which methods are appropriate with his data.

6.1.1 Picture displays

The principle is to draw one picture for each unit of a data-matrix; each variate contributes to the picture. The set of pictures may be displayed in an array or superimposed on ordinations or, where appropriate, on a geographical map. Figure 6.1 shows examples of three basic displays: *glyphs* (Anderson, 1960), *stars*, and *faces* (Chernoff, 1973). With glyphs the length of each line is proportional to the value taken by one of the variates; there are as many lines as there are variates. The length of each arm of the star is similarly obtained from the variates, thus the stars will be p-pointed for p-dimensional data. Chernoff (1973) gives rules for the construction of each face for up to 18 variates. Since Chernoff's original paper other forms of humanoid rep-

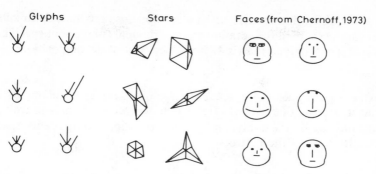

Figure 6.1   Three types of picture display

resentations have been suggested and used. The ability to interpret these displays obviously depends on the arrangement of the individual pictures within the overall display. Also the allocation of variates to the different parts of each picture affects the interpretation, possibly misleadingly.

We note also the recent work of Kleiner and Hartigan (1980): the form of their pictures (*trees, castles* and *ships*) is derived from a preliminary analysis of the variates.

6.1.2 Units plotted in two dimensions

The arbitrariness of the displays mentioned in Section 6.1.1 does not appeal to us. Instead we prefer to represent the units as points in two-dimensions, possibly with extra information superimposed.

For p variates we might consider plotting all the $\frac{1}{2}p(p-1)$ scatter diagrams (see, for example, the six-views display of four-dimensional data discussed by Tukey and Tukey in Chapter 10).

6.1.3 Principal components analysis

Each two-dimensional plot is the projection of points representing the n units in p dimensions, onto a plane within the p-dimensional space. Furthermore, the p axes defining these planes are orthogonal. A rotation of these axes so that most of the structure of the data could be displayed in a few of the $\frac{1}{2}p(p-1)$ planes would obviously be helpful. *Principal components analysis* does this, by maximizing the variation within the data that is displayed in the first few dimensions. This is equivalent to minimizing the sum-of-squares of the residual distances of each point from the fitted plane. Gnanadesikan and Kettenring (1972) suggest that the final dimensions may be useful for the detection of outliers.

If $\mathbf{X}$ is the $n \times p$ data-matrix with column-means zero and, optionally, unit column variances, then the rotation to the principal component space is given by the $p \times p$ orthogonal matrix $\mathbf{L}$ from the spectral decomposition:

$$\mathbf{X}^{\mathrm{T}}\mathbf{X} = \mathbf{L}\mathbf{\Lambda}\mathbf{L}^{\mathrm{T}}$$

where the eigenvalues $(\lambda_1 \geq \lambda_2 \geq, \ldots, \geq \lambda_p \geq 0)$ are the elements of the diagonal matrix $\mathbf{\Lambda}$. (The superscript ^{T} denotes vector or matrix transpose.) The coordinates of the individuals in the principal components space are given as the rows of the matrix

$$\mathbf{Z} = \mathbf{X}\mathbf{L}$$

and thus the plots are of e.g. (z_{i1}, z_{i2}). The amount of variation contained in the jth principal direction is given by λ_j. Since $\mathbf{L}$ is an orthogonal matrix the inter-point distances in the original p dimensions are preserved in the principal-component space, and are approximated in the plot of (z_{i1}, z_{i2}).

Hartigan (1975) gives some data on the rates of 7 different crimes (variates) for 16 American cities (units). Figure 6.2 is a plot of the cities in the first two principal components: this contains 84% of the total variation.

An alternative approach to principal-component analysis proceeds via the *singular-value decomposition*

$$\mathbf{X} = \mathbf{U}\mathbf{\Sigma}\mathbf{V}^{\mathrm{T}}$$

where the columns of $\mathbf{U}$ ($n \times p$) are orthogonal, $\mathbf{V}$ ($p \times p$) is an orthogonal matrix and the singular values $(\sigma_1 \geq \sigma_2 \geq, \ldots, \geq \sigma_p \geq 0)$ form the diagonal matrix $\mathbf{\Sigma}$. It is easy to show that $\mathbf{V} = \mathbf{L}$, $\mathbf{\Sigma}^2 = \mathbf{\Lambda}$ and $\mathbf{Z} = \mathbf{U}\mathbf{\Sigma}$. Expanding, the

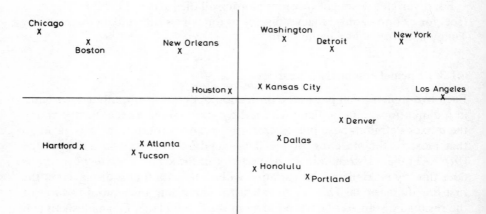

Figure 6.2   First two scores from principal components analysis of rates of 7 types of crime in 16 American cities

decomposition gives

$$x_{ij} = \sum_{k=1}^{p} u_{ik}\sigma_k v_{jk}$$

or

$$x_{ij} = \sum_{k=1}^{p} z_{ik} v_{jk}$$

and the plot of the units in the first two-dimensions approximates the data as

$$x_{ij} = z_{i1}v_{j1} + z_{i2}v_{j2}$$

with residual

$$e_{ij} = \sum_{k=3}^{p} z_{ik} v_{jk}.$$

The relevance of the matrix V is explained in Section 6.1.6.

6.1.4 Putting extra information on a point plot

We might wish to display extra dimensions $(3, 4, \ldots, q$ for $q \leq p)$ on a two-dimensional point plot. This plot could be of two of the original variates (from the X matrix) or of two of the new variates (from the Z matrix). The extra variates can be used to construct a picture as in Section 6.1.1, or some variant of it, for each individual; these are then displayed at the points given by the first two variates.

If any of the original variates are qualitative, different colours or symbol shapes can be used to represent the different possible values.

In some situations there is a constraint on a set of variates that allows us to reduce the dimensionality by one. A common example is when three percentages must total 100; then the points must lie on a plane in the three dimensions, and within an equilateral triangle on that plane. Thus the points can be plotted within a triangle in two dimensions. Such a plot is said to be in *barycentric* coordinates.

As an example we show in Figure 6.3 the percentages of cows, sheep and pigs for 20 English counties for 1971 (data from MAFF, 1971). A technique due to Ross (reported by Gower, 1967) has been used to add, for each of the countries, northings and eastings from a point near Leicester. This technique is of the same general class as those discussed in Section 6.1.1. Some aspects of the structure are immediately apparent: the predominance of pig farming in East Anglia and neighbouring counties, and the tendency towards sheep farming in Kent and in the North of England (also in the other moorland counties).

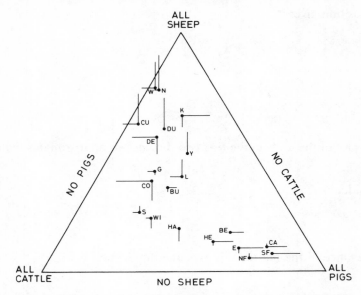

Figure 6.3 Proportions of pigs, sheep and cattle in 20 English counties (barycentric coordinates). The lengths of vertical and horizontal lines of each point give northings and eastings from an origin near Leicester.

Key:

BE	Bedfordshire	HE	Hertfordshire
BU	Buckinghamshire	K	Kent
CA	Cambridgeshire	L	Lancashire
CO	Cornwall	NF	Norfolk
CU	Cumberland	N	Northumberland
DE	Devon	S	Staffordshire
DU	Durham	SF	Suffolk
E	Essex	W	Westmorland
G	Gloucestershire	WI	Wiltshire
HA	Hampshire	Y	Yorkshire

6.1.5 Displaying goodness-of-fit

The plot of (z_{i1}, z_{i2}) gives only an approximation to the spread of the points in p dimensions. The eigenvalues give an overall assessment of the goodness-of-fit but they do not indicate which points, or interpoint relationships, are poorly approximated. In this section we suggest a number of techniques for adding such information to a two-dimensional plot. For illustration we use the city crime data of Section 6.1.3.

We can consider the distance between the plotted point (z_{i1}, z_{i2}) and the true point $(z_{i1}, z_{i2}, \ldots, z_{ip})$ as a residual, e_i. It is not difficult to show that

$$e_i^2 = \sum_{j=3}^{p} e_{ij}^2$$

where e_{ij} is the residual for x_{ij}, as defined above. The value of e_i can usefully be placed beside the plotted point, or as suggested by Dr. P. A. Tukey, the size of the plotted symbol could be inversely proportional to the value e_i; thus the more accurately positioned points are emphasized. The first possibility is shown in Figure 6.4. Note that in general it is not possible to give signed residuals. This is most easily seen by considering the projection of points in three dimensions onto a straight line. The residuals are the distances of the points from the line, but the points cannot be said to lie on one side of the line or the other.

We can also use the familiar idea of inter-point distance by constructing a minimum spanning tree. A *spanning tree* is a set of straight line segments joining pairs of points such that there are no closed loops and a path exists between all pairs of points; a *minimum spanning tree* is that with minimum length. This can be superimposed on the two-dimensional plot to highlight those plotted points which are much nearer or further than is consistent with the true length being minimum. Gower and Ross (1969) give an algorithm for this; see also Ross (1972).

A slightly different idea is to draw on the plot (directed) vectors from each point to its nearest neighbour in p dimensions. If A is the nearest neighbour of B, then B need not be the nearest neighbour of A; hence plotted arrows may or may not occur in pairs on the lines. In fact these lines always form part of the minimum spanning tree and so the two ideas can be combined.

We have drawn the minimum spanning tree for the city crime data in Figure 6.5; the arrows on the straight-line segments show the nearest neighbour vectors. There are discrepancies, signified by the long lines, in each corner of

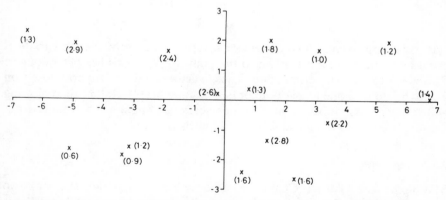

Figure 6.4   Principal-components scores for crime rates in 16 cities (as in Figure 6.2) with associated residuals

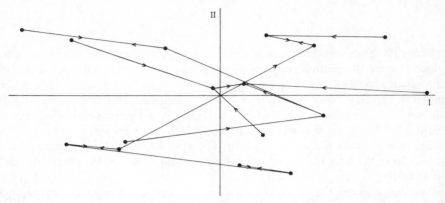

Figure 6.5   Figure 6.2 with superimposed minimum spanning tree. The arrows point at the nearest neighbour of each point

the plot, suggesting that the two-dimensional approximation is not particularly good in these regions. A better-fitting minimum spanning tree occurs later in Section 6.1.8.

6.1.6 Representation of variates

In the preceding sections we have concentrated on point plots for the n units; in this section we suggest a method for plotting the variates.

The variates can be considered as p unit vectors from the origin in the direction of the axes of the original p-dimensional space. These vectors join the origin to the points with coordinates given by the rows of the unit-matrix I_p. Projecting these points onto the principal axes gives new coordinates in the matrix

$$\mathbf{B} = \mathbf{IL} = \mathbf{L}$$

and so an approximate two-dimensional representation of the ith variate is given by a line joining the origin to the point (l_{i1}, l_{i2}). This has been done in Figure 6.6 for the city crime data. These vectors could be superimposed on Figure 6.2 to give one form of biplot (see Section 6.1.7). Rather than plotting unit vectors, it might be useful to plot projections of points at a distance from the origin equal to the standard error of each variate.

6.1.7 The biplot

The *biplot* (see Gabriel, Chapter 8) of a matrix $\mathbf{X}$ finds the best rank-two approximation to $\mathbf{X}$ in the form $\mathbf{X}_{(2)} = \mathbf{A}_{(2)}\mathbf{B}_{(2)}^{\mathrm{T}}$ where $\mathbf{A}_{(2)}$ is $n \times 2$ and $\mathbf{B}_{(2)}$ is $p \times 2$. Graphically the rows and columns of $\mathbf{X}$ are jointly represented by the

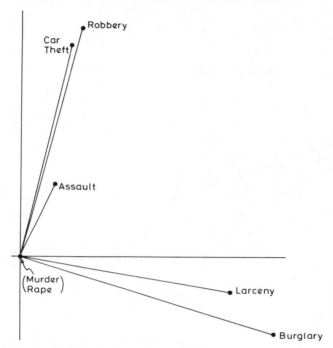

Figure 6.6 Projection of unit variates corresponding to the seven types of crime onto the space of the first two principal components. When this figure is combined with Figure 6.2, one form of biplot is obtained. Variables (crimes) considered are oblique directions in two dimensions

points (a_{i1}, a_{i2}) and (b_{j1}, b_{j2}), respectively. Eckart and Young (1936) show that the approximation can be obtained from the singular-value decomposition of $\mathbf{X}$, thus

$$\mathbf{A}_{(2)} = \mathbf{U}_{(2)} \, \mathbf{\Sigma}^{\alpha}_{(2)}$$
$$\mathbf{B}_{(2)} = \mathbf{V}_{(2)} \, \mathbf{\Sigma}^{1-\alpha}_{(2)}$$

where $\mathbf{U}_{(2)}$ and $\mathbf{V}_{(2)}$ are the first two columns of $\mathbf{U}$ and $\mathbf{V}$, respectively, $\mathbf{\Sigma}_{(2)}$ is diag(σ_1, σ_2), and α is some constant open to choice.

In the original paper on the biplot (Gabriel, 1971), its application to principal-component analysis was described. If the parameter α is set to 1, the combined plot of those of Sections 6.1.3 and 6.1.6 is obtained. The usefulness of setting $\alpha = 0$ is also mentioned: now the lengths of the vectors for the variates approximate their standard deviations (other inferences can be drawn—we refer the reader to the original paper).

As an example Figure 6.7 shows the second form of the biplot (i.e. with

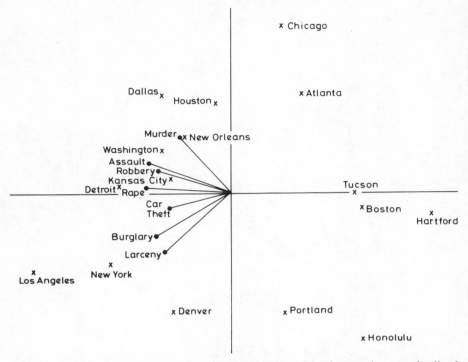

Figure 6.7   A two-dimensional biplot of the cities and crimes using standardized variates. This can be compared with the combination of Figures 6.2 and 6.6 which used unstandardized variates

$\alpha = 0$) for the city crime data, after the variates have been standardized to unit variance. The differences between this plot and Figure 6.6 (e.g. the vectors for the two crimes murder and rape) illustrate the effect that standardization can make to a principal-components analysis. Note the equivalence to a principal-components analysis supplemented by plotting vectors for the variates.

Bradu and Gabriel (1978) propose using the biplot as a diagnostic tool when the original data are considered as a two-way table. They suggest that the table might have row and column means subtracted before the rank-two approximation is found, and that the parameter α should have the value $\frac{1}{2}$. If the original data are y_{ij} this gives

$$x_{ij} = y_{ij} - \mu - r_i - c_j,$$

where μ is an overall mean and r_i and c_j are row and column effects, respectively. Thus the diagnostic biplot models the data as:

$$y_{ij} = \mu + r_i + c_j + a_{i1}b_{j1} + a_{i2}b_{j2} + e_{ij},$$

where e_{ij}, the error from the rank-two approximation, is defined in a similar way to that given in Section 6.1.3. Bradu and Gabriel (1978) interpret collinearities in the biplot as suggesting restrictions on the parameters above.

6.1.8 Correspondence analysis

Correspondence analysis (see Greenacre, Chapter 7) is appropriate to nonnegative data, for example tables of counts or percentages. The analysis provides a joint plot of points representing both the rows and columns of the table.

The original data, y_{ij}, are transformed by dividing each y_{ij} by $\sqrt{(r_i c_j)}$ where r_i and c_j are row and column totals, respectively. Thus

$$\mathbf{X} = \mathbf{R}^{1/2}\mathbf{Y}\mathbf{C}^{1/2},$$

where $\mathbf{R}$ and $\mathbf{C}$ are diagonal matrices of row and column totals. Again the singular-value decomposition of $\mathbf{X}$ is formed

$$\mathbf{X} = \mathbf{U}\boldsymbol{\Sigma}\mathbf{V}^T$$

and the matrices holding coordinates for the rows and columns are

$$\mathbf{A} = \mathbf{R}^{-1/2}\mathbf{U}\boldsymbol{\Sigma}^{\beta}$$
$$\mathbf{B} = \mathbf{C}^{-1/2}\mathbf{V}\boldsymbol{\Sigma}^{\beta}.$$

The parameter β depends on variants of the method; $\beta = 0$, $\frac{1}{2}$ or 1 are usual. A consequence of the initial transformation of $\mathbf{Y}$ is that $\sigma_1 = 1$ and the corresponding first columns of $\mathbf{A}$ and $\mathbf{B}$ are constant ($=1$ when the data total one). Thus the plot of interest is of the points (a_{i2}, a_{i3}) and (b_{j2}, b_{j3}).

Again we can specify a model for the data. Since

$$\mathbf{Y} = \mathbf{R}^{1/2}\mathbf{X}\mathbf{C}^{1/2} = \mathbf{R}^{1/2}\mathbf{U}\boldsymbol{\Sigma}\mathbf{V}^T\mathbf{C}^{1/2} = \mathbf{R}\mathbf{A}\boldsymbol{\Sigma}^{1-2\beta}\mathbf{B}^T\mathbf{C}$$

the plotted terms relate to the difference between the y_{ij} and their expectations, as proportions, under the assumption of row/column independence:

$$\frac{y_{ij} - r_i c_j}{r_i c_j} = z_{i2}b_{j2}\sigma_2^{1-2\beta} + a_{i3}b_{j3}\sigma_3^{1-2\beta} + e_{ij}.$$

For illustration we use some data concerning 16 European countries and 20 types of food (from Hartigan, 1975); y_{ij} is the percentage of households in country j that stock food i. The plot resulting from a correspondence analysis with $\beta = 0$ is shown in Figure 6.8. It can be shown that when the vectors from the origin to a row-point and to a column-point are close the appropriate cell of the table is likely to be larger than expected under row/column independence; conversely, diametrically opposed row and column points indicate a value lower than expected. Here we note the relations between the Scandinavian countries and crispbread (positive) and yoghurt (negative). The distances

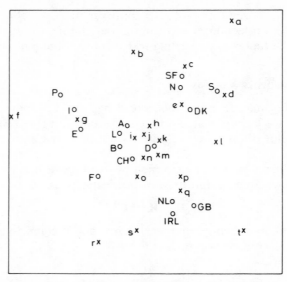

Figure 6.8   A correspondence analysis of percentages of households in 16 European countries having each of 20 types of food

Key:
Foodstuffs: *a* Crispbread, *b* Ground coffee, *c* Frozen fish, *d* Frozen vegetables, *e* Instant potato, *f* Garlic, *g* Olive oil, *h* Margarine, *i* Oranges, *j* Butter, *k* Tea, *l* Sugarless sweeteners, *m* Biscuits, *n* Apples, *o* Soup (packaged), *p* Jam, *q* Tinned fruit, *r* Yoghurt, *s* Instant coffee, *t* Soup (tinned)

Countries: *A* Austria, *B* Belgium, *CH* Switzerland, *D* West Germany, *E* Spain, *F* France, *GB* Great Britain, *I* Italy, *IRL* Ireland, *L* Luxembourg, *N* Norway, *NL* Holland, *P* Portugal, *S* Sweden, *SF* Finland

between the locations for the countries in all 16 dimensions have been used to construct a minimum spanning tree, which is superimposed on plot (b_{j3}, b_{j2}) of the countries in Figure 6.9: note that this is quite similar to a geographical map of Europe, apart from the points representing Spain and Portugal.

It will be evident that principal-components analysis, the biplot, and correspondence analysis have much in common, through their central use of the singular-value decomposition with its least-squares properties. Another method for analysing rectangular two-way tables for joint row and column representation is *multidimensional unfolding*, discussed in Section 6.2.2.

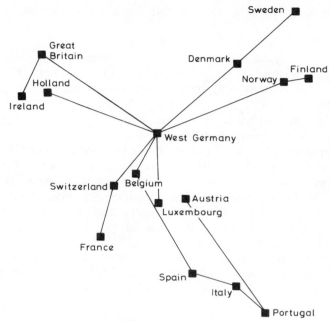

Figure 6.9 Minimum spanning tree fitted to the full 15-dimensional correspondence analysis solution superimposed on a rotated plot of countries from Figure 6.8

6.2 DATA AS A SYMMETRIC MATRIX

When a set of data consists of all the pairwise associations between n objects, the data can be formed into a symmetric matrix of order n. Thus m_{ij} is a measure of similarity, dissimilarity or distance, between objects i and j, and in this section we assume this to equal m_{ji} (the case when m_{ij} is not equal to m_{ji}, is discussed in Section 6.3.

Ordination methods, discussed in Sections 6.2.1 and 6.2.3, locate the objects in some number of dimensions such that the inter-object associations are approximately preserved. Thus if the data are inter-town road distances we expect a two-dimensional ordination to approximate a geographical map.

6.2.1 Metric scaling

The methods of *metric scaling*, for example, *principal coordinate analysis* (Gower, 1966), use the data values m_{ij} directly (cf. Section 6.2.3). If the data are m_{ij}, principal-coordinate analysis finds locations in t dimensions ($a_{i1}, a_{i2},$

$\ldots, a_{it})$ for the n objects so that the inter-point squared-distance:

$$d_{ij}^2 = \sum_{k=1}^{t} (a_{ik} - a_{jk})^2$$

approximates $m_{ii} + m_{jj} - 2m_{ij}$. This is appropriate when the data are similarities (see Section 6.5) because self-similarities are unity and the approximation becomes $d_{ij}^2 \sim 2(1 - m_{ij})$. When m_{ij} are distances, self-distances are zero and hence $d_{ij}^2 \sim -2m_{ij}$, which implies that to approximate distance δ_{ij} it is appropriate to set $m_{ij} = -\frac{1}{2}\delta_{ij}^2$.

The computational process of principal coordinates is similar to that of principal components analysis. The matrix $\mathbf{M}$ is *doubly-centred*, which means that it is transformed to $(\mathbf{I} - \mathbf{N})\mathbf{M}(\mathbf{I} - \mathbf{N})$ where $\mathbf{N}$ is the matrix all of whose values are $1/n$. The eigenvectors of the transformed matrix are normalized to have sum-of-squares equal to their corresponding eigenvalues. The coordinates of the ith point to be plotted are the ith values of the t vectors corresponding to the t biggest eigenvalues.

A special case of principal coordinate analysis occurs when the data are Euclidean distances which have been obtained from an original $n \times p$ data matrix (see Section 6.1) of values y_{ij} by using

$$\delta_{ij}^2 = \sum_{k=1}^{p} (y_{ik} - y_{jk})^2.$$

Now the locations for the objects in t dimensions will be precisely those of the objects relative to the first t principal components obtained from the original data $\mathbf{Y}$. Thus there is a duality between a principal coordinate analysis operating on a dispersion (or R-) matrix and principal component analysis operating on a distance (or Q-) matrix. A similar duality exists with canonical variate analysis when Mahalanobis squared-distances are used as the values δ_{ij} in a principal coordinate analysis. Note that the principal coordinate analysis is very general because it can operate formally on any distance, similarity or dissimilarity matrix. However with some coefficients the fitted Euclidean configuration may not be real, and care has to be taken in interpretation. This situation is easily recognized because negative eigenvalues occur in the analysis, which will lead to difficulties if they dominate the positive eigenvalues.

Nathanson (1971) gives the Mahalanobis squared-distances between 10 types of galaxy: ellipticals, irregularly shaped galaxies, and eight spiral forms. Principal coordinate analysis has been used for these data and the two-dimensional solution is shown in Figure 6.10, where the morphological diagrams of Nathanson (1971) have been used to locate the points. It is interesting to see that the points approximately lie on an arc of a circle with the irregular galaxies at its centre. Along the circumference of the circle there is a trend from the dense galaxies (elliptical) to the most tenuous galaxies of spiral form.

Figure 6.10   A principal-coordinate analysis of Mahalanobis
distances between ten types of galaxy

As in Section 6.1 additional information may be superimposed on two-dimensional metric-scaling configurations. A useful device occurs when the original data y_{ij} all take values 0 or 1. Now a similarity matrix $\mathbf{M}$ can be calculated and used as the basis of a metric scaling. Then the quantitiies $\Sigma_{j=1}^{p} y_{ij}$ $(i = 1, 2, \ldots, n)$ are trivally calculated and may be plotted on the two-dimensional diagram. Banfield and Gower (1980) discuss how the interpretation of such annotated diagrams reveals discrepancies in the two-dimensional approximation, allows other useful quantities to be calculated and also may offer direct interpretational advantages. With continuous variables the quantities $(1/p)\Sigma y_{ij} = y_{i.}$ (say) are often termed size variables, at least in biological applications. These may be plotted in the same way.

Hartigan (1975) gives some data relating to 30 types of car. There are 13 variables, each being a type of repair; a car scores one for a repair if that particular repair is required more frequently than usual, otherwise the score is zero. A simple matching similarity coefficient is suitable here which allows a principal components analysis of the binary data; the locations of the cars relative to the first two principal axes are shown in Figure 6.11, with the $y_{i.}$ values superimposed. It is clear that the $y_{i.}$ values increase as the points become more distant from the point with $y_{i.} = 0$. This is a common feature of these plots showing that 'size' (in this case number of faults) is a major contribution to the dispersion of the plotted points.

A further device is to work in the space orthogonal to size, so that the data are transformed to $y_{ij} - y_{i}$. In matrix form the principal coordinate analysis operates on

$$\mathbf{M} = \mathbf{Y}\mathbf{Y}^{T} - p\mathbf{y}\mathbf{y}^{T}$$

where $\mathbf{y}$ is the vector of size estimates. A two-dimensional approximation may be found in the usual way and the values $y_{i.}$ superimposed. This has been done with the car data in Figure 6.12.

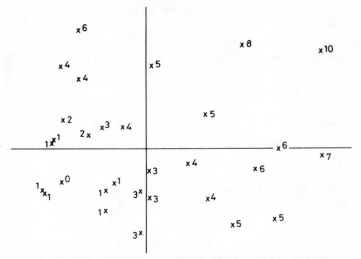

Figure 6.11 A principal coordinate analysis of 30 models of car showing for each model the total number of faults where each car model was worse than average

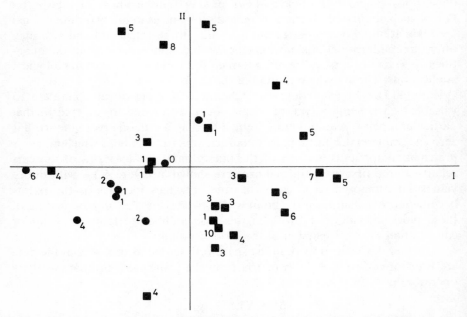

Figure 6.12 A principal coordinate analysis of 30 models of car after removing a 'size' component corresponding to the fault rating. Number of faults as in Figure 6.11 are associated with each model. Key: ● European models; ■ American models

Note that the size trend is no longer present. The cars with most faults tend to lie on the periphery of the diagram, those with least towards the centre. Thus we can imagine concentric contours of equal numbers of faults. Of the 30 types of car, eight are European, the rest being American: this classification is shown on the diagram. It can be seen that the European cars occupy one sector of the plot in Figure 6.12, suggesting that European cars tend to suffer from different combinations of faults than American cars. The range in the number of faults is similar for both groups, but more European cars seem to have fewer faults than do American cars.

Clearly a similar device can be used when y is replaced by any linear combination of the data values.

The term 'principal coordinate analysis' is most often encountered with biological applications; in psychometrics the equivalent method is termed *classical scaling* (to differentiate from non-metric scaling). Other forms of metric scaling exist, which obtain their approximations by minimizing different goodness-of-fit criteria, which, of course, lead in turn to (slightly) different two-dimensional configurations. The graphical properties remain virtually unchanged and need not detain us.

6.2.2 Multidimensional unfolding

When the data M have missing values, metric scaling is in general impracticable. One special case of importance is when M has the form of Figure 6.13, where only the $r \times s$ two-way table has available data. Coordinates can still be found for the $r + s$ points, giving another form of analysis for a two-way table. Computation is more complicated, but *metric unfolding* methods have been

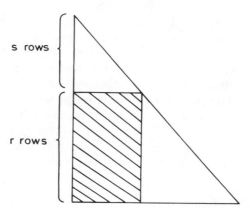

Figure 6.13 Multidimensional unfolding. The hatched area shows the part of a complete distance-matrix that is available for analysis

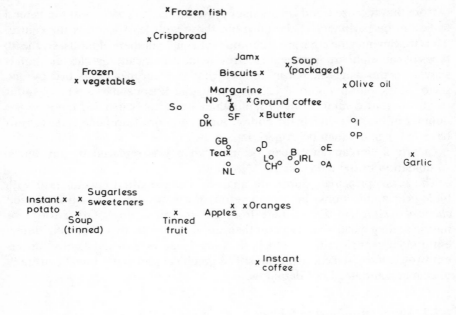

Figure 6.14   A multidimensional unfolding of the data described in Figure 6.8. Key to countries as in Figure 6.8

discussed by Schonemann (1970), Gold (1973) and Greenacre (1978). Nevertheless reliable computational methods still need development and it is more usual to use non-metric scaling methods (see Section 6.2.3) for multidimensional unfolding, although these too have certain deficiencies.

The result of a two-dimensional non-metric unfolding is shown in Figure 6.14; the data are those used in Section 6.1.8, after subtracting the values from 100 to obtain measures of distance rather than similarity. Notice that the locations for the countries are more tightly bunched in the centre of the plot than in Figure 6.8. This particular analysis seems less satisfactory than the correspondence analysis solution, probably because, in unfolding, the additional structure of row-column distance approximations has to be incorporated in the plot. Also, because the data can be considered to be contingencies, correspondence analysis has a special relevance.

6.2.3 Non-metric scaling

In essence, *non-metric scaling* is similar to its metric counterparts in that locations are found for the n objects that approximately maintain associations between the objects. However this is done via an ordinal scale in such a way that the goodness-of-fit criterion depends only on the rankings of the values m_{ij} and not on their absolute values. Various criteria are available and a fuller account of non-metric multidimensional scaling is given by Kruskal and Wish (1977).

6.2.4 Considering a symmetric matrix as a two-way table

A symmetric matrix can be analysed as a two-way table. The methods of Section 6.1 will not give much additional information, for the singular-value decomposition of a symmetric matrix is of the form $\mathbf{U\Sigma U}^T$, giving the same vectors for both rows and columns. However, multidimensional unfolding (Section 6.2.2) gives useful simplifications. Each of the n objects is doubly represented, once as a row of the table and once as a column. Omitting the diagonal elements may be preferable: that is, the data for the row-column combination of the objects with themselves is discarded. Considerable dimension reduction, compared with standard methods, can be obtained with this method. Particularly dramatic is that a regular simplex of n points, which normally requires $n-1$ dimensions, can be represented exactly in one dimension.

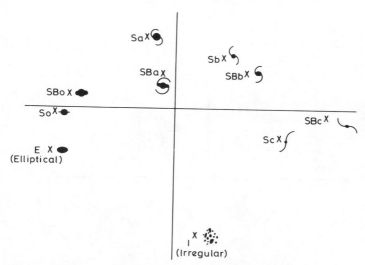

Figure 6.15 A non-metric multidimensional unfolding of the symmetric matrix of Mahalanobis distances between the types of galaxy. The zero diagonals have been ignored. The solution is in three dimensions, the first two of which are exhibited in the figure. The picture displays (from Nathanson, 1971) describe the form and shape of the galaxies and the labels indicate a standard astronomical classification

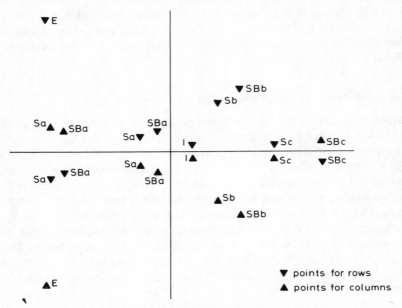

Figure 6.16   As Figure 6.15, but dimensions 1 and 3

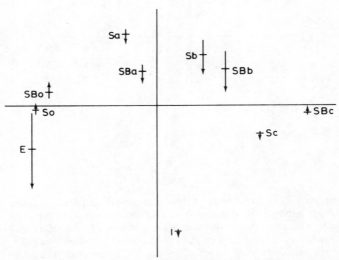

Figure 6.17 A combination of all three dimensions from Figures 6.15 and 6.16

We have used multidimensional unfolding (Section 6.2.2) in its non-metric form to find pairs of locations in three dimensions for the 10 galaxy types. Various phenomena can occur when symmetric matrices are analysed in this way; two of particular importance are as follows. The first is coincidence of the row and column points for each object within some dimensions: this is illustrated in Figure 6.15, where it can be seen that the row and column points coincide in dimensions one and two. The second phenomenon is shown in Figure 6.16: the third dimension of the unfolding solution gives a reflection of the row points to the column points (and vice versa) in dimension one. The size of this reflection, which represents the discrepancy between the row and column locations, can be superimposed on the first two dimensions of the solution, as shown in Figure 6.17. In Figures 6.15 and 6.17 the points representing the galaxies tend to lie on an arc of a circle, and at the centre, as in Figure 6.10.

6.3 ASYMMETRIC SQUARE TABLES

All methods available for rectangular tables are potentially available for square tables. However there is an important special class of data where the rows and columns are similarly classified, giving a square table **A**, but the data values are not symmetric as they were in Section 6.2. A feature of such tables is that the rows and columns are classified by the same entities but in different modes. Examples are emigration/immigration data, international trade figures, confusion matrices in psychometrics, social mobility data, etc. This section is illustrated by data from Hartigan (1975) giving the percentage of people of one country who speak the language of another.

Methods are of two kinds; those that model the whole table and those that separately model the symmetric and skew-symmetric components of the data. We shall briefly describe two of the first class of models before going on to describe in some detail one of the second class.

Young (1975) proposed fitting the model

$$m_{ij} = \sum_{k=1}^{t} w_{ik}(x_{ik} - x_{jk})^2$$

where w_{ik} are positive weights. The coordinates x_{ik} ($k = 1, 2, \ldots, t$) are plotted for the ith point, giving a Euclidean representation, apart from the set of weights at each point. Asymmetry is allowed for because w_{ik} and w_{jk} differ in general. This model with its associated graphics is reminiscent of individual scaling discussed in Section 6.4. Another important class of models, discussed by Harshman (1978), sets

$$y_{ij} = \sum_{u=1}^{t} \sum_{v=1}^{t} x_{iu} r_{uv} x_{jv}$$

or equivalently

$$Y = XRX^T.$$

Clearly when R is symmetric, the model fits a symmetric matrix. When R is asymmetric, so is Y. The solution is not unique, for any orthogonal matrix Q may be chosen and X replaced by XQ and R replaced Q^TRQ. This would not affect any plot of X whose rows are treated as coordinates, but it might be worth choosing a rotation Q that simplifies R, drawing on the techniques of factor rotation and the idea of simple structure used in factor analysis. Chino (1978) has discussed a variant of the Harshman model in which R is restricted to a very special form.

Often, attempts to model asymmetry in a single simple model are not successful. We suspect that this may be because symmetry and departures from symmetry may be induced by separate processes. An approach that analyses symmetry and skew-symmetry separately has been suggested by Gower (1977) who writes

$$Y = M(\text{symmetric}) + N(\text{skew-symmetric}).$$

Because $\Sigma y_{ij}^2 = \Sigma m_{ij}^2 + \Sigma n_{ij}^2$ the two parts may be viewed independently. Clearly M may be analysed by the methods discussed in Section 6.2. To analyse the skew-symmetric N, we use the least-squares property of the Eckart–Young theorem adapted for this special case. The singular value decomposition of N has form $N = U\Sigma JU^T$ where U and J are orthogonal and $\Sigma = \text{diag}(\sigma_1, \sigma_1, \sigma_2, \sigma_2, \ldots)$ with last value zero when n is odd. J is block diagonal with 2×2 blocks containing the values

$$\begin{pmatrix} 0 & 1 \\ -1 & 0 \end{pmatrix},$$

with unity in the last diagonal position when n is odd. The best two-dimensional fit is given by

$$n_{ij} = \sigma_1(u_{i1}u_{j2} - u_{i2}u_{j1})$$

which may be regarded as the model fitted. If the points with coordinates P_i(i.e. u_{i1}, u_{i2}) are plotted, the geometrical interpretation is that n_{ij} is approximated by the area of the triangle with vertices at P_i, P_j and the origin, O. The areas of triangles OP_iP_j and OP_jP_i are equal but opposite in sign, thus modelling the skew-symmetry. Therefore, unlike the distance models of symmetry, the position of the origin is important; however, rotations leave area unchanged as do scalings of one axis by a factor λ (say) coupled with an inverse scaling λ^{-1} of the other axis. As with diagrams that use distance as the interpretive device, a pair of close points P_i and P_j indicate a small value of n_{ij}, which however remains small when P_i and P_j are distant, but collinear with the origin. The locus of points P_k such that triangles OP_iP_j and OP_iP_k have equal area (i.e. $n_{ij} = n_{ik}$) is a line through P_j paralle to OP_i. Thus the geometry of the space representing skew-symmetry in terms of areas is a novel one that needs care in interpreting. In particular the familiar concept of distance does not apply.

Gower (1977, 1980) and Constantine and Gower (1978) discuss analyses based on the area interpretation of skew-symmetry, paying special attention to the case when all the points are collinear. This corresponds to the most simple form of skew-symmetry in which $n_{ij} = n_i - n_j$. We discuss here an analysis of data from Hartigan (1975) who gives for eleven European countries a table of the percentage of persons in each country who speak the language of the other. The diagram representing the skew-symmetric part of this table is given in Figure 6.18. We see that the languages spoken locally (at least in Europe) lie approximately on a line through the origin indicating that about equal numbers (probably few) speak the other's language. The international languages (English, French and German and to some extent Swedish, which is a language widely known throughout Scandinavia and Finland) lie to one side, giving many large areas. This reflects obvious facts, such as that many more Dutch people speak English than vice versa. The relationship between English and German suggests that enough German is spoken by Englishmen to go some way towards cancelling out the amount of English spoken by Germans. English and French are nearly collinear with the origin as would happen if the other language was equally well-known in both countries. The diagram focuses attention on such matters, which can be examined in detail by referring to the original data. With large data sets the diagram

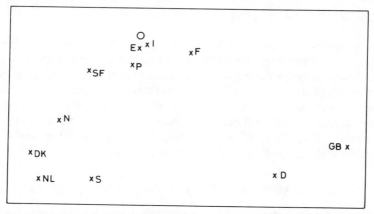

Figure 6.18   Canonical analysis of the skew-symmetric components of data giving the percentages of people in each of 11 European countries who speak the language of each of the other 10 countries. The origin is marked by a circle and the key to countries is as in Figure 6.8

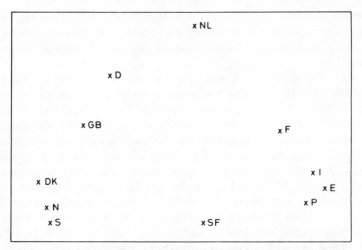

Figure 6.19 Principal-coordinate analysis of the symmetric component of the data described in Figure 6.18

gives a valuable initial scrutiny of the data not feasible for data in tabular form.

For the same data we have also analysed the symmetric part **M**, shown in Figure 6.19. The romance, germanic and scandinavian groups separate out well, with Finnish distant from all other languages. Some of the separations are greater than might be expected at first sight. For example Dutch and German are not close. This is because although many Dutch people speak German, few Germans speak Dutch, diluting the association between the two.

Ideally the two analyses of **M** and **N** should be combined. Certainly if models can be fitted to each separately, it is sufficient to add the two components. However, there can be difficulties in doing this. For example even the simple multiplicative model $y_{ij} = m_{ij}p_j$ has only a simple structure between symmetric and skew-symmetric parts if the data are transformed to logarithms, and even then there are certain difficulties in uniqueness of parameterization. Thus the ideal of combining the two parts of the analysis is not easily achieved, but it should always be kept in mind.

6.4 GRAPHICAL METHODS WITH 3-WAY DATA

In this section we mention a class of models that have received much attention in recent years. Suppose we have a set of m data matrices or distance matrices. Then each may be analysed by the methods discussed in Sections 6.1 and 6.2, and associated plots produced. The question arises as to how to combine the plots with some kind of average configuration together with an indication of how the individual plots differ from the average. A combined analysis is possible only when the same n units occur in all analyses. Two rather different methods are discussed below, but others exist.

6.4.1 Individual scaling

Suppose distances d_{ijk} are given between the ith and jth units for the kth configuration. It is required to find an average configuration in t dimensions given in the $n \times t$ matrix X such that the kth configuration arises by weighting the sth axis of the average by a value w_{ks}. Thus

$$d_{ijk}^2 \sim \sum_{s=1}^{t} w_{ks}(x_{is} - x_{js})^2.$$

The configuration given in X is usually termed the *group average* and may be plotted in the usual way. The weights w_{ks} may also be plotted. When $t = 2$, the weights (and group average configuration) give two-dimensional plots. Weights near the 45° line indicate an individual configuration close to that of the group average. Weights close to an axis are associated with an individual diverging maximally from the group average.

Carroll and Chang (1970) describe a method for calculating X and the weights w_{ks} ($k = 1, 2, \ldots, n; s = 1, 2, \ldots, t$) which is incorporated in a widely used computer program, INDSCAL. The same model can be fitted by optimizing different criteria of goodness-of-fit incorporated in ALSCAL (Takane, Young and de Leeuw, 1977) and in SMACOF-I (Heiser and de Leeuw, 1979).

We illustrate the method with anthropometric data relating to ten humanoid populations, some represented by many skulls, some by a single skull. Variables are measured on six regions of the skull (upper jaw, articular region, basicranium, cranial vault, face, balance region). For each region, Mahalanobis distances between all pairs of populations were calculated and six configurations produced by canonical variate analysis. Thus this set of six Mahalanobis distance matrices represent the 'individuals' in an INDSCAL analysis. Figure 6.20 shows the group-average space fitted in $t = 2$ dimensions. Populations 6 and 9, each of which are represented by single skulls, stand out as remote from the other eight populations. Figure 6.21 shows the weights for each region. Because the points representing all regions lie quite near the 45° line of equal weights, it seems that there is little evidence that the Mahalanobis distance matrices differ much among the groups. The cranial vault, face and upper jaw regions diverge most from the average, but this divergence is not very strong.

A feature of individual scaling analysis that is unusual among the methods discussed so far is that coordinate axes may not be rotated. This is because

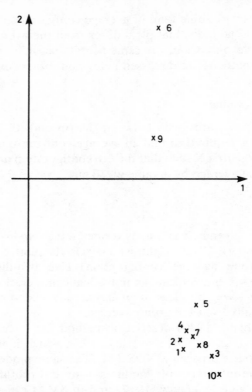

Figure 6.20   The group-average display for a Individual Scaling Analysis (INDSCAL). Each individual corresponds to one of 6 regions of the skull (upper jaw, articular, basicranium, cranial vault, face, balance). For each region Mahalanobis distances have been calculated between 10 humanoid populations. Key: 1 Modern homo sapiens, 2 Late pleistocene homo sapiens, 3 Neanderthal, 4 Pekin homo erectus, 5 Australopithicus Africanus, 6 East Rudolf hominids No. 406, 7 East Rudolf hominids No. 1813, 8 East Rudolf hominids No. 3733, 9 Olduvai hominids No. 5, 10 Olduvai hominids No. 24

rotation of the axes in the group-average space induces change in the estimated weights, that are not consistent with the model being fitted.

6.4.2 Generalized Procrustes analysis

Individual scaling analysis operates on m distance-matrices, which may of course have been derived from m data-matrices. *Generalized Procrustes*

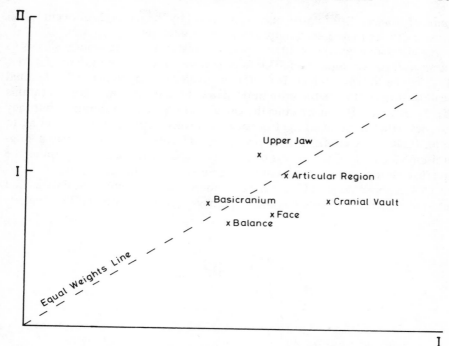

Figure 6.21   Individual scaling analysis: Weightings for the 6 skull regions of
the 2 dimensions of the group-average axes given in Figure 6.20

analysis operates on m matrices, each of size $n \times p$ and giving the coordinates
of n points in p dimensions, which may of course have been derived from
distance matrices. If $\mathbf{X}_1$ and $\mathbf{X}_2$ are two such $n \times p$ matrices, an orthogonal
Procrustes analysis fits one to the other by using the rigid body motions of
translation and orthogonal transformations. A least-squares goodness-of-fit
criterion is used that minimizes the sum over all n pairs of the squared distance
between corresponding points. The problem has a straightforward analytical
solution, involving the singular-value decomposition of $\mathbf{X}_1^T\mathbf{X}_2$—see Sibson
(1978) for a recent review.

A further transformation that may be required in Procrustes fitting prob-
lems is to scale $\mathbf{X}_1$ relative to $\mathbf{X}_2$ by a factor ρ. This is a simple and useful
extension, but the scaling of $\mathbf{X}_2$ relative to $\mathbf{X}_1$ is not simply related to the
scaling of $\mathbf{X}_1$ to $\mathbf{X}_2$. This difficulty is most simply resolved by first scaling $\mathbf{X}_1$
and $\mathbf{X}_2$ to have equal (say unit) sums-of-squares. Any additional scaling is then
invertible and turns out to be equivalent to the special case of generalized
Procrustes analysis (discussed below) in which $m = 2$.

One way of handling m data sets $\mathbf{X}_1, \mathbf{X}_2, \ldots, \mathbf{X}_m$ is to perform all $\binom{m}{2}$
pairwise Procrustes analyses and build up the symmetric matrix of residual

sums-of-squares. This matrix may be analysed by the methods of Section 6.2.
Gower (1971b) gives an example of such an analysis.

An alternative extension to m sets is to transform simultaneously all sets to
fit an average configuration. This is *generalized Procrustes analysis* (Gower,
1975). The average, which is analogous to the group average of individual
scaling, turns out to be the arithmetic mean of the transformed configurations
$X_1, X_2, \ldots, X_m$. Because of this the calculations have to be iterative, but they
are nevertheless quite straightforward. It is convenient, but not essential, to
refer the average configuration to its principal axes. The transformed configurations for each of the m sets can be displayed on the same diagram as the
average configuration, and examined for unusually large residuals.

This has been done in Figure 6.22 for the same anthropometric data as that
used to illustrate individual scaling. We have however restricted this analysis

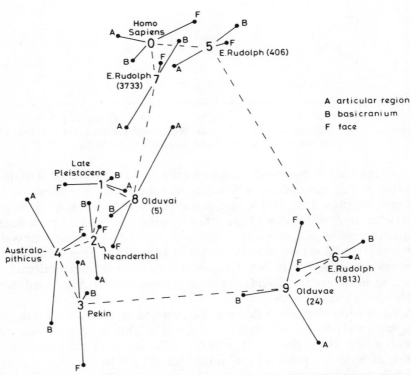

Figure 6.22   A generalized Procrustes analysis of the data described in Figure
6.20 but including only the three skull regions given by A, articular region; B,
basicranium; F, face. The centroids for each population are indicated by the
large digits 0–9, and are analogous to the group-average space of Figure 6.20.
The lines joining the centroid to points representing regions give residuals
indicating the discrepancies amongst regions

to only three skull regions (face, basicranium and articular region). The configurations being fitted are the canonical variate means of the ten populations. As previously, the same two single skulls stand out as outliers. The plotted residuals suggest that the articular region gives a rather different description of the differences between the populations, but this cannot be compared with the individual scaling analysis because of the fewer regions of the skull being considered. Associated with generalized Procrustes analysis is an analysis of variance which summarizes the main features (see Gower, 1975).

A further generalization occurs when different weights are to be associated with each configuration. An example of such an analysis is given in Chapter 13 by Everitt and Gower, who also indicate the modifications to the numerical process that are required.

6.5 HIERARCHICAL REPRESENTATION

The methods of *hierarchical classification* are legion (see, for example, Everitt, 1974) and commonly operate on a matrix of similarities between the n objects. This is a $n \times n$ symmetric matrix with values in the range 0–1, and value 1 on the diagonal. Gower (1971a) describes a general method for constructing such a matrix from an original units × variates data matrix. However, any symmetric matrix $\mathbf{M}$ (see Section 6.2) with constant diagonal value is acceptable.

In this section we are not concerned with algorithms for hierarchical classification but merely mention some graphical methods that can aid the interpretation of a hierarchical classification of a set of objects, however obtained.

6.5.1 Classification order

Hierarchical classification defines a reordering of the n objects so that similar objects are close together in the new order. A *dendrogram* is a binary tree that shows the hierarchical merging of groups of objects with an associated scale showing the levels of similarity at which the different groups merge.

6.5.2 Shading

Sneath (1957) suggests that the similarity matrix for the objects in classification order can be displayed in a shaded form: higher densities of shading are used for larger similarities.

For illustration we will use a set of data from Kendall (1975): 48 applicants for a job were assessed on 15 characteristics (e.g. appearance, keenness to join), each being scored on a 0–10 scale. Figure 6.23 shows the shading, together with a 'hanging' dendrogram for a furthest-neighbour cluster

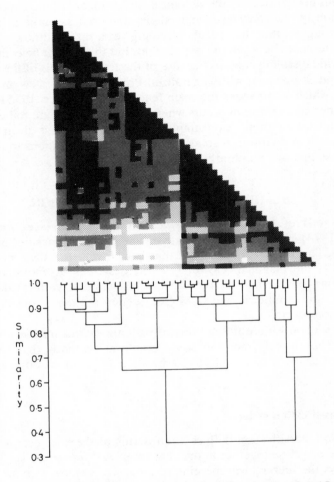

Figure 6.23   A similarity matrix based on scores for 15 qualities of 48 applicants for a job. The hanging dendrogram shows a furthest-neighbour cluster analysis, the end points of which correspond to the 48 applicants in a sorted order.

Key: □ Similarities   0–75%
        ⧄   75–89%
        ■   89–100%

Figure 6.24 A threaded dendrogram of a furthest-neighbour cluster analysis

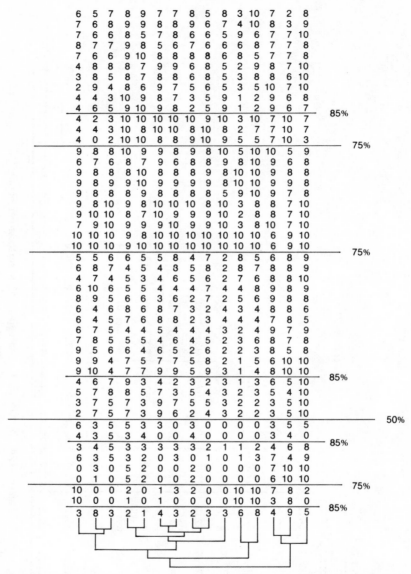

Figure 6.25   Scores for the 15 qualities of 48 applicants for a job, rearranged by a furthest-neighbour analysis amongst the variates. The rows correspond to the 48 applicants who are arranged in the same order as in Figure 6.23. The horizontal lines separate the applicants into the major clusters at levels of 50%, 75% and 85% similarity

analysis. We feel that the two parts of this display complement each other: the dendrogram shows the grouping, but not the separate similarities; conversely, the shade diagram shows the similarities, but does not clearly show the grouping. Another ingenious and concise way of exhibiting both types of information is due to Hartigan—see Figure 6.24 where the dendrogram is threaded through the matrix of similarities, here transformed correlations, between the 15 variables.

6.5.3   Reordering of the data matrix

If the original data are of the units × variates type, the rows of the data matrix can be displayed in the classification order. It is convenient to transform the variates to common origin and scale. Such a display is shown in Figure 6.25; the 0–10 form of the variate values makes the transformation unnecessary. For Figure 6.25 the 15 variables as well as the units have been hierarchically classified. The columns of the matrix are appropriately reordered, and the dendrogram is shown. The horizontal lines in Figure 6.25 delimit the groups of applicants obtained at three classification thresholds.

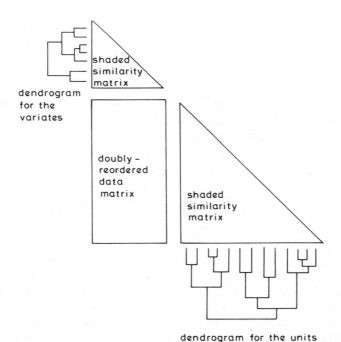

Figure 6.26   A schematic way of combining row and column hierarchical analyses

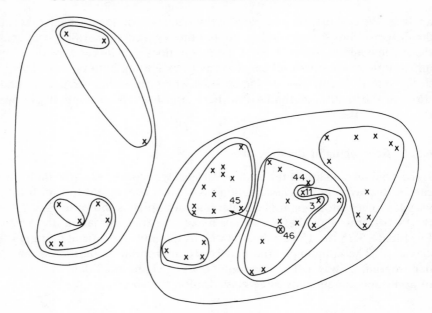

Figure 6.27 A combination of furthest-neighbour cluster analysis (thresholds as in Figure 6.25) with a principal coordinate analysis of the similarity matrix shown in shaded form in Figure 6.23

Obviously, these types of display can be grouped together in a number of ways. A display such as that shown schematically in Figure 6.26 would give a comprehensive hierarchical representation.

6.5.4 Ordination

We can use the similarity matrix to provide an ordination of the objects, such as that provided by principal coordinate analysis (Section 6.2.1). Hierarchical classification and ordination may be viewed as complementary ways of exhibiting sets of points in a multidimensional space. The former attempts to preserve closeness whilst the latter attempts to preserve distance. Combining both types of information in one diagram can be very useful. Figure 6.27 shows the 48 applicants plotted against the first two principal coordinates; this contains 67% of the variation. The grouping of the objects at three different thresholds is also shown; the distortion near points 44, 11 and 3 can be seen, also point 46 appears to be totally misplaced (as it should be in the same cluster as point 45).

REFERENCES

Anderson, E. (1960) A semigraphical method for the analysis of complex problems. *Technometrics*, **2**, 387–91.

Banfield, C. F. and Gower, J. C. (1980) A note on the graphical representation of multivariate binary data. *Applied Statistics*, **29**, 238–45.

Bradu, D. and Gabriel, K. R. (1978) The biplot as a diagnostic tool for models of two-way tables. *Technometrics*, **20**, 47–68.

Carroll, J. D. and Chang, J. J. (1970) Analysis of individual differences in multidimensional scaling via an *n*-way generalization of 'Eckart–Young' decomposition. *Psychometrika*, **35**, 283–319.

Chernoff, H. (1973) Using faces to represent points in *k*-dimensional space graphically. *J. Amer. Statist. Assn.*, **68**, 361–8.

Chino, N. (1978) A graphical technique for representing the asymmetric relationships between *N* objects. *Behaviormetrika*, **5**, 23–40.

Constantine, A. G. and Gower, J. C. (1978) Graphical representation of asymmetric matrices. *Applied Statistics*, **27**, 297–304.

Eckart, C. and Young, G. (1936) The approximation of one matrix by another of lower rank. *Psychometrika*, **1**, 211–318.

Everitt, B. S. (1974) *Cluster analysis*. London: Heinemann.

Gabriel, K. R. (1971) The biplot graphic display of matrices with applications to principal components analysis. *Biometrika*, **58**, 453–67.

Gnanadesikan, R. and Kettenring, J. R. (1972) Robust estimates, residuals and outlier detection with multiresponse data. *Biometrics*, **28**, 81–124.

Gold, E. M. (1973) Metric unfolding: data requirement for unique solution and clarification of Schonemann's algorithm. *Psychometrika*, **38**, 555–69.

Gower, J. C. (1966) Some distance properties of latent root and vector methods used in multivariate analysis. *Biometrika*, **53**, 325–38.

Gower, J. C. (1967) Multivariate analysis and multidimensional geometry. *The Statistician*, **17**, 13–25.

Gower, J. C. (1971a) A general coefficient of similarity and some of its properties. *Biometrics*, **27**, 857–72.

Gower, J. C. (1971b) Statistical methods of comparing different multivariate analyses of the same data. In Hodson, F. R., Kendall, D. G., and Taŭtu, P. (eds.) (1971). *Mathematics in the Archaeological and Historical Sciences*, pp. 139–49. Edinburgh: University Press.

Gower, J. C. (1975) Generalised Procrustes analysis. *Psychometrika*, **40**, 33–51.

Gower, J. C. (1977) The analysis of asymmetry and orthogonality. In Barra, J. *et al* (eds.) (1977). *Recent Developments in Statistics*. Amsterdam: North Holland, pp. 109–123.

Gower, J. C. (1980) Problems in interpreting asymmetric chemical relationships. In Bisby, F. (Ed.) (1980). *Chemosystematics: principles and practice*. New York: Academic Press.

Gower, J. C. and Ross, G. J. S. (1969). Minimum spanning trees and single linkage cluster analysis. *Applied Statistics*, **18**, 54–64.

Greenacre, M. J. (1978) Some objective methods of graphical display of a data matrix. *Special Report*, University of South Africa.

Harshman, R. (1978) Models for analysis of asymmetric relationships among *N* objects or stimuli. Paper presented at the first joint meeting of the Psychometric Society and the Society for Mathematical Psychology.

Hartigan, J. A. (1975) *Clustering Algorithms*. New York; Wiley.

Heiser, W. and de Leeuw, J. (1979) How to use SMACOF-I. A program for metric multidimensional scaling. *Internal Report*, Department of Data Theory, University of Leiden.

Kendall, M. G. (1975). *Multivariate Analysis*. London: Griffin.

Kleiner, B. and Hartigan, J. A. (1981) Representing points in many dimensions by trees and castles. *J. Amer. Statist. Assn.* **76**, 260–9.

Kruskal, J. B. and Wish, M. (1977) *Multidimensional scaling*. The Sage series on Methodology in the Social Sciences. Beverly Hills, California and London: Sage Publications.

M.A.F.F. (1972) *Agricultural statistics 1970–1971*. London: HMSO.

Nathanson, J. A. (1971) Applications of multivariate analysis in astronomy. *Applied Statistics*, **20**, 239–49.

Ross, G. J. S. (1972) Discussion of Sibson, R. (1972) Order invariant methods for data analysis. *J. Roy. Statist. Soc. B*, **34**, 343–4.

Schonemann, P. H. (1970) On metric multidimensional unfolding. *Psychometrika*, **35**, 349–66.

Sibson, R. (1978) Studies in the robustness of multidimensional scaling: Procrustes statistics. *J. Roy. Statist. Soc., B*, **40**, 234–8.

Sneath, P. H. A. (1957) The application of computers to taxonomy. *J. Gen. Microbiol*, **17**, 201–26

Takane, Y., Young, F., and de Leeuw, J. (1977) Non-metric individual differences multidimensional scaling: an alternating least squares method with optimal scaling features. *Psychometrika*, **42**, 7–67.

Williams, W. T. and Gillard, P. (1971) Pattern analysis of a grazing experiment. *Aust. J. Agric. Res.*, **22**, 245–60.

Young, F. W. (1975) An asymmetric Euclidean model for multi-process asymmetric data. In *U.S.-Japan Seminar on Theory, Methods and Applications of Multidimensional Scaling and Related Techniques*, Univ. of California, pp. 79–88.

CHAPTER 7

Practical Correspondence Analysis

M. J. Greenacre, *University of South Africa*

Correspondence analysis, as practised by a group of French statisticians since the early 1960s, is theoretically equivalent to a number of techniques which have appeared independently in different contexts since the mid 1930s, for example:

simultaneous linear regression

a special case of canonical correlation analysis

reciprocal averaging

dual scaling.

Correspondence analysis is primarily a technique for displaying the rows and columns of a two-way contingency table as points in corresponding low-dimensional vector spaces. This geometric approach in defining, describing and interpreting the technique broadens its base so that it may be extended, with suitable care, to the display of a wide range of data matrices.

In this chapter several applications of correspondence analysis are described which demonstrate its versatility as an exploratory statistical tool. These include the graphical display of:

frequency data

data in the form of ratings

'heterogeneous' data, i.e. observations on continuous and discrete variables.

7.1 INTRODUCTION

Correspondence analysis is primarily a technique for displaying the rows and the columns of a two-way contingency table as points in corresponding low-dimensional vector spaces. These spaces may be superimposed to obtain a joint display (see Figure 7.1). With suitable care the analysis may be extended to display other matrices of nonnegative data.

It is theoretically equivalent to a number of techniques which have appeared independently in the statistical literature since the mid 1930s, for

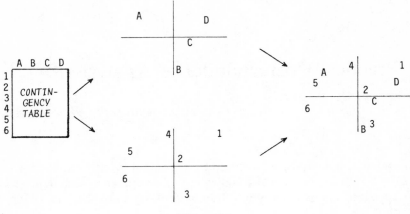

Figure 7.1

example:

> simultaneous linear regression (e.g. in the article by Hirschfeld, 1935, where we find one of the earliest formulations of the problem);

> reciprocal averaging (as used in statistical ecology, e.g. in the work of Hill 1974);

> dual (or optimal) scaling (in the pioneering work of Guttman 1941, 1946, and more recently in the work of Nishisato, 1978).

It may also be described as a special case of canonical correlation analysis. Recall that canonical correlation analysis is the study of linear relationships between two sets of variables. Call these Y and Z. The basic problem is to find the linear combinations of the variables Y and Z which have maximum correlation (Figure 7.2a). Correspondence analysis and discriminant analysis may be described as special cases of this problem.

In discriminant analysis, one of the sets of variables, Z say, is a logical matrix indicating the groups to which the sampling units belong (Figure 7.2b). The rows of Z contain zeros apart from a 1 in the appropriate column to indicate the group membership, so that Z is really a single qualitative variable defining a partition of the sampling units into groups. The canonical correlations would measure the ability of the variables in Y to linearly discriminate between these groups.

Correspondence analysis may be described as a further special case of this problem, where both Y and Z are logical matrices indicating two different partitions of the sampling units (Figure 7.2c). In this sense correspondence analysis may be called a double discriminant analysis, where the dependence of two partitions of the same sampling units is investigated. Alternatively, the

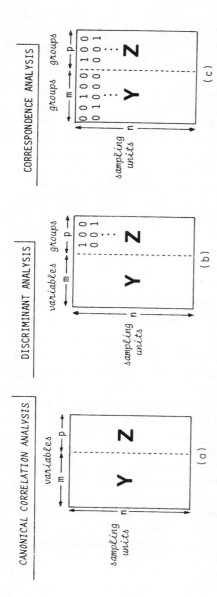

Figure 7.2 Discriminant analysis (b) and correspondence analysis (c) as special cases of canonical correlation analysis (a). In each case the objective of the analysis can be described as maximizing the correlation of linear combinations **Yu** and **Zv** of the 2 sets of columns

analysis may be considered as studying the dependence of two qualitative variables, hence its applicability to the two-way contingency table Y^TZ. (The superscript ^{T} denotes a matrix transpose.)

The name 'correspondence analysis' is a translation of the French 'analyse des correspondances', the name given by a group of French statisticians who have been applying this method to data since the early 1960s (see, for example, Benzécri, 1973 and Lebart, Morineau and Tabard, 1977). The approach of this group is to define, describe and interpret the analysis in a geometric framework. The analogy with canonical correlation analysis gives a very restrictive view of the problem, whereas the geometric approach of the French school gives a much broader view of correspondence analysis, widening its field of application to other types of data matrices apart from contingency tables. This approach also presents correspondence analysis as a unifying technique in exploratory multidimensional data analysis, linking up with the rationale of classification, regression and clustering. It is one of the techniques which have led to the elaboration of a new statistical philosophy, particularly strong in this group of French statisticians, led by Prof. Jean-Paul Benzécri, where supreme importance is placed on inductive strategies and reasoning in data analysis.

7.2 GEOMETRIC DEFINITION OF CORRESPONDENCE ANALYSIS: A SIMPLE EXAMPLE

The geometry of correspondence analysis is very similar to Karl Pearson's geometric description of principal components analysis, which he published in 1901, preceding Hotelling's statistical definition by over 30 years (Hotelling, 1933). Pearson posed the problem of finding the lines and planes of closest fit to a cloud of points in multidimensional Euclidean space. The closeness of the points to a line, plane, or in general to a low-dimensional subspace, is defined as the sum of squared distances from the points to the subspace: $\Sigma_i z_i^2$ in Figure 7.3. Correspondence analysis is conveniently described in these terms, by defining firstly a cloud of points in a multidimensional vector space, secondly the metric structure on this space, and thirdly the fit of this cloud to a variable low-dimensional subspace onto which the points are projected for display and interpretation. Remember that there are two problems of this nature: the display of a cloud of points representing the rows of a contingency table and similarly, the columns. As suggested by the name 'correspondence' analysis, these two problems are very closely linked.

As a simple illustration consider a small data matrix (Figure 7.4) which contains the frequencies of three antelope tribes in five African game reserves (antelope tribes: *Aepycerotini*, e.g. impala; *Tragelaphini*, e.g. eland, kudu; *Antilopini*, e.g. gazelle, springbok; game reserves: Kruger Park, Wankie,

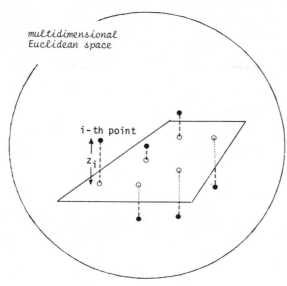

Figure 7.3

Kalahari, Serengeti, and Ngorongoro). This is a 5 × 3 submatrix of a larger data matrix which will be discussed later as an application (in Section 7.3.1).

We shall discuss the display of the rows (i.e. the game reserves) alone for the moment.

The point vector representing a row is defined as the row vector divided by the sum of its elements. Such a vector is known as a *profile*, in this case a row profile. In our example where the data consist of frequencies, the profile of a game reserve is simply its vector of relative antelope frequencies, a vector in three-dimensional space (Figure 7.5). Actually because the sum of the elements of each profile is 1, the game-reserve profiles lie in a two-dimensional subspace.

			antelope tribes			*row totals*
			AEP	TRA	ANT	
	Kruger	KRU	153 000	11 124	0	164 124
	Wankie	WAN	8 000	5 450	0	13 450
game reserves	*Kalahari*	KAL	0	6 569	24 041	30 610
	Serengeti	SER	65 000	9 500	190 000	264 500
	Ngorongoro	NGO	0	400	5 000	5 400
	column totals		226 000	33 043	219 041	478 084

Figure 7.4

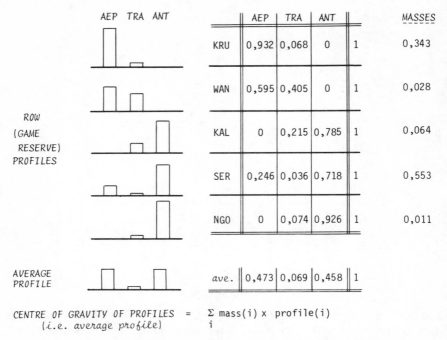

	AEP	TRA	ANT		MASSES
KRU	0,932	0,068	0	1	0,343
WAN	0,595	0,405	0	1	0,028
KAL	0	0,215	0,785	1	0,064
SER	0,246	0,036	0,718	1	0,553
NGO	0	0,074	0,926	1	0,011
ave.	0,473	0,069	0,458	1	

ROW (GAME RESERVE) PROFILES

AVERAGE PROFILE

CENTRE OF GRAVITY OF PROFILES = $\sum_i$ mass(i) x profile(i)
  (i.e. average profile)

Figure 7.5   Set of row profiles and row masses for the data matrix in Figure 7.4,
as well as the average row profile (or centre of gravity)

The *average row profile* is the profile of the column totals of the data matrix, thus the average game-reserve profile is the vector of the three antelope totals divided by the grand total. The average row profile is the weighted average, or centre of gravity, of the row profiles, where each row profile is weighted proportionally to the respective row sum in the original data matrix. We in fact define a set of *row masses* (or *weights*) which add up to 1 by dividing each of these original row sums by the grand total. In our example a game-reserve mass, given in the last column of Figure 7.5, is the total number of antelope in the reserve divided by the grand total. Hence while the profile representing the game reserve is independent of the total number of antelope counted in the reserve, this total will be used as a measure of the profile's importance in the analysis. (Note that Pearson's principal components analysis does not contain this idea of weighting the points and in that context we can think of all the points as having equal mass.)

Next it is necessary to define a distance, or metric, in the space of the profiles. In correspondence analysis a generalized Euclidean metric is used, where each squared difference in coordinates is divided by the respective element of the average profile. This is reminiscent of chi-squared formulations, where squared differences between frequencies are weighted inversely by the expected frequency, and is accordingly named the *chi-squared metric*. Denoting the row profiles in general by the vector $\mathbf{a}_i^T$ and forming the diagonal matrix $\mathbf{D}_c$ with the average row profiles $\mathbf{c}$, we have that the squared distance is the quadratic form with matrix $\mathbf{D}_c^{-1}$, i.e. the squared distance between row profiles $\mathbf{a}_i^T$ and $\mathbf{a}_{i'}^T$ is

$$d^2(\mathbf{a}_i, \mathbf{a}_{i'}) \equiv (\mathbf{a}_i - \mathbf{a}_{i'})^T \mathbf{D}_c^{-1}(\mathbf{a}_i - \mathbf{a}_{i'}).$$

In our example this choice of distance means that in the computation of distances between game-reserve profiles the larger differences in the relative frequencies of the more numerous antelope tribes are reduced, while the smaller differences between the rarer tribes are increased. This tends to equalize the contributions of the rare and frequent tribes to the metric structure of the space. This choice of distance is also essential for the geometrical correspondence and symmetry of the rows and the columns, which will be discussed later.

So far we have defined the cloud of row-profile points with masses in a space structured by the chi-squared metric. The problem consists in finding the p-dimensional subspace which is closest to all the points. The measure of closeness is defined as the weighted sum of squared distances from the points to the subspace, where the weights are once again the row masses. It is not difficult to show the intuitive result that a subspace of closest fit should include the centre of gravity of the points. If r_i denotes the mass of the ith

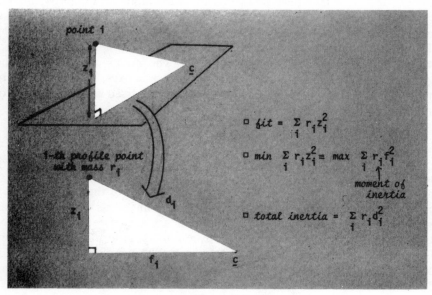

Figure 7.6

point, and z_i the distance of this point to the subspace, then the problem is to find the subspace that minimizes $\sum_i r_i z_i^2$ (see Figure 7.6). Because the triangle formed by the centre of gravity, the point and its projection has a fixed-length hypotenuse d_i, the problem is by Pythagoras' theorem equivalent to maximizing $\sum_i r_i f_i^2$, where f_i is the distance of the ith point's projection from the centre of gravity.

Suppose for ease of discussion that the subspace is one-dimensional, that is we are looking for the line of closest fit. Then this $\sum_i r_i f_i^2$ can be called the *moment of inertia* of the points along the line, since this is a sum of mass × squared distance. The line along which the moment of inertia is maximized is called the first *principal axis of inertia*. In the general case of profile points in an m-dimensional space, there are m-1 orthogonal principal axes and respective moments of inertia. The sum of the moments of inertia along all the principal axes is called the *total inertia* of the cloud of points and is equal to $\sum_i r_i d_i^2$. The total inertia is identical to Pearson's mean-squared contingency coefficient calculated on the contingency table, i.e. the chi-squared statistic divided by the total of the matrix. This quantity is used as a measure of the total variation within the data matrix and is decomposed along principal axes, analogous to the decomposition of the total variance of a set of variables in principal components analysis along principal axes of variance. Geometrically, inertia may be thought of as weighted spread or dispersion.

As in principal components analysis, the principal axes solution is contained ultimately in the form of an eigen-equation, where the eigenvalues $\lambda_1 \geq \cdots \geq \lambda_{m-1} \geq 0$, in descending order, are the moments of inertia, and the respective eigenvectors $\mathbf{u}_1, \ldots, \mathbf{u}_{m-1}$ are the principal axes of inertia (for computational details see, for example, Lebart, Morineau and Tabard, 1977). The axes are orthonormal in the metric $\mathbf{D}_c^{-1}$, i.e. $\mathbf{u}_j^T \mathbf{D}_c^{-1} \mathbf{u}_{j'} = \delta_{jj'}$, and form a new basis in the space of the row profiles. The points are displayed and interpreted in the subspace of the first few principal axes, and the quality of the display is gauged by the moments of inertia expressed as percentages τ of the total inertia:

$$\tau_\alpha = 100 \times \lambda_\alpha \bigg/ \sum_{k=1}^{m-1} \lambda_k \qquad (\alpha = 1, \ldots, m - 1).$$

In our example the line of closest fit (or maximum inertia) explains 87% of the total inertia (Figure 7.7). Thus we have lost 13% of the inertia of the 5 game reserve points by projecting them onto the line. This display is thus an approximate representation of the points in a space of reduced dimension (here the dimension has been reduced from 2 to 1). Interpreting an axis consists intuitively in examining how the points spread out along the axis, for example this axis clearly reveals a split of the 5 reserves into two groups. However, in practice the interpretation does go deeper geometrically.

We can examine the contributions made by each point to the moment of

Figure 7.7   Projection of row points (game reserves) of Figure 7.4 onto
their first principal axis of inertia

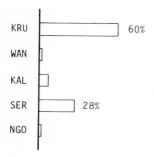

Figure 7.8   Percentage contributions by row profile
points to first principal axis (these are the terms of the
sum $\Sigma_i r_i f_i^2 = \lambda_1$ expressed as a percentage of λ_1)

inertia of the axis, in other words we look at the terms of $\Sigma_i r_i f_i^2$ (Figure 7.8).
These are usually expressed as percentage contributions, so that in our
example it is seen that the points KRUger and SERengeti contribute the
most to the orientation of this axis (60% and 28% respectively).

As well as the inertia contributions of the points to the axes we can also
examine the angles between the point vectors and the axes (see Figure 7.9). It
is convenient to examine the squared cosines of these angles because for each
point the sum of the squared cosines over the complete set of orthogonal

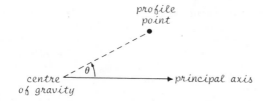

SQUARED COSINES OF ANGLES BETWEEN ROW PROFILE POINTS
AND FIRST PRINCIPAL AXIS

KRU : 0,996   ($\theta = 3,6°$)
WAN : 0,222   ($\theta = 61,9°$)
KAL : 0,617   ($\theta = 38,2°$)
SER : 0,964   ($\theta = 10,9°$)
NGO : 0,993   ($\theta = 4,8°$)

Figure 7.9

principal axes equals 1. If $\cos^2 \theta$ is high, then θ is low and the vector can be said to lie in the direction of the axis, or correlate with the axis. In our example, the game reserves KRUger and SERengeti which contributed the most to the first axis also make small angles with the axis. The point NGOrongoro, although contributing very little to the orientation of the axis, nevertheless correlates very highly with it. The examination of the contributions of the profile points to each axis as well as the angles between the point vectors and the axes aid immensely in the interpretation of the basic graphical display.

Up to now we have considered the projection of the cloud of row profiles onto a low-dimensional subspace to obtain an interpretable display (represented schematically in Figure 7.10a). Everything that has been said applies in a similar, symmetric fashion to the columns of the data matrix—as if the matrix were transposed and the whole argument repeated (see Figure 7.10b).

Firstly a cloud of column profiles with masses is defined in n-dimensional space. Secondly the space is structured by the generalized Euclidean metric with matrix $\mathbf{D}_r^{-1}$, where $\mathbf{r}$ is the average column profile, in fact just the vector of row masses defined previously. Thirdly the subspaces of closest fit are obtained by identifying the principal axes of inertia of the cloud of column points.

There is a duality in the formulations and solutions of this pair of dimension-reducing problems and this duality and symmetry is at the heart of the geometric correspondence of the eventual graphical displays. Notice, for example, the dual roles played by the masses, weighting the points in one space and defining the metric in the other space.

In our example, the 3 antelope profiles lie in 5-dimensional space, but being only 3 points they occupy a 2-dimensional subspace. The total inertia of this cloud turns out to be identical to the total inertia of the cloud of game

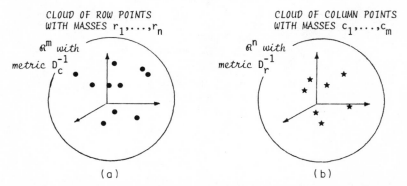

Figure 7.10   Dual analyses in correspondence analysis: the analysis of the row points (Figure 7.10a) and the analysis of the column points (Figure 7.10b) are symmetric

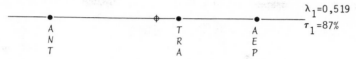

Figure 7.11   Projection of column points (antelope tribes) of
Figure 7.4 onto their first principal axis of inertia

reserve points in their 2-dimensional subspace, and the first principal axis of
inertia explains the same percentage (87%) of this inertia (see Figure 7.11).
This is the first justification for the name *correspondence* analysis.

In addition there is a correspondence of the positions of the row and
column points on the axes. If the vector **f** contains the co-ordinates of the
game reserves along the first principal axis, with moment of inertia λ, and if **b**
denotes the profile of an antelope tribe, say ANTilopini, then the co-ordinate
of the point ANT with respect to the first principal axis in its space is simply
$\mathbf{b}^T\mathbf{f}$ divided by $\sqrt{\lambda}$ (see Figure 7.12). Because the elements of the profile **b** add
up to 1, $\mathbf{b}^T\mathbf{f}$ is the weighted average or centre of gravity of the co-ordinates of
the game reserves where the weights are the elements of the antelope profile
b. Thus the point ANT tends towards the direction of the game reserves in
which it is the most prominent. There is a further scale expansion of $1/\sqrt{\lambda}$,
which is understandable since there is a symmetric transition formula from
the set of antelope points to the individual game-reserve points and the sets
cannot both be centres of gravity of each other.

These linear mappings between the co-ordinates **f** of the row points and **g** of
the column points with respect to any principal axis (with moment of inertia

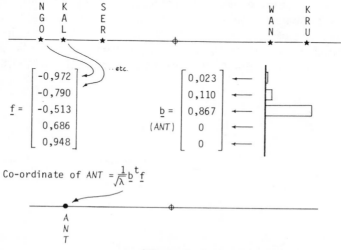

Figure 7.12

λ) in their respective spaces, are called the *transition formulae*:

$$\mathbf{g} = \frac{1}{\sqrt{\lambda}} \mathbf{B}^{\mathrm{T}} \mathbf{f},$$

$$\mathbf{f} = \frac{1}{\sqrt{\lambda}} \mathbf{A}^{\mathrm{T}} \mathbf{g}.$$

These are essentially the equations defining the equivalent analysis known as *reciprocal averaging*, now used extensively in ecological studies (e.g. Hill, 1973, 1974). Here **A** and **B** denote the matrices of row and column profiles respectively.

The transition formulae imply the following eigen-equations:

$$\mathbf{A}^{\mathrm{T}} \mathbf{B}^{\mathrm{T}} \mathbf{f} = \lambda \mathbf{f},$$

$$\mathbf{B}^{\mathrm{T}} \mathbf{A}^{\mathrm{T}} \mathbf{g} = \lambda \mathbf{g}.$$

Solving for **f** and **g** simultaneously can be rephrased as a singular-value decomposition (*basic structure*) problem. However, computationally this usually consists of solving the eigen-equation of smaller dimension and using the appropriate transition formula to transform to the results of the dual problem.

Two features have been demonstrated. Firstly, that the inertias and their decompositions along the principal axes are identical in the two clouds of points. Secondly, because of the transition formulae, it is clear that in their respective subspaces a row point is attracted to the region of the column points for which the row profile is large, and vice versa. These are the reasons justifying the merging of the displays into one and the representation of the row and column points on the same principal axes (see Figure 7.13). There are advantages and disadvantages of this simultaneous display. Clearly an advantage is the very concise graphical display expressing the correspondence between the two sets of points vis-a-vis the principal axes. But here there is the almost inevitable danger of placing a false interpretation on the distances between row and column points. It should be remembered that in terms of the

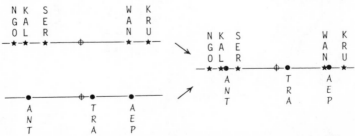

Figure 7.13   Merging of displays in Figures 7.7 and 7.11 into a simultaneous display of the row and column points

transition formulae, the positions of *all* the game reserves collectively determine the position of *each* antelope tribe, and vice versa. It is not valid to comment on the proximity of a single game reserve and an antelope tribe in the display, since no such distance has been defined or intended (see Greenacre, 1978, for further discussion of this point). Instead we should try to assign names to the principal axes by examining the corresponding spreads of the two sets of points along the axes.

How many axes should be interpreted? Can we say that an axis reflects a significant spread in the data? Lebart has published approximate significance tests for the percentages of inertia along successive axes in the cases of two-way contingency data and rank order data (see Lebart and Fénelon, 1971; Lebart, Morineau and Tabard, 1977). These provide a formal test of the null hypothesis that a principal axis is due to random dispersion of the points.

However, correspondence analysis may be applied to other types of data matrices, in fact to any data where the notions of profile, mass, chi-squared distance and inertia make sense. In these cases a more pragmatic guideline would be to inspect a graphical display of the percentages of inertia (for example, in Figure 7.14 it seems that there are three axes worthy of interpretation), and then simply to carry any interpretation as far as is reasonable. With sufficient knowledge of the problem at hand, one would realize when a given scatter of points along an axis is residual fluctuation rather than an interesting pattern.

7.3 APPLICATIONS OF CORRESPONDENCE ANALYSIS

For further discussion of the theoretical aspects of correspondence analysis, particularly the algebraic duality of the corresponding graphical displays, see Benzécri *et al.* (1973). At this point we will discuss briefly three applications of correspondence analysis in the fields of ecology, psychology and meteorology.

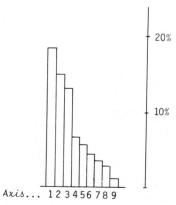

Figure   7.14   Percentages of
inertia

7.3.1 Display of frequency data in ecology

The first example is the graphical display of the complete data matrix relating
to the frequencies of 9 antelope tribes in a set of 16 game reserves. The game
reserves from which census figures were obtained are shown on the map of
Africa in Figure 7.15.

Notice the varying sizes of the reserves which will be reflected in the wide
range of total antelope counted in each reserve. The game-reserve profiles, or
vectors of relative antelope frequencies, are now points in an 8-dimensional
space and are given masses proportional to their respective antelope total.
This means that if a correspondence analysis were performed on these data as
they stand, the larger reserves like KRUger and SERengeti would be assigned
huge masses compared to the smaller reserves. There is in fact no ecological

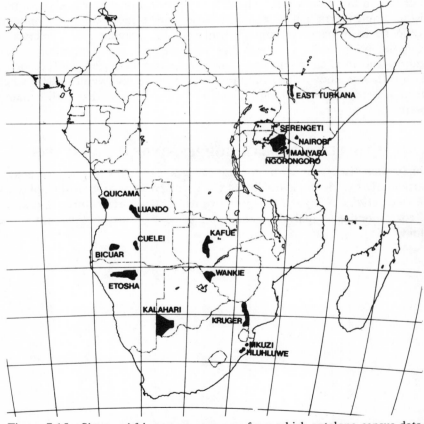

Figure 7.15   Sixteen African game reserves from which antelope census data
were obtained

significance in assigning masses to game reserves proportional to their total antelope population, since it is primarily history and politics that have determined the sizes of the reserves. This is a case where correspondence analysis should not be applied to the raw data. In consultation with the palaeo-ecologist, Dr. E. Vrba,* involved in this study (reference will be made later to the palaeontological importance of this data set), it was decided that the most meaningful way to weight the game reserves in the circumstances was in terms of the number of antelope per unit area. In this way more importance is placed on the areas more favourable to antelope. Reallocation of such masses is performed simply by dividing the frequencies in each reserve by the surface area of the reserve. Notice that such a multiplicative transformation of each row does not alter the row profiles (i.e. the game-reserve profiles) at all, only the mass associated with each profile. The metric in the space of the game reserve profiles is, of course, altered, as well as the antelope profiles in their 8-dimensional space; but this is an advantage since less emphasis is placed on the antelope tribes which had high mass just because they were present in the larger reserves.

The correspondence analysis was thus applied to the matrix of antelope frequencies per square kilometre. Four interpretable axes resulted and interpretation consisted mainly of comparing the spread of the game reserves and antelope tribes along these axes to supplementary information on the reserves like rainfall, bush cover, altitude, longitude, biomass, tribal diversity, etc.

For example, the projection of the game reserves and antelope tribes onto the first principal axis is shown in Figure 7.16. Above each reserve point a code indicates the reserve's category of bushcover—L for low bushcover, M for medium and H for high. It is immediately clear that all the reserves with low bushcover are on the negative side of this axis and there is a wide gap between these and the other reserves. It was concluded that this principal axis, which is determined solely by the profiles of antelope frequencies in the reserves, is due to the environmental variable, bushcover. Antelope tribes which lie on the negative side of this axis would thus be associated with low bushcover reserves.

The interpretation continued in the same vein and the second, third and fourth axes were attributed to the supplementary variables, longitude, biomass and rainfall, respectively. For example, Figure 7.17 shows the display of the points in two dimensions and the ordination of the reserves along the second axis (the vertical axis) turns out to be almost identical to their west-to-east longitude across Africa.

A further interesting aspect of this particular analysis is the way these

---

*Dr. E. Vrba, Transvaal Museum, Pretoria, South Africa. Note that the full results of this study are being prepared for publication by Greenacre and Vrba.

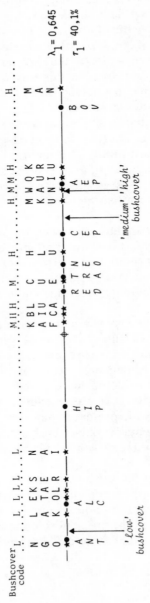

Figure 7.16 Simultaneous display of 16 game reserves (★) and 9 antelope tribes (●) on their corresponding first principal axis of inertia. Above the game-reserve mnemonics a category (*L*—low, *M*—medium, *H*—high) of bushcover is given. (The names of the reserves can be deduced from Figure 7.15—here LAK refers to Lake Turkana, or East Turkana. The names of the antelope tribes are not relevant to our discussion here, and a key to their mnemonics in this and subsequent figures has been omitted.) Note that the three categories of bushcover can also be displayed as supplementary points on the principal axis

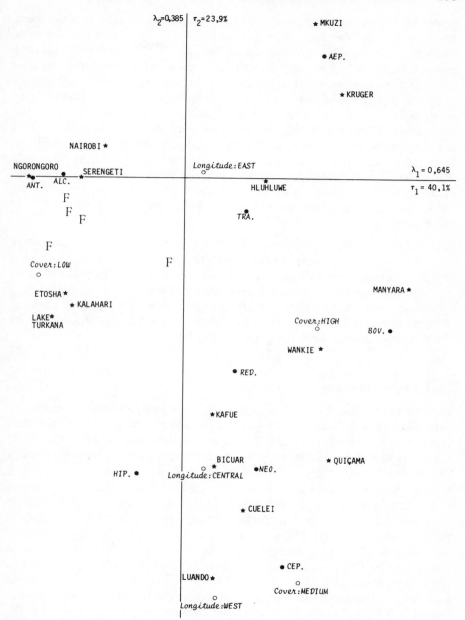

Figure 7.17   Games reserves (rows) and antelopes tribes (columns) in the plane of the first two principal axes of inertia, as well as supplementary rows (fossil sites, denoted by *F*), and supplementary columns (environmental categories of bushcover and longitude)

graphical displays may be used to display comparable fossil frequency data. There were in fact five fossil sites in Southern Africa where skulls of the same antelope tribes have been found, dating back to $1\frac{1}{2}$–$2\frac{1}{2}$ million years ago, the period called Plio-Pleistocene. Each site thus has a profile across the antelope tribes and its position with respect to the principal axes may be investigated using the appropriate transition formula. Geometrically these 5 profiles may be thought of as points with zero mass so that they do not influence the orientation of the axes, but can be projected onto the axes *a posteriori*. Their positions in the plane of the first two principal axes are also shown in Figure 7.17. It turned out that four of these sites correlate highly with the first axis and lie well to the negative side of the axis, suggesting that in the Plio-Pleistocene the fossil sites were part of a low bushcover environment.

The main aspects of correspondence analysis which should be stressed in this example are:

(1)   the importance of the row and column masses: the masses must have meaning in the context of the application;
(2)   the ability to display supplementary rows and/or columns in the space of the corresponding principal axes. In this example the supplementary rows were the fossil sites and the supplementary columns the environmental information, so that all the data involved in this study could be incorporated in the same graphical display.

7.3.2 Display of ratings in psychology

The geometric idea inherent in correspondence analysis may be applied to data other than frequencies, and the next example deals with multidimensional data in the form of ratings. This sort of data is common in the social sciences and this particular study was concerned with evaluating students of clinical psychology at the University of South Africa.

Each student was evaluated twice, once before attending a practical course in psychotherapeutic strategies and then again after the course. He or she was videotaped twice in a psychotherapist–patient situation. The student was the therapist and the patient's role was played by a professional psychologist. At a later date the videotaped interviews were presented in random order to three other experienced psychologists who were asked to judge the student according to a set of 19 criteria. The judges had no previous knowledge of the students and did not know which of the interviews were recorded before the course or after the course. They simply observed the student therapist and awarded him ratings from 0 to 10 for each criterion. For example, criterion 4 was: 'The therapist is in control of the relationship', and a low rating (e.g. 2.0) would indicate a poor control on the part of the student, while a high rating (e.g. 7.8) would indicate good control. Another criterion was: 'The therapist is aware of the emotional aspects of the interview, i.e. he does not only concentrate on the content.'

The data matrix thus consists of 19 columns and there are 6 rows for each student, his evaluations by each of the three judges before and after the course. To display these data by correspondence analysis, we should once again consider the values of the row and column masses. Our conclusion is that if the analysis is applied to the matrix as it is, then the masses are quite arbitrary. Firstly, higher masses would be assigned to students who have a higher total rating—this has little meaning when the criteria are mostly bipolar and there is no real reason why the 0 to 10 scale should not be a 10 to 0 scale, for instance. Actually the 19 criteria had been worded so that a rating of 10 corresponded to the favourable aspect of the criterion, but this was not always clear *a priori*. As for the column masses, there is no justification for giving more importance to the criteria which received generally higher ratings than others.

A neat solution to this problem is to perform what is called a *doubling* of the data. This means that alongside each column is added a new column representing the complementary rating, in this case 10 minus the actual rating. There are now 38 columns in the matrix and, for example, if a student had been given a rating of 3.2 for criterion j (this column is now labelled $j+$) then there is a complementary rating of 6.8 in the doubled column (labelled $j-$) (Figure 7.18). Now the sum of each row is exactly 190 (since there are 19 pairs of columns, each pair of values adding up to 10) and so each evaluation of the student receives the same mass, which seems satisfactory. Also the sum of the original column sum and its doubled column sum is constant, so that each criterion receives the same mass which is distributed between the two

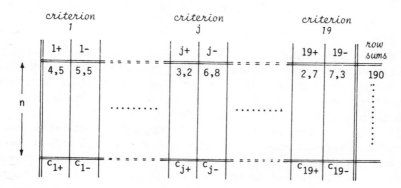

For all $j=1,\ldots,19$: $c_{j+} + c_{j-} = $ constant $(=10n)$

Figure 7.18   Doubling of a data matrix of ratings to balance the poles of a bipolar scale

points representing the two poles of the criterion, the rating and its complement.

Here again we do not need to dwell on the actual results of the analysis, except to say that the first axis does turn out to be a 'bad' to 'good' feature in the evaluations (see Figure 7.19). Most of the '+' points oppose strongly their

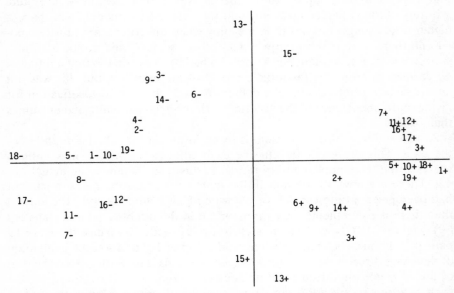

Figure 7.19   Correspondence analysis of the columns of the doubled data matrix of ratings, showing projections onto the plane of the first two principal axes of the points corresponding to the two poles of each criterion

'−' counterparts, with a few exceptions that lie more on the second axis. The first axis thus provides a condensed rating of each student's ability to apply the correct psychotherapeutic strategies. The criteria which determine the second axis are interesting because they are orthogonal to, and in this sense independent of, the 'bad' to 'good' scale.

The corresponding display of the row points shows graphically the individual evaluations of each student. It is interesting to look at the positions of the 6 points for each student. For example, in Figure 7.20a it is apparent that judges 1 and 2 gave similar ratings, while judge 3 gave lower ratings both before and after the course, and that all three judges rated the student higher after the course. Figure 7.20b shows closer agreement amongst the judges and a large improvement after the course.

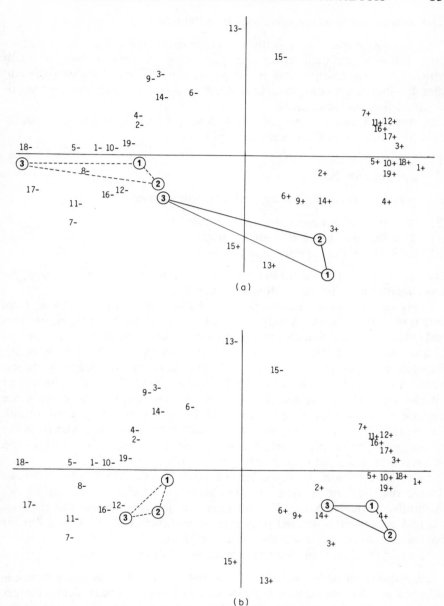

Figure 7.20   The corresponding display of the 6 row points relating to two students ((a) and (b), respectively). The dashed lines link up the evaluations of the student by the three judges before the course, and the solid lines the evaluations after the course

7.3.3 Displays of heterogeneous data in meteorology

The final example deals with meteorological data from a weather-modification experiment in an important river catchment area in South Africa. The experiment is still in the preliminary stages where weather and rainfall patterns are being investigated before the actual statistical and physical cloud-seeding experiment.

In this particular experiment, the following five principal weather situations have been identified in the area of interest:

(1)   fair weather days;
(2)   general rain days;

and then three categories of days with cumulus clouds:

(3)   days that do not meet the seeding criteria;
(4)   days that do meet the seeding criteria and
(5)   days where the cumulus contains hail.

The experiment centres around the type 4 situations which will form the experimental units in the randomized experiment.

Every day a radiosonde attached to a balloon is released at 9 a.m. local time transmitting data back to base while it ascends into the atmosphere. This and other information are assembled at a meeting of the project members at 11 a.m. where a forecast of the weather situation for the day is made. Depending on this forecast are a number of decisions as to the daily operations—for example which planes should be made ready for reconnaissance or for cloud-seeding. Of course, in the experimental phase of the project, the forecast determines whether the day is declared an experimental unit or not. At the end of the day, when the actual weather has been observed from the air and on radar, a final classification is made. Correspondence analysis can be used here as an aid to forecasting the weather type.

In the introduction, correspondence analysis was described in the form of a double discriminant analysis, or the canonical correlation analysis of two qualitative variables Y and Z. This idea can now be extended to the case where Y represents a number of qualitative variables $Y_1, \ldots, Y_s$ and Z is the final classification of the weather situation (Figure 7.21a).

The variables available for forecasting are of different types:

quantitative variables: variables measured on a continuous scale; these can be scalars like temperatures, pressures and other meteorological measurements; or wind vector variables, wind speeds and directions at different levels in the atmosphere.

qualitative variables: e.g. the so-called 'synoptic code', in this case a code from 1 to 7 which classifies the morning pressure system over Southern Africa.

In order to use data on all these variables in a global analysis, an obvious answer is to reduce them all to qualitative form Thus the range of a continuous variable like surface temperature is divided into, say, three intervals and each day is categorized as low, medium or high surface temperature. The category boundaries may be chosen, for example, to place approximately the same number of days in each category. The wind data can also be categorized after examining the histograms of wind directions and speeds. Here it was decided to recode the wind vector into 9 categories, three categories of speed by three categories of direction.

After a total recoding of the data in this manner we obtain a logical matrix of the required form, where each submatrix $\mathbf{Y}_j$ corresponds to one of the original variables. The correspondence between the classification $\mathbf{Z}$ and the variables in $\mathbf{Y}$ is condensed into the contingency table $\mathbf{Z}^T\mathbf{Y}$ which is just the accumulations of the rows of $\mathbf{Y}$ for each of the $p = 5$ weather situations (see Figure 7.21b). The correspondence analysis of this matrix reveals graphically the correspondence between the weather types and the set of predictor variables.

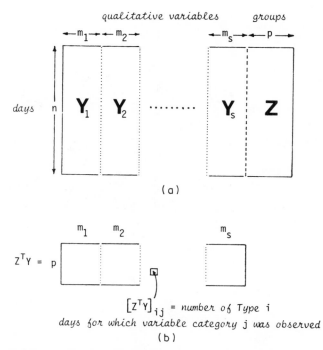

Figure 7.21   (a) Generalization of the scheme of Figure 7.2(c); (b) condensation of the data into a set of two-way contingency tables

Briefly, as far as the results are concerned, correspondence analysis yields a display showing the type 1 fair weather days and the type 2 general rain days to be the most separable groups, while the other three categories lie relatively close together (Figure 7.22). This is a confirmation of the difficulty experienced by the forecasters in distinguishing between categories 3, 4 and 5 in their forecasts. The corresponding spread of the categories along the axes gives the explanation for the separation of the weather types, and it is useful to link up the points representing the categories of each variable.

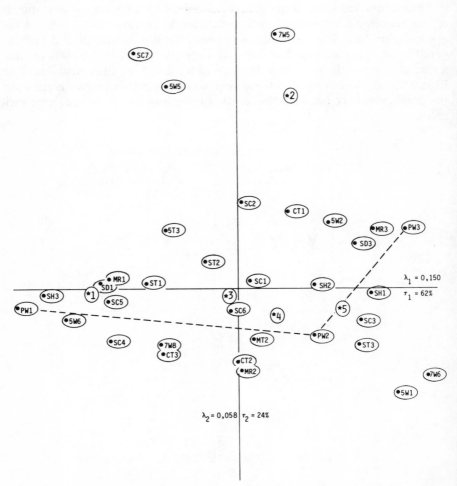

Figure 7.22 Correspondence analysis of weather types (1*, 2*, 3*, 4*, 5*) and categories of predictor variables (e.g. PW1, PW2 and PW3 refer to precipitable water 'low', 'medium' and 'high')

Furthermore the days themselves may be represented on the same axes. The point representing weather type i is in fact the centre of gravity of the subcloud of type i days in the rows of the matrix $\mathbf{Y}$. By defining $\mathbf{Y}$ as a set of n supplementary rows in the correspondence analysis of $\mathbf{Z}^T\mathbf{Y}$ (Figure 7.23), the days are projected onto the discriminant subspace (Figure 7.24).

Now this permits the construction of a classification rule for new observations. Given the values for the variables on a new day we form the logical vector of categorized data and compute its position with respect to the principal axes, using the appropriate transition formula. Having situated this new day in the discriminant space, we may identify the historical days closest to it. If in the neighbouring 10 day-points, say, there is a majority of type 1 days, then the forecast would be a type 1 (Figure 7.25). The very identification of the past days closest to the day in hand in the subspace which best discriminates between the weather types is interesting information to the forecasters. It is also interesting to consider the radius of the neighbourhood which encloses 10 days (Figure 7.25). Finally some allowance should be made for the *a priori* frequencies of the 5 weather types.

Note that a standard discriminant analysis is applicable only to the continuous data and cannot handle qualitative data or wind directions, but it does handle the full information content of the continuous data. Using correspondence analysis to set up the discriminant space has the advantage of allowing all types of variables to be included after suitable recoding, but in the case of continuous variables there is clearly a loss of information in replacing a value on a continuous scale by its corresponding category. This loss of information may be attenuated in a number of ways, for example using the coding scheme shown in Figure 7.26. Here the indicated value of the continuous variable is recoded not strictly as $(1, 0, 0)$ but as $(\frac{3}{4}, \frac{1}{4}, 0)$ to indicate that it lies close to category 2. This improves the recoding of values which lie near the boundaries of the categories.

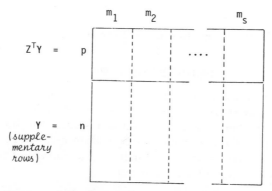

Figure 7.23 The days are added as supplementary rows to the contingency table $\mathbf{Z}^T\mathbf{Y}$

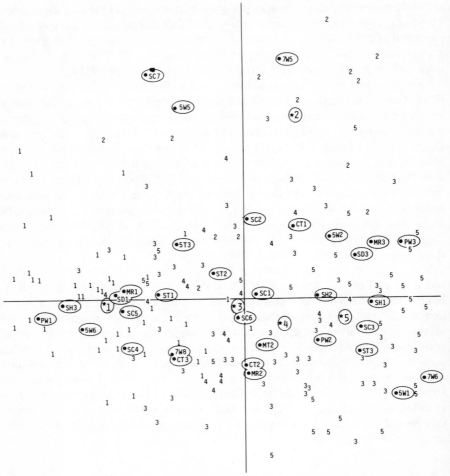

Figure 7.24   The days themselves are represented on the same axes as in Figure 7.22

7.4 CONCLUDING REMARKS

We have demonstrated how correspondence analysis provides a framework for exploring a wide range of data matrices. The analysis essentially handles a matrix, where a certain total positive mass has been distributed amongst the cells of the matrix. The raw data matrix is often recoded to obtain a matrix where this mass distribution has meaning in the context of the study. Three examples of this recoding have been shown:

(1)   reweighting the rows (or columns) by a multiplicative transformation of each row (or column) (for example, as in the game reserves data);

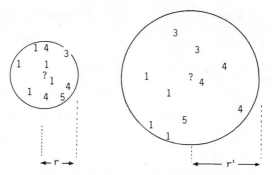

Figure 7.25   Possible neighbourhoods of new
days (denoted by '?') to aid in the classification
of these days according to weather type

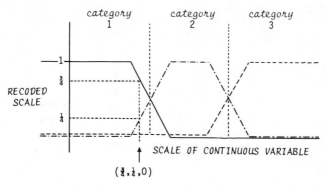

Figure 7.26   Recoding a continuous variable as a generalized
qualitative variable with three categories

(2) doubling the rows (or columns), which can be thought of as a counter-
     balancing of the mass (for example, as in the ratings data);
(3) transforming from other data spaces into a mass space (as in the final
     example where continuous variables are mapped to qualitative variables,
     or to generalized qualitative variables).

REFERENCES

Benzécri, J.-P. (1973) *L'analyse des correspondances.* (Volume 2 of *L'analyse des Données*), Paris: Dunod.
Greenacre, M. J. (1978) Some objective methods of graphical display of a data matrix. Translation of doctoral thesis (Université de Paris, VI), published as *special report* by UNISA, Pretoria.

Guttman, L. (1941) The quantification of a class of atributes: A theory and method of scale construction. In Horst, P. *et al.* (eds.) (1941). *The Prediction of Personal Adjustment.* Bulletin No. 48, New York: The Social Science Research Council, 319–48.

Guttman, L. (1946) An approach for quantifying paired comparisons and rank order. *Ann. Math. Statist.*, **17**, 144–63.

Hill, M. O. (1973) Reciprocal averaging: an eigenvector method of ordination. *J. Ecology*, **61**, 237–49.

Hill, M. O. (1974) Correspondence analysis: a neglected multivariate method. *Applied Statistics*, **23**, 340–54.

Hirschfeld, H. O. (1935) A connection between correlation and contingency. *Proc. Camb. Phil. Soc.*, **31**, 520–4.

Hotelling, H. (1933) Analysis of a complex of statistical variables into principal components. *J. Educ. Psychol.*, **24**, 417–41, 498–520.

Lebart, L. and Fénelon, J.-P. (1971) *Statistique et informatique appliquées.* Paris: Dunod.

Lebart, L., Morineau, A., and Tabard, N. (1977) *Techniques de la description statistique.* Paris, Dunod.

Nishisato, S. (1978) Optimal scaling of paired comparison and rank order data: an alternative to Guttman's formulation. *Psychometrika*, **43**, 263–71.

Pearson, K. (1901) On lines and planes of closest fit to a system of points. *Phil. Mag.* ser. 6, **2**, 559–72.

CHAPTER 8

Biplot Display of Multivariate Matrices for Inspection of Data and Diagnosis*

K. R. Gabriel, *University of Rochester, NY, USA*

In this chapter, I will discuss the *biplot* as a graphical multivariate technique, and I shall start by showing what a biplot is. I will then explain and illustrate its use in two applications: (1) in inspecting data matrices and (2) in diagnosing models to fit data. I will end by making some comments on advantages of this particular method as compared to other displays of multivariate data.

8.1 THE BIPLOT

A biplot (Gabriel, 1971, 1980) is a graphical display of a matrix $\mathbf{Y}$ of n rows and m columns by means of markers $\mathbf{a}_1, \mathbf{a}_2, \ldots, \mathbf{a}_n$ for its rows and markers $\mathbf{b}_1, \mathbf{b}_2, \ldots, \mathbf{b}_m$ for its columns. These markers are chosen in such a way that the inner product $\mathbf{a}_i^T\mathbf{b}_j$ represents y_{ij}, the i,jth element of $\mathbf{Y}$ (The superscript ^{T} denotes a vector or matrix transpose.) Now, if we assemble all the $\mathbf{a}$ markers as rows of a matrix $\mathbf{A}$ and all the $\mathbf{b}$ markers as rows of a matrix $\mathbf{B}$, then this inner-product relationship means that matrix product $\mathbf{AB}^T$ represents the matrix $\mathbf{Y}$ itself.

Let me make a remark about terminology. The prefix 'bi' in 'biplot' does not refer to its being two-dimensional but indicates that it is a *joint* display of rows and of columns of the matrix $\mathbf{Y}$. When we have an analogous three-dimensional display, we refer to that as a 'bimodel'; the prefix 'bi' again indicates that it is a joint display of rows and columns; the ending 'model' signifies that it is not plotted in the plane but uses further dimensions.

A simple example of a biplot is given in Figure 8.1. The 4×3 matrix $\mathbf{Y}$ can be factorized as the product $\mathbf{AB}^T$, $\mathbf{A}$ being 4×2, $\mathbf{B}^T$ being 2×3. The biplot displays the rows of $\mathbf{A}$, i.e., $\mathbf{a}_1^T, \mathbf{a}_2^T, \mathbf{a}_3^T$ and $\mathbf{a}_4^T$, as well as the rows of $\mathbf{B}$, i.e., $\mathbf{b}_1^T, \mathbf{b}_2^T$ and $\mathbf{b}_3^T$. The first row of $\mathbf{A}$, i.e., the vector (2,2) is displayed as the point $\mathbf{a}_1$; the second row (2,1) is displayed as the point $\mathbf{a}_2$, and the other two rows as points $\mathbf{a}_3$ and $\mathbf{a}_4$. The columns of $\mathbf{B}^T$ are displayed as arrows $\mathbf{b}_1, \mathbf{b}_2$ and $\mathbf{b}_3$. The distinction between arrow display for columns and point display for rows is

*The work presented in this chapter was supported by Contract N00014-80-C-0387 from the Office of Naval Research, USA.

147

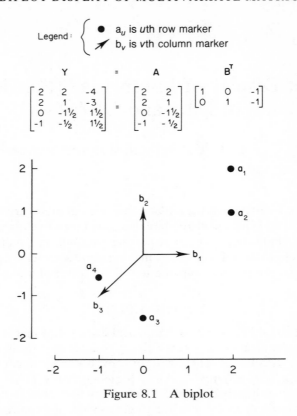

Figure 8.1   A biplot

convenient: the viewer immediately sees which are row markers and which are column markers.

The inner-product interpretation of this biplot can be seen from Figure 8.2, which shows two of the elements of $\mathbf{Y}$. Element $y_{2,3}$ is represented on the biplot by the inner product of $\mathbf{a}_2$ and $\mathbf{b}_3$. This inner product can be visualized by taking the direction through vector $\mathbf{b}_3$ and projecting the vector $\mathbf{a}_2$ onto it. The projection of $\mathbf{a}_2$ onto that direction is $3/\sqrt{2}$ units long; the length of $\mathbf{b}_3$ itself is $\sqrt{2}$ units; the product is $3/\sqrt{2} \times \sqrt{2} = 3$. Hence the inner product is -3; the negative sign reflects the fact that the projection is in the direction opposite to that of the vector projected upon. Indeed, element $y_{2,3}$ is equal to -3. For another example, take element $y_{3,3}$; the inner product of $\mathbf{a}_3$ with $\mathbf{b}_3$ is visualized by projecting $\mathbf{a}_3$ onto the direction through $\mathbf{b}_3$. (This is the same direction that was used before.) The projection is of length $3/(2\sqrt{2})$; the vector projected onto is of length $\sqrt{2}$; they are both in the same direction. Therefore, the inner product is $+[3/2\sqrt{2})] \times \sqrt{2} = 3/2$, which is indeed the value of $y_{3,3}$.

The matrix $\mathbf{Y}$ could be biplotted exactly because it was of rank two. In

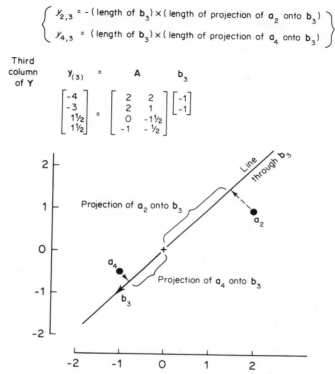

$$\left\{ \begin{array}{l} y_{2,3} = -(\text{length of } b_3) \times (\text{length of projection of } a_2 \text{ onto } b_3) \\ y_{4,3} = (\text{length of } b_3) \times (\text{length of projection of } a_4 \text{ onto } b_3) \end{array} \right\}$$

Third
column $y_{(3)}$ =   A b_3
of Y

$$\begin{bmatrix} -4 \\ -3 \\ 1\frac{1}{2} \\ 1\frac{1}{2} \end{bmatrix} = \begin{bmatrix} 2 & 2 \\ 2 & 1 \\ 0 & -1\frac{1}{2} \\ -1 & -\frac{1}{2} \end{bmatrix} \begin{bmatrix} -1 \\ -1 \end{bmatrix}$$

Figure 8.2   Inner product representation of matrix elements
on the biplot of Figure 8.1

general, an exact biplot of a matrix is possible only if the matrix is of rank one or two, because the biplot itself is planar. For a matrix of higher rank several steps have to be taken in order to display it by an approximate biplot. The first step is to approximate the matrix Y by a matrix $Y_{[2]}$ of rank 2. The second step is to factorize this rank 2 approximation $Y_{[2]}$ as a product AB^T of a matrix $A_{(n \times 2)}$ and a matrix $B^T_{(2 \times m)}$. The third step is to take each row of matrix A as a row marker a and each column of matrix B^T as a column marker b. These markers are then plotted as an *approximate* biplot of the original matrix Y.

We next consider each of these three steps of approximation, factorization and display. The best-known method for lower-rank approximation is due to Householder and Young (1938). It minimizes the sum of squares of the deviations of elements of Y from elements of the reduced rank matrix $Y_{[2]}$. However, this method cannot be applied directly when weights are involved. The elegant mathematical relations that were used by Householder and Young break down as soon as one uses weighted least squares and multiplies the squared deviation $(y_{i,j} - y_{[2]i,j})^2$ by a weight $w_{i,j}$. An algorithm is available

(Gabriel and Zamir, 1979), which allows this more general approximation. For special kinds of weights, Haber (1975) found an earlier solution. Another method of fitting lower rank matrices is by adaptive fits (McNeil and Tukey, 1975), and yet further methods might become available.

Factorization of the rank 2 approximation $Y_{[2]}$ is always possible. Matrices $A_{(n \times 2)}$ and $B_{(m \times 2)}$ that satisfy $Y_{[2]} = AB^T$ must exist. That follows from the definition of the rank of a matrix. However, such a factorization is not unique. In fact, if we post-multiply A by any 2×2 nonsingular R and premultiply B^T by the inverse R^{-1}, the resulting $(AR)(R^{-1}B^T)$ factorization is just as valid as the original AB^T factorization. We therefore have a choice as to which factorization to biplot. Note that transformation by a nonsingular matrix consists of a rotation of axes, a scaling along the new axes and another rotation, whereas the transformation by the inverse consists of the same rotations with a scaling which is reciprocal to the first one. This may help to give an idea of how different factorizations and different biplots are related. (An illustration of alternative factorizations and the resulting biplots was given by Gabriel, 1971).

The non-uniqueness of the factorization has some advantages for the statistician, who may choose a factorization which has desirable data-analytic or statistical features. For instance, one particularly attractive factorization is referred to as the GH^T factorization. This has orthonormal columns for G and therefore satisfies $Y^TY = HH^T$, which is especially useful if the rows of Y represent individuals and the columns represent variables. Then Y^TY is n times the estimated variance-covariance matrix, and so the inner products of the rows h of H in a GH^T biplot represent the covariances, and the squared lengths of the h's represent the variances. The cosines between h-vectors therefore represent the correlations between the variables. This biplot is useful in many statistical applications.

8.2 INSPECTION OF DATA

Next, I consider uses of the biplot. I will first describe the use of the biplot for inspecting data matrices. It is particularly useful for studying large data matrices, where 'eyeballing' the large collection of numbers is quite impractical. Biplot display makes it much easier to see the main features of the matrix. For convenience, I will illustrate this with a moderate size example. I should stress that I will not use the biplot to analyse the data statistically, and certainly not to test it for significance. Rather, I will use it for 'looking at the data'.

Table 8.1 shows the table of *per capita* protein consumption in 25 European countries; the rows are countries and the columns are nine different sources of protein. This matrix is biplotted in Figure 8.3 after the mean of each column has been subtracted from the entries in the column. The points, or row markers, represent countries; the arrows, or column markers, represent

Table 8.1 European protein consumption (grams per head per day)

	Meat (Grazing animals)	Pigs and poultry	Eggs	Milk	Fish	Cereals	Starchy foods	Pulses, nuts, oil-seeds	Fruits, vegetables
Albania	10.10	1.40	0.50	8.90	0.20	42.30	0.60	5.50	1.70
Austria	8.90	14.00	4.30	19.90	2.10	28.00	3.60	1.30	4.30
Belg. Luxem.	13.50	9.30	4.10	17.50	4.50	26.60	5.70	2.10	4.00
Bulgaria	7.80	6.00	1.60	8.30	1.20	56.70	1.10	3.70	4.20
Czechoslovakia	9.70	11.40	2.80	12.50	2.00	34.30	5.00	1.10	4.00
Denmark	10.60	10.80	3.70	25.00	9.90	21.90	4.80	0.70	2.40
East Germany	8.40	11.60	3.70	11.10	5.40	24.60	6.50	0.80	3.60
Finland	9.50	4.90	2.70	33.70	5.80	26.30	5.10	1.00	1.40
France	18.00	9.90	3.30	19.50	5.70	28.10	4.80	2.40	6.50
Greece	10.20	3.00	2.80	17.60	5.90	41.70	2.20	7.80	6.50
Hungary	5.30	12.40	2.90	9.70	0.30	40.10	4.00	5.40	4.20
Ireland	13.90	10.00	4.70	25.80	2.20	24.00	6.20	1.60	2.90
Italy	9.00	5.10	2.90	13.70	3.40	36.80	2.10	4.30	6.70
Netherlands	9.50	13.60	3.60	23.40	2.50	22.40	4.20	1.80	3.70
Norway	9.40	4.70	2.70	23.30	9.70	23.00	4.60	1.60	2.70
Poland	6.90	10.20	2.70	19.30	3.00	36.10	5.90	2.00	6.60
Portugal	6.20	3.70	1.10	4.90	14.20	27.00	5.90	4.70	7.90
Rumania	6.20	6.30	1.50	11.10	1.00	49.60	3.10	5.30	2.80
Spain	7.10	3.40	3.10	8.60	7.00	29.20	5.70	5.90	7.20
Sweden	9.90	7.80	3.50	24.70	7.50	19.50	3.70	1.40	2.00
Switzerland	13.10	10.10	3.10	23.80	2.30	25.60	2.80	2.40	4.90
United Kingdom	17.40	5.70	4.70	20.60	4.30	24.30	4.70	3.40	3.30
USSR	9.30	4.60	2.10	16.60	3.00	43.60	6.40	3.40	2.90
West Germany	11.40	12.50	4.10	18.80	3.40	18.60	5.20	1.50	3.80
Yugoslavia	4.40	5.00	1.20	9.50	0.60	55.90	3.00	5.70	3.20
Average	9.83	7.90	2.94	17.11	4.28	32.25	4.28	3.07	4.14

Source: A. Weber (1973) Agrarpolitik im Spannungsfeld der internationalen Ernaehrungspolitik. Kiel, Institut fuer Agrarpolitik und Marktlehre (Mimeographed).

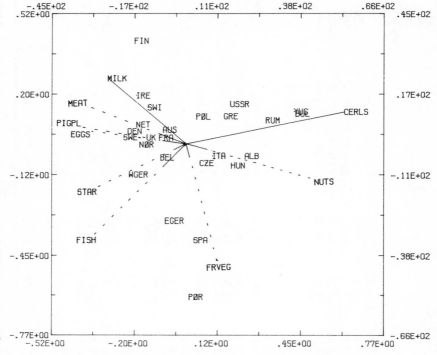

Figure 8.3   **GH**^T biplot of European protein consumption

sources of protein. This happens to be a **GH**^T biplot, so that the lengths of the arrows represent the variances of the different sources of protein and the angles represent their correlations. The centre of this biplot is at the European mean, or centroid, of all these sources of protein. The goodness of fit of $Y_{[2]}$ is of the order of 0.85: that is, the biplot displays 85% of the sum of squares of the mean-centred data matrix **Y**.

Looking at the configuration of the nine sources of protein, the most striking thing we see is that there is a very large variance for cereals and a somewhat large one for milk, but that the variances are relatively small for all the other sources of protein. The correlations are also interesting. On the left-hand side of the plot are all the animal sources of proteins; the angles between them are fairly small, which indicates high correlations between animal sources. Countries with high protein consumption from meat appear also to have high protein consumption from eggs, poultry, milk, etc. The marker for cereals is on the right side of the biplot, at an angle of about 180° to the markers for animal sources. Evidently, countries that have a high consumption of protein from animal sources have relatively low consumption of cereal protein and vice versa. Next, we note that the markers for fruit and vegetables (and for fish (?)) are at about 90° to those for both animal sources and cereals. Apparently these sources of protein are pretty much uncorrelated with animal and cereal proteins.

It is interesting to consider which countries are typical of each source: i.e., which countries have high consumption of each kind of protein. For that purpose, the row markers can be displayed by means of three different symbols—1 for Western and Northern Europe, 2 for Eastern Europe, and 3 for Mediterranean countries. This simple device makes it easy to see that Eastern European countries are on the right of the biplot along with cereals; these countries consume much protein from cereals. Western and Northern European countries are on the left along with markers for animal protein. Mediterranean countries are partly towards the bottom of the biplot, which indicates that fruit and vegetables, nuts, and fish are relatively important sources of protein for them.

This example illustrates an important feature of the biplot. It displays not only the configuration of the variables (i.e., of the sources of protein) and the scatter of the individuals (i.e., of the countries) but it also relates the two. It is able therefore to reveal, for example, not only that consumption of cereal proteins is negatively correlated with consumption of animal proteins, but—and this is the special feature of the biplot—it also identifies countries which are typical users of cereal protein and countries which mostly use animal proteins. This joint display of countries *and* sources justifies the use of the prefix 'bi'.

Another method of displaying particular groups of countries on the biplot is the use of a concentration ellipse for the points of each group of interest. (A concentration ellipse is the two-dimensional analogue of a one standard deviation interval about the mean. It is centred on the points' centroid and its 'shadow' in any direction is a univariate 'mean ±SD interval' for the variate displayed in that direction; see Dempster, 1969, Chapter 7.) The usefulness of this concentration ellipse display is in summarizing a large number of points of each group by a simple figure.

The biplot of Figure 8.3 is shown again in Figure 8.4 with the countries' row markers replaced by concentration ellipses for the three groups. This shows very clearly the northern and western European group to be on the left, in the animal protein direction, the eastern group on the right in the cereal direction and the Mediterranean group to have a very elongated scatter in the nuts, fish, fruit and vegetable directions. It is obvious that the eastern European group is much more heterogeneous than the western and northern European group and the shape of the Mediterranean scatter makes one doubt whether that should really be considered as a single group.

Use of concentration ellipses is of particular importance when large sets of data need to be displayed and there are more row markers than can be displayed effectively. Figure 8.5 shows a biplot of breast-tissue samples which

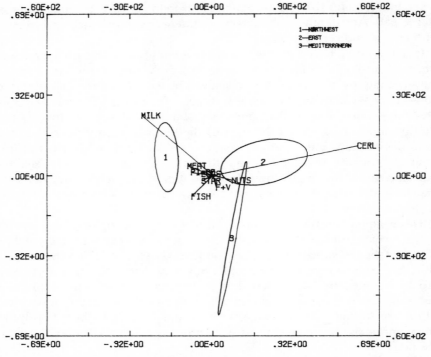

Figure 8.4 **GH**^T biplot of European protein consumption with concentration
ellipses for groups of countries

were analysed for enzyme activity. (The data are due to Dr. Russell Hilf of
the Department of Biochemistry at the University of Rochester.) The activity
of several enzymes and other phenomena were measured on each of several
hundred breast-tissue samples which had also been classified into four diagnostic groups: normal tissue (Group 4), cancerous tissue (Group 1) and two
kinds of benign growths (Groups 2 and 3). When all the 700-odd points were
displayed on the biplot, it was very difficult to distinguish the four groups
of points. But the biplot with the concentration ellipses of the four groups—
Figure 8.5—is much easier to grasp. One sees a clear distinction between the
scatters of the cancerous and the normal tissues; each shows different enzyme
activities. The two benign-growth groups are intermediate between the preceding two in enzyme activities.

It is at times useful to consider only the variance–covariance configuration.
Thus, in a **GH**^T biplot one might omit the markers for individuals (rows) and
display only the variables' (columns) **h**-markers. This will be referred to as an
h-plot. One reason for wishing to ignore the individuals could be that they

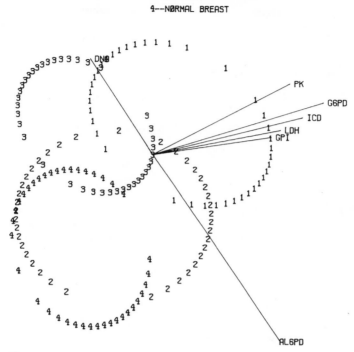

Figure 8.5   Biplot of enzyme activity data for samples of breast tissue with concentration ellipses for four types of diagnosis.

might be mere samples, or replicates, from a population, and it is only the population as an aggregate that is of interest. At times, one might want to use several **h**-plots and compare the variance–covariance configurations of several different populations.

An interesting example comes from the first randomized rainmaking experiment in Israel. Days were randomly allocated to have clouds seeded either in the north or in the centre of Israel. Figures 8.6 and 8.7 are **h**-plots of the precipitation in eight sub-areas of Israel—Figure 8.6 for centre-seeded days, Figure 8.7 for north-seeded days (Corsten and Gabriel, 1976). The two **h**-configurations are, at first glance, very similar. At the top of each display is the **h** marker for the south, then come the markers for the three sub-areas of the centre of Israel, then, at the bottom of the displays, are the markers for the north of Israel, and for the 'buffer zone' between the north and the centre.

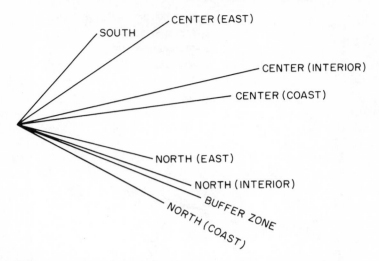

Figure 8.6 **H**-plot of variance–covariance of precipitation in Israel—centre-seeded days. (From Corsten and Gabriel, 1976. Reproduced by permission of The Biometric Society)

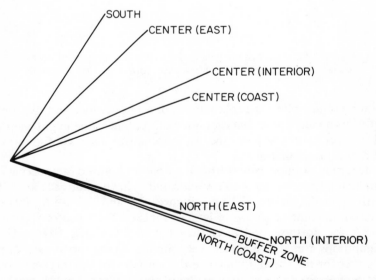

Figure 8.7 **H**-plot of variance–covariance of precipitation in Israel—north-seeded days. (From Corsten and Gabriel, 1976. Reproduced by permission of The Biometric Society)

Both displays show that there was high correlation between sub-areas within the north, average correlation among the centre sub-areas and rather low correlation between the centre and the north.

Despite the overall similarity of the configurations of north-seeded and centre-seeded days, some differences are revealed by closer inspection of Figures 8.6 and 8.7. The most striking difference is that the correlations were considerably higher in the north when seeding was carried out in the north. Also, when one compares the lengths of vectors on the two **h**-plots, one readily sees that the variances of the northern sub-areas were larger when the north was seeded whereas the variances of the centre sub-areas were larger when the centre was seeded. The explanation for these findings may be that the effect of seeding was (1) to make the seeded sub-areas more similar to each other and (2) to augment the variance of rainfall in the seeded area (the means were also augmented, though this is not shown on the **h**-plots).

A somewhat more elaborate example is the data in Table 8.2 of three different cranial measurements of subspecies of anteaters, collected at six geographical locations (Reeve, 1940, quoted by Seal, 1964). The matrix that would be biplotted here is the 6×3 table of the 6 sample means of the logarithms of the 3 cranial measurements. Since these are averages of samples, it is appropriate when calculating their rank-2 approximation to weight them by the sample sizes and the inverse of the matrix of sums of

Table 8.2 Means and error sums of squares and products of anteater data

Locality	Number of skulls	Z_1	Z_2	Z_3	Subspecies
		Means			
1. Sta. Marta, Columbia	21	2.054	2.066	1.621	*Instabilis*
2. Mina Geraes, Brazil	6	2.097	2.100	1.625	*Chapadensis*
3. Matto Grosso, Brazil	9	2.091	2.095	1.624	*Chapadensis*
4. Sta. Cruz, Bolivia	3	2.099	2.102	1.643	*Chapadensis*
5. Panama	4	2.092	2.110	1.703	*Chiriquensis*
6. Mexico	5	2.099	2.107	1.671	*Mexicana*
Total	48				

Within localities sum of squares and products (42 d.f.)

	Z_1	Z_2	Z_3
Z_1	0.013631	0.012769	0.016438
Z_2	0.012769	0.012923	0.017135
Z_3	0.016438	0.017135	0.036152

The variables Z_1, Z_2, Z_3 are common logarithms of, respectively, basal length excluding the premaxilla, occipito nasal length and greatest length of nasals.

squares and products about the means. This weighting is identical to that used in one-way multivariate analysis of variance (Gabriel, 1972).

On the resulting biplot, referred to as a $\mathbf{JK}^T$-biplot (see Figure 8.8) each point represents a sample from one location and each arrow represents a log characteristic measured (one of the three variables). What is immediately evident is that the three samples of sub-species *Chapadensis* are very similar; they are very close together on this biplot. The location of *Chiriquensis* and the location of *Instabilis* are quite far from these three biplot locations and from each other. *Mexicana* is located between *Chiriquensis* and *Chapadensis*. Also, the general direction of the variables is up and slightly to the right, hence that is the direction of larger crania. This indicates that *Instabilis* is a smaller type of anteater, whereas *Chiriquensis, Mexicana* and *Chapadensis* are all larger. The difference between *Chapadensis* and *Chiriquensis*, on the other hand, is not one of overall size but one of a contrast between the different variables. *Chiriquensis* is relatively larger on the third variable (greatest nasal length) whereas *Chapadensis* is relatively larger on the first two variables. The two sub-species are thus seen to have different profiles of the variables.

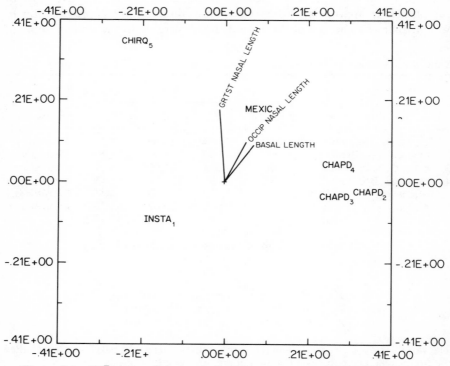

Figure 8.8 $\mathbf{JK}^T$ biplot of anteaters by subspecies and cranial measurements

This **JK**^{T} biplot differs from the **GH**^{T} biplots described above. Amongst other things, weights were used in fitting it. However, because of the particular weights used, biplot distances represent Mahalanobis distances between the different samples. Thus, the Mahalanobis distances between the *Chapadensis* samples are small; the one between *Mexicana* and *Chapadensis* is less then that between *Chiriquensis* and *Chapadensis*, etc.

The Mahalanobis distance is closely related to Hotelling's T^2 except that the latter is scaled by the sum of the reciprocals of the sample sizes. It is possible to approximate the Hotelling T^2 test between pairs of samples by drawing circles around the biplot sample markers, where the radii of the circles depend on the critical point used for testing and on the sizes of the samples (Gabriel, 1972). This is illustrated in Figure 8.9. The interpretation of these 'comparison circles' is clear. Circles which intersect show a non-significant comparison; disjoint circles show a significant comparison. Thus, the three circles for *Chapadensis* overlap very much with each other and also with the *Mexicana* circle. This indicates that there are no significant differences between the three *Chapadensis* samples, nor between them and the *Mexicana* sample. *Mexicana* is not significantly different from *Chiriquensis*

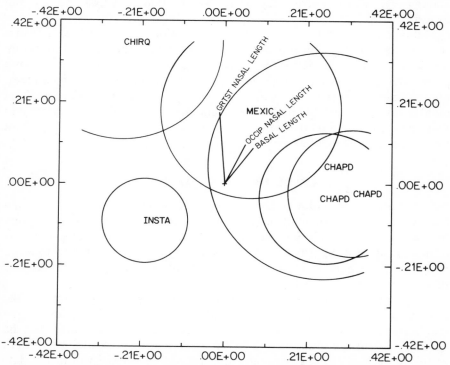

Figure 8.9   **JK**^{T} biplot of anteaters with 5% experimentwise comparison circles

either. However, *Mexicana* is significantly different from *Instabilis*. In fact, *Instabilis* is found to be significantly different from everything else, and *Chiriquensis* is also different from *Chapadensis*. The general conclusions are (1) that *Instabilis* indeed differs from the rest of the anteaters and is a smaller type; (2) the larger anteaters are of at least two groups (one containing *Chiriquensis*, the other *Chapadensis*). *Mexicana* could belong to either of these groups; there are no significant differences which would indicate to which.

The graphical test used here is an approximation to Hotelling's T^2. In many cases such a Gaussian test may not be valid and more robust tests may be needed. It may, for example, be possible to carry out re-randomization tests directly on biplots. We are currently trying out the 'multiple response permutation procedures' of Mielke, Berry, and Johnson (1976) for that purpose. Let me stress, however, that I see a very limited role for significance testing in the exploration of such multivariate data. In most multivariate situations, we have a fair number of samples and a fair number of variables, and we are rarely concerned with a test of an overall null hypothesis for all samples and all variables. Instead we usually want to find out what sort of differences exist and between which samples they occur. We are trying to explore rather than to test.

Multivariate analysis is essentially an exploratory technique rather than a confirmatory method. Indeed, by the time one gets to the stage of confirmation and sets up a well-defined null hypothesis for testing, one usually knows pretty well which particular variable, or what linear combination of variables, one is really interested in, so that the testing becomes univariate and not multivariate. I submit that multivariate analysis is principally exploratory and that techniques such as the biplot are usually very much more to the point than most tests of significance.

8.3 DIAGNOSIS OF MODELS

Another use of the biplot is that of diagnosing models which will fit a data matrix. This use is particularly important because statisticians really have very few techniques available for inspecting a data matrix and deciding what sort of model will fit it. Statistics textbooks have ample material on how to test a model once we have formulated it, but little or nothing on how to select a model, except by trial and error.

A biplot may be used to diagnose a model by looking for a pattern on the display and then inferring mathematically what model that implies for the data matrix. For example, if the row markers are seen to be collinear, and the column markers are also noted to be collinear, and the two lines are at right angles to each other, one may infer that an additive model will fit the data closely, i.e., $y_{i,j} = \alpha_i + \beta_j$, for some set of α_is and β_js. If, for another instance, one observes row markers and column markers to be on two non-perpendicular lines, one can infer that a concurrent model fits the data, i.e., $y_{ij} = \eta + \alpha_i \beta_j$, for some η, α_is and β_js. (This, by the way, is a reparametrization of Tukey's one-degree-of-freedom-for-non-additivity model.) Also, if one observes that all markers, for both rows and columns, are on one and the same line, it is obvious that the matrix is of rank one and so the model is $y_{ij} = \alpha_i \beta_j$.

Table 8.3 shows these and some other rules of diagnosis derived by Bradu and Gabriel (1978). The first line indicates that, when the row markers are collinear, the data may be fitted by a columns regression model. (This model is due to Mandel (1961). It expresses each column as a linear regression on given row effects α_i). The next line of Table 8.3 similarly shows that, when the column markers are collinear, each row can be modelled as a linear regression on fixed column βs. When both row markers and column markers are collinear, a concurrent model is diagnosed (as noted above), unless these two lines are at $90°$ to each other, in which case an additive model is diagnosed (as also noted above).

The rules of Table 8.3 apply even if some of the biplot markers are not on these lines. In such cases, the diagnoses apply to the subtable of the rows and columns whose markers are collinear. This is quite a remarkable feature of the biplot. It makes it possible to diagnose models not only for the entire matrix, but also for any submatrices. Most importantly, all these diagnostic indicators are very simple. The eye very easily picks up a straight line, even when it fits only some of the row markers or some of the column markers.

Here are some further examples. Bradu and Grine (1979) considered cranial measurements for a number of specimens of fossils (see Table 8.4). This table has a large number of missing values, so that ordinary techniques for fitting were inappropriate. Bradu and Grine therefore used the algorithm

Table 8.3 Some biplot diagnostic rules

Row markers $\mathbf{a}_i$	Col. markers $\mathbf{b}_j$	The model for $Y_{i,j}$ is:
collinear	—	$\beta_j + \alpha_i \delta_j$ columns regression
—	collinear	$\alpha_i + \gamma_i \beta_j$ rows regression
collinear	collinear	$\mu + \gamma_i \delta_j$ concurrent
collinear lines at $90°$ to each other	collinear	$\alpha_i + \beta_j$ additive

(Bradu and Gabriel, 1978).

Table 8.4 Thirty measurements on 26 specimens of Diademodontine crania (From Bradu and Grine, 1979. Reproduced by permission of the *South African Journal of Science*)

Variable	\	\	\	\	\	\	\	\	\	\	\	\	Specimen	\	\	\	\	\	\	\	\	\	\	\	\	\
	1	2	3	4	5	6	7	8	9	10	11	12	13	14	15	16	17	18	19	20	21	22	23	24	25	26
1	275	230	287	177	—	—	134	74	92	112	142	—	—	84	47	127	193	205	260	232	130	172	51	247	197	187
2	305	230	331	194	—	—	147	76	99	120	154	—	170	—	53	135	—	238	280	253	139	185	19	258	209	209
3	130	98	—	83	73	76	55	39	45	48	58	—	74	36	23	61	90	95	122	90	58	80	19	—	89	82
4	158	118	171	108	—	—	86	36	52	61	88	63	—	44	21	70	103	110	143	142	72	92	32	149	104	105
5	177	131	216	108	—	—	93	44	57	69	95	63	97	—	33	78	—	143	163	163	81	105	—	160	122	125
6	138	—	145	92	97	77	64	38	52	65	71	—	79	—	29	72	93	104	130	114	69	85	27	115	99	100
7	96	88	97	62	67	61	42	24	33	43	49	—	52	—	19	47	63	69	84	76	47	60	19	74	65	71
8	107	78	119	—	75	67	54	31	—	42	61	48	—	—	17	56	82	88	103	93	55	68	—	—	85	75
9	114	138	131	64	—	—	54	22	29	37	60	—	60	—	—	41	—	—	64	95	42	52	—	—	54	57
10	160	205	187	125	108	—	83	43	53	69	90	—	116	58	—	92	126	—	167	144	86	100	32	145	123	—
11	260	144	303	184	—	—	136	70	82	109	141	—	167	—	17	133	—	223	263	241	131	163	—	—	200	194
18	253	126	207	130	—	—	115	66	65	93	115	92	106	—	28	63	—	—	230	218	100	138	—	—	174	153
19	200	126	197	105	128	—	96	61	60	76	93	68	92	48	26	52	—	—	166	160	74	115	—	180	—	—
20	59	42	58	37	39	32	29	24	22	25	28	27	32	24	10	24	41	—	56	53	26	36	11	53	39	37
21	48	42	46	31	37	29	28	18	20	—	24	—	36	17	9	—	33	42	47	40	—	30	11	36	34	—
22	64	56	68	37	52	41	30	22	22	26	29	—	36	—	9	—	41	49	68	58	—	37	12	48	43	—
23	23	21	—	18	17	—	13	12	8	12	—	—	13	10	6	14	14	—	25	17	12	13	8	17	15	—
24	64	47	72	35	51	—	36	17	18	28	40	33	31	20	6	17	—	—	70	78	31	43	8	—	49	41
26	159	98	99	66	—	58	75	44	54	58	44	56	48	34	12	34	64	64	132	111	62	87	19	142	—	65
28	93	29	36	22	38	—	32	28	39	44	48	44	18	12	8	32	—	64	92	77	45	55	8	90	67	65
29	33	36	29	20	30	19	19	12	16	—	28	16	36	22	8	31	27	22	36	22	17	23	8	30	23	23
30	58	49	62	35	42	39	30	19	21	25	28	23	33	16	9	37	37	24	60	54	26	35	10	56	38	37
37	83	55	—	52	51	—	41	32	—	24	32	30	37	—	16	37	45	—	—	75	75	—	—	—	—	—
38	62	52	82	53	42	38	32	28	28	25	29	30	34	34	15	31	45	53	69	63	—	46	—	54	46	42
39	53	50	71	47	35	32	32	23	39	24	28	24	30	22	13	31	42	—	66	49	—	36	14	40	43	—
42	30	34	44	27	—	26	24	14	20	23	28	23	—	16	13	27	33	—	36	40	25	28	—	31	33	—
43	25	32	35	31	11	20	20	15	14	18	21	20	—	16	8	22	25	14	32	24	14	21	—	22	30	10
47	17	12	20	8	11	12	9	3	4	6	—	37	8	3	3	6	11	14	—	18	—	10	13	22	—	10
51	100	80	120	71	—	—	44	28	23	28	39	—	41	—	13	36	—	80	86	69	34	55	13	—	69	—
52	68	54	62	35	—	44	38	—	—	38	34	—	29	—	—	27	49	50	73	63	34	42	—	56	50	50

developed by Gabriel and Zamir (1979) for weighted least squares and introduced zero weights for the missing values and unit weights for present values. The resulting biplot is shown in Figure 8.10. It is quite remarkable how closely the row markers cluster around one line and the column markers along another line. Using the diagnostics of Table 8.3, Bradu and Grine inferred that a concurrent model would fit the data very closely, as indeed it did. We note, however, that the angle between the lines is very close to 90° and thus suspect that an additive model would also have fitted pretty well.

A more complex example is data of gamma radiation (Table 8.5) classified by distance from the radiation source, number of intervening plates, the metal of which these plates consisted and two replications. This is a four-way layout so one has to confound several classifications in the rows and/or in the columns before one can display it in a biplot, as that is a matrix display. One way of doing this is to consider the data in the matrix form of Table 8.5, with the metals, distances and replications confounded in the rows, and only the number of plates appearing in the columns. This matrix, after subtracting the

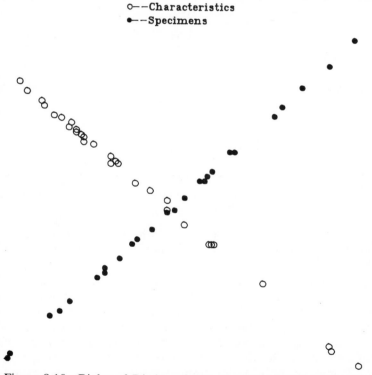

o--Characteristics
●--Specimens

Figure 8.10 Biplot of Diademodontine crania data (From Bradu and Grine, 1979. Reproduced by permission of the *South African Journal of Science*)

Table 8.5   Absorption of gamma radiation by lead and aluminium

Row	Distance d in cm	Replic.	Number of plates p				
			1	3	6	7	10
			Lead				
1	3.8		1.801	1.765	1.696	1.670	1.606
2	5.2		1.621	1.572	1.516	1.486	1.425
3	6.0	I	1.526	1.481	1.406	1.401	1.333
4	9.0		1.222	1.169	1.102	1.078	1.010
5	12.5		0.973	0.939	0.862	0.850	0.781
6	3.8		1.805	1.768	1.704	1.680	1.615
7	5.2		1.609	1.572	1.511	1.482	1.408
8	6.0	II	1.494	1.461	1.387	1.324	1.315
9	9.0		1.233	1.208	1.130	1.111	1.046
10	12.5		0.978	0.930	0.870	0.844	0.779
			Aluminium				
11	3.8		1.834	1.818	1.811	1.790	1.777
12	5.2		1.632	1.613	1.600	1.603	1.597
13	6.0	I	1.509	1.482	1.476	1.454	1.447
14	9.0		1.249	1.224	1.204	1.211	1.179
15	12.5		0.976	0.971	0.966	0.960	0.943
16	3.8		1.916	1.913	1.884	1.887	1.871
17	5.2		1.732	1.723	1.698	1.696	1.674
18	6.0	II	1.632	1.624	1.592	1.588	1.579
19	9.0		1.344	1.341	1.312	1.311	1.290
20	12.5		1.118	1.118	1.106	1.086	1.066

From Mandel (1969). Reproduced by permission of U.S. National Bureau of Standards.

overall mean, is biplotted in Figure 8.11, in which the column markers represent numbers of plates, and each row marker represents a combination of metal, distance and replication.

The biplot (Figure 8.11) of the radiation data clearly shows a linear pattern for the number of plates. The pattern for the row markers is not so immediately obvious. However, if for each of the ten distance–metal combinations, we average two replications, we find that these ten average markers lie on a non-rectangular lattice. The metals form two parallel lines and the distances form another five parallel lines. What model can be diagnosed from such a pattern? It may be useful to go through the algebraic steps of modelling for this case. Starting from any origin we can model the line for the column markers $\mathbf{b}_p = \boldsymbol{\alpha} + \lambda_p \boldsymbol{\beta}$ where λ_p is a parameter for the number of plates p and

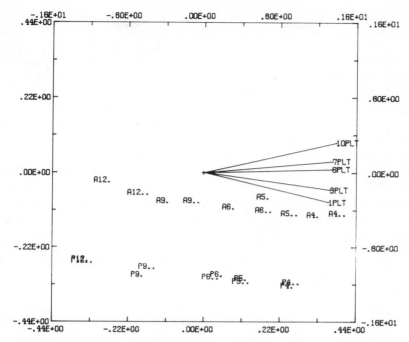

Figure 8.11   Biplot of gamma radiation data: Aluminium (A), Lead (P), number of plates (PLT), replications (.) or (. .) and distance.

$\boldsymbol{\beta}$ is in the direction in which the column markers lie. We can also model the row markers for the average of the two replications as $\mathbf{a}_{m,d\cdot} = \phi_d\boldsymbol{\gamma} + \psi_m\boldsymbol{\delta}$ with parameter ϕ_d depending on the distances d, and parameter ψ_m on the metals m. Vector $\boldsymbol{\gamma}$ would be in the direction of the parallels for the metals whereas $\boldsymbol{\delta}$ would be in the direction of the parallels for the distances. To see the form of the model for the data, we take the inner product

$$\mathbf{a}_{m,d}^{\mathrm{T}}\mathbf{b}_p = (\phi_d\boldsymbol{\gamma}^{\mathrm{T}} + \psi_m\boldsymbol{\delta}^{\mathrm{T}})(\boldsymbol{\alpha} + \lambda_p\boldsymbol{\beta})$$
$$= \phi_d\boldsymbol{\gamma}^{\mathrm{T}}\boldsymbol{\alpha} + \psi_m\boldsymbol{\delta}^{\mathrm{T}}\boldsymbol{\alpha} + \phi_d\lambda_p\boldsymbol{\gamma}^{\mathrm{T}}\boldsymbol{\beta} + \psi_m\lambda_p\boldsymbol{\delta}^{\mathrm{T}}\boldsymbol{\beta}.$$

This models the average $y_{d,m,p.}$ by an effect due to distance, plus an effect due to metal, plus two multiplicative effects, i.e., interaction terms, one of distance with plates and the other of metals with plates.

However, there is still more to be gleaned from the biplot of Figure 8.11. The lines for lead and for aluminium are virtually parallel and pretty much at right angles to the line for plates. In terms of our parametrization, this means the vector $\boldsymbol{\beta}$ is orthogonal to vector $\boldsymbol{\gamma}$. Therefore, the inner product $\boldsymbol{\beta}^{\mathrm{T}}\boldsymbol{\gamma}$ is zero and that term vanishes from the model. Defining $\pi_d = \phi_d\boldsymbol{\gamma}^{\mathrm{T}}\boldsymbol{\alpha}$, and $\sigma_p = \boldsymbol{\delta}^{\mathrm{T}}\boldsymbol{\alpha} + \lambda_p\boldsymbol{\delta}^{\mathrm{T}}\boldsymbol{\beta}$, one obtains the model $y_{d,m,p.} = \pi_d + \psi_m\sigma_p$. As ψ_m takes on only two values, this results in two additive submodels, one for each metal. The distance effects π_d are the same for both metals, but the number of plate effects differ by a constant of proportionality. Indeed this kind of model could be fitted to these data. Note also that this example illustrates diagnosis for subtables: rule four of Table 8.3 indicates directly an additive model for the data of each metal. (See Kester, 1979, for further rules.)

Further parametrization could be effected by noting that the distances along the lines through the column markers were pretty much proportional to the number of plates and therefore the parameters σ_p could be expressed as linear in the number of plates. Similarly, the parallel lines for distances were spaced pretty much proportionally to the distances from the source of radiation and so π_d could be presented as a linear, or perhaps more precisely as a quadratic, expression in the distance d. The actual model that was fitted was an elaboration of the above and included linear and quadratic terms in the number of plates and in the distances from the source of radiation.

This is not only an instance of successful modelling but also shows the method by which a pattern observed on the biplot is translated algebraically into a model for the data.

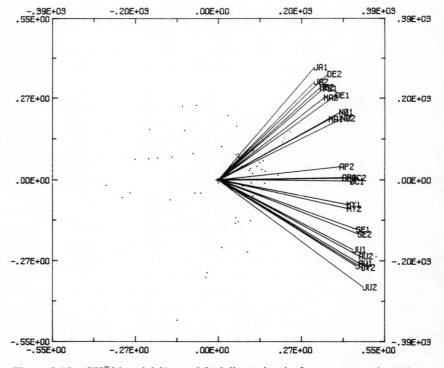

Figure 8.12   **GH**^{T} bimodel (1st and 2nd dimensions) of temperature data: dots – stations, lines – months

All the models that we have diagnosed so far have been linear or bilinear in the various effects. It may be of interest to consider an instance in which such modelling was not sufficient. The example is one of mean monthly temperatures during the 24 months of 1951 and 1952 at 50 stations on the American continents (Brier and Meltesen, 1976). The data were biplotted after the average temperatures for all 50 stations were subtracted out; the degree of goodness-of-fit was 96%. See Figure 8.12. (This analysis is reported in Tsianco, 1980.)

There is nothing particularly revealing about the scatter of row markers for the stations, shown in Figure 8.12. But the column markers fan out in a rather systematic manner. At first sight they would seem to be collinear and suggest a rows regression model. However, the order of the different months is interesting. It reveals a very similar configuration for the two years, with January at the top, then February and December, then March and November, and, somewhat farther down, April, October and May, then June, August, July and September. What sort of model does this suggest?

We note that the time sequence is systematic, going down from January to February, then to March and further down till June, then going up from July

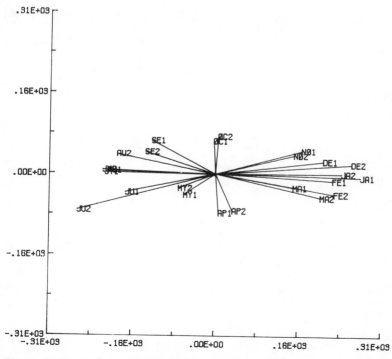

Figure 8.13   **GH**^T bimodel (2nd and 3rd dimensions) temperature data
(stations omitted)

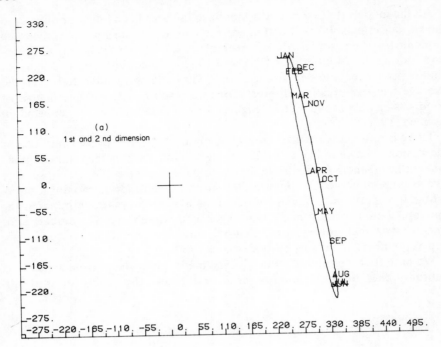

(a)
1st and 2 nd dimension

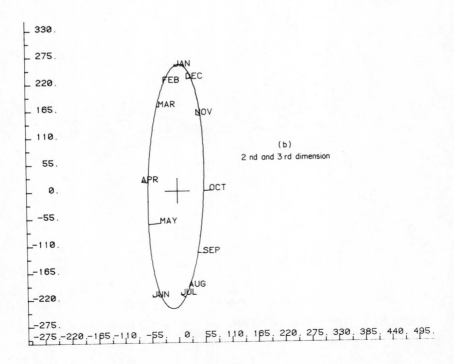

(b)
2 nd and 3 rd dimension

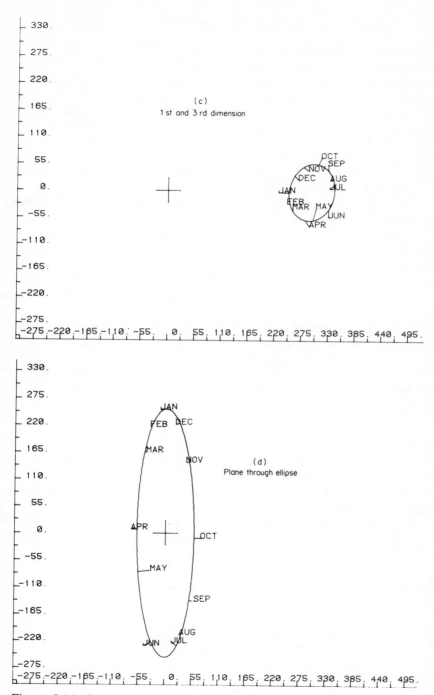

Figure 8.14   Projections of ellipsoid fitted to monthly temperature data (1951, 1952 average): (a) 1st and 2nd dimension; (b) 2nd and 3rd dimension; (c) 1st and 3rd dimension; (d) Plane through ellipse

to December. This suggests that the time sequence may really be three-dimensional, the up-down-up movement on the biplot being complemented by a further change in a third dimension separating Spring from Autumn. It is therefore worthwhile to fit a bimodel (i.e., a three-dimensional analogue of a biplot) and to look at the plane of the second and third dimension: that is, to essentially inspect the entire configuration from the right-hand side. This is shown in Figure 8.13, in which the column markers are displayed on the plane of the second and third axes of the bimodel. Now we see a clear elliptical pattern from Winter on the right, through Spring at the bottom, Summer on the left and Autumn on top.

Another way of visualizing this is by means of ellipses fitted to the three-dimensional **h** configuration. Figure 8.14 shows several projections of these fitted ellipses as viewed from the front (that is along the first and second dimensions) as viewed from the side, as we saw a moment ago; as viewed from the top; and as viewed orthogonally to the plane of the ellipse. (Note that in Figure 8.14 the individual months are shown as averages for the two years and so there are only 12 markers instead of the 24 of Figure 8.13. Also note that these are *not* concentration ellipses.)

What can be inferred from this elliptic pattern about models suitable for the data? What we are modelling by an ellipse is the configuration of the **h**-vectors of the $\mathbf{GH}^T$ bimodel. **Y** is displayed by the rank-3 matrix product $\mathbf{GH}^T$, and we are not considering the **G** factor but only the 24 columns of **H**, each having three elements. These **h**s have an elliptical configuration which we may model as

$$\mathbf{h}_j = \boldsymbol{\mu} + \boldsymbol{\alpha} \cos \theta_j + \boldsymbol{\beta} \sin \theta_j$$

for three-element vectors $\boldsymbol{\mu}$, $\boldsymbol{\alpha}$ and $\boldsymbol{\beta}$ and angles $\theta_1, \ldots, \theta_{24}$. This familiar parametrization of an ellipse represents the centre by $\boldsymbol{\mu}$, the major axis by $\boldsymbol{\alpha}$, the minor axis by $\boldsymbol{\beta}$ and the points along it by angles θ_j.

So far we have a model for the **h**s as observed on the bimodel. But our real concern is to obtain a model for the data matrix itself, i.e., for the elements $y_{i,j}$. Now, the bimodel representation is $y_{i,j} = \mathbf{g}_i^T \mathbf{h}_j$ for a row $\mathbf{g}_i^T$ of **G** and one of the vectors $\mathbf{h}_j$. In view of the elliptical modelling of the latter, we obtain

$$y_{i,j} = \mathbf{g}_i^T \boldsymbol{\mu} + \mathbf{g}_i^T \boldsymbol{\alpha} \cos \theta_j + \mathbf{g}_i^T \boldsymbol{\beta} \sin \theta_j.$$

This can be simplified by the following reparametrization:

$$\eta_i = \mathbf{g}_i^T \boldsymbol{\mu}, \qquad \psi_i \cos \phi_i = \mathbf{g}_i^T \boldsymbol{\alpha} \qquad \text{and} \qquad \psi_i \sin \phi_i = \mathbf{g}_i^T \boldsymbol{\beta}.$$

The model then becomes

$$y_{i,j} = \eta_i + \psi_i \cos \phi_i \cos \theta_j + \psi \sin \phi_i \sin \theta_j,$$

and, by the ordinary laws of trigonometry, that equals

$$y_{i,j} = \eta_i + \psi_i \cos(\phi_i + \theta_j).$$

This simple harmonic model for the data has thus been shown to have been diagnosed by means of the bimodel.

This model makes a lot of meteorological sense. η_i is a station average temperature; ψ_i is the amplitude of the annual harmonic variation in temperature, and when the model was fitted, these amplitudes were found to be larger farther from the equator and smaller close to the equator, as one would expect (Tsianco, 1980). The harmonic cosine element has its phases in terms of two arguments, ϕ_i depending on the station i and θ_j depending on the month j. Tsianco found θ_j to change from month to month by almost exactly $2\pi/12$, as one would expect from the annual cycle of temperature. He found the fitted values of ϕ_i to be much the same for all North American stations and again much the same for all South American stations. The difference between the northern and the southern ϕ_is was π, which is what one would expect since it is well-known that it is warm in the north when it is cold in the south and vice versa.

This example has shown how inspection of a biplot/bimodel may lead to observation of a pattern which can be modelled and how such a model can lead to a model for the data themselves. It has also shown that the resulting model is in accord with what we know about meteorology. Thus, biplot/bimodel inspection and consequent modelling for the data may give physically appropriate models.

8.4 SOME GENERAL COMMENTS

It may be in order to state the sequence in which I think display and modelling should be applied. One should begin by fitting the biplot or bimodel to a data matrix; from inspection of this display one might be able to infer a model or formulate a description of the data. Before one could conclude that this was an appropriate description, one should look at the residuals and ask whether they might be related to the fit of the biplot or the model, and/or whether they might be heteroscedastic. If so, one should look for forms of re-expression in the hope of yielding more homogeneous, less systematic, residuals from the next fit. This sequence of fitting, looking at residuals, and re-expression should be iterated until one is satisfied that the residuals are mainly noise.

Whilst doing these inspections of residuals, one should not merely look at general patterns of residuals but also spot outliers. In fact, this would seem to be an essential preliminary stage in all inspection of data. If there are extreme outliers, one must check the records from which the data came. Most of the time one would find gross errors which need to be corrected. In some cases, unexplained outliers would remain. It is extremely important to note unexplained outlying residuals in reporting analyses, even if they are omitted from the following fits and modelling because the methods of fitting might be unduly influenced by them. Scientists who are interested in the data often find the outliers to be the most fascinating and instructive part of the whole data set. We, as applied mathematicians, enjoy finding patterns and fitting models and get the satisfaction of mathematical elegance of presentation of these regularities. But this may be of little interest to the scientists who are looking for new and unexpected phenomena rather than for neat formulation of patterns with which they are already familiar. It may well be that much of the progress of science is in finding the unexpected (the outliers) and being led to new ideas rather than in systematizing and parametrizing the familiar.

Let me make some final remarks about biplot display in comparison to a number of other techniques of data analysis. There are a number of steps in biplot display:

(1) we start with a matrix $\mathbf{Y}$;
(2) we compute a reduced rank approximation $\mathbf{Y}_{[2]}$;
(3) we factorize that as $\mathbf{Y}_{[2]} = \mathbf{AB}^T$; and
(4) we display the $\mathbf{a}$s and $\mathbf{b}$s in a biplot (or bimodel).

Regularities that are in the original data can generally be expected to remain in the reduced-rank approximation and therefore to be expressed in the factorization and to appear as patterns on the biplot. So matrix regularities will be displayed as biplot patterns. But scientific inference must proceed in the opposite direction. One observes the biplot patterns and tries to infer about the data. This is possible to the extent that the steps of approximation, factorization and display are reversible. Indeed, display is reversed by visualization and factorization by inner product multiplication. But the approximation step is reversible only as well as the goodness-of-fit of the reduced-rank approximation. Often these approximations are very close and then one can say that the steps back from the biplot to the data can be retraced almost exactly. A number of examples have been presented above which show how one may parametrize a relationship, or pattern, on the biplot and then retrace the steps to see what model suits the data matrix.

The possibility of reproducing the data, at least approximately, from the biplot/bimodel display is a unique feature of this particular method. There are a number of other methods, such as multidimensional scaling or correspondence analysis, in which one starts from a matrix, calculates a function of the matrix (e.g., interpoint distances, correlations, etc.) and then produces some map of these distances or correlations by metric or non-metric methods. If there are regularities in the data then these maps of distances or correlations should reflect them. But we cannot even approximately retrace the step from the map of distances, or correlations, to the original data. This is because the distance, or correlation, functions which have been used to summarize the data are generally not one-to-one functions. Hence one cannot reproduce the data. One may model the distances, or correlations, but one cannot model the data by any of these other methods. The biplot seems to be unique in that it permits going back the extra step to the original data.

In summary, two main uses of the biplot have been presented. One is to inspect data matrices and look for patterns and relationships. In that use the biplot is very similar to several other methods. The other use of the biplot is to diagnose models to fit the data. For that purpose the biplot seems to be unique.

REFERENCES

Brier, G. W. and Meltesen, G. T. (1976) Eigenvector analysis for prediction of time series. *Journal of Applied Meteorology*, **15**, 1307–12.

Bradu, D. and Gabriel, K. R. (1978) The biplot as a diagnostic tool for models of two-way tables. *Technometrics*, **20**, 47–68.

Bradu, D. and Grine, F. E. (1979) Multivariate analysis of Diademodontine crania from South Africa and Zambia. *South African Journal of Science*, **75**, 441–8.

Corsten, L. C. A. and Gabriel, K. R. (1976) Graphical exploration in comparing variance matrices. *Biometrics*, **32**, 851–63.

Dempster, A. P. (1969) *Continuous Multivariate Analysis*, Reading, Mass.: Addison-Wesley.

Gabriel, K. R. (1971) The biplot–graphic display of matrices with application to principal component analysis. *Biometrika*, **58**, 453–67.

Gabriel, K. R. (1972) Analysis of meteorological data by means of canonical decomposition and biplots. *Journal of Applied Meteorology*, **11**, 1071–7.

Gabriel, K. R. (1980). Biplot. In Johnson, N. L. and Kotz, S. (eds.) (1980) *Encyclopedia of Statistical Sciences* Vol. 1., New York: Wiley.

Gabriel, K. R. and Zamir, S. (1979) Lower rank approximation of matrices by least squares with any choice of weights. *Technometrics*, **21**, 489–98.

Haber, M. (1975) The singular value decomposition of random matrices. *Ph. D. Thesis*, Hebrew University, Jerusalem.

Householder, A. S. and Young, G. (1938) Matrix approximation and latent roots. *Am. Math. Monthly*, **45**, 165–71.

Kester, N. (1979) Diagnosing and fitting concurrent and related models for two-way and higher-way layouts. *Ph.D. Thesis*, University of Rochester, New York.

McNeil, D. R. and Tukey, J. W. (1975) Higher-order diagnosis of two-way tables. *Biometrics*, **31**, 487–510.

Mandel, J. (1961) Non-additivity in two-way analysis of variance. *J. Amer. Statist. Assn.*, **56**, 878–88.

Mandel, J. (1969) The partitioning of interaction in analysis of variance. *Journal Nat. Bur. Stand. (US)*, **73B**, 309–28.

Mielke, P. W., Berry, K. J., and Johnson, E. S. (1976) Multi-response permutation procedures for a priori classifications. *Communications in Statistics, Theory-Methods*, **A5** (*14*), 1409–24.

Reeve, E. C. R. (1940) Relative growth of anteaters. *Proc. Zool. Soc. Lond.*, **A110**, 47–80.

Seal, H. L. (1964) *Multivariate Statistical Analysis for Biologists* New York: Wiley.

Tsianco, M. C. (1980). Use of biplots and 3D-bimodels in diagnosing models for two-way tables. *Ph.D. Thesis*, University of Rochester, New York.

CHAPTER 9

Statistical Applications of Real-Time Interactive Graphics

D. F. Andrews, *University of Toronto*

This chapter presents two applications of real-time interactive graphical displays for the assessment and comparison of statistical models. Simulated motion is used to display three- and higher-dimensional data structures. These structures are designed to exhibit characteristics of fitted models. They may be used for designed experiments and multiway tables.

9.1 INTRODUCTION

Graphical display has traditionally played an important rôle in the statistical analysis and presentation of data. More recently the availability of computers has made the routine use of graphical displays fast and inexpensive. These displays are typically static, two-dimensional representations: scatter plots for example.

Scatter plots are useful for displaying two-dimensional information. If data are three-dimensional, selected scatter plots may reveal the underlying structure. However, the consolidation of information presented in several displays requires some skill. If the data, considered as points in $\mathbb{R}^3$, are rotated and the moving two-dimensional projection displayed, it is much easier to identify the nature of the three-dimensional structure.

The development of terminals with local processing makes possible the simulation of motion and hence the display of three-dimensional characteristics. While the constraints of publication currently restrict the *presentation* of results to static displays, motion is available for displays to guide statistical analysis. We shall consider two such applications.

The comparative assessment of several contemplated statistical models involves both numerical summaries of the quality of each fitted model and an understanding of the terms and form of each model. Sometimes this assessment may be aided by graphical display. For example Mallows (1973) advocates a display of adjusted residual sums of squares for the comparison of all possible regressions. His C_p plot presents graphically the residual sums of squares from many regression models so that the good models may be readily identified. An alternative display designed to exhibit the relation between terms of a model is presented in Section 9.2.

The selection of a model or of models depends, however, not only on an aggregate measure of the size of residuals. Fitting increasing numbers of terms can only make residuals smaller *and* increase the variability of the corresponding predicted values. An additional term may for example greatly reduce the size of one residual and increase the uncertainty involved in the predicted values of the corresponding observation. In Section 9.3 we present a method for displaying, *simultaneously*, the size of residuals and the predictive variability. The differences between these characteristics of models may be readily compared. In Section 9.4 a computational procedure for the display of rotations is outlined.

9.2 DISPLAYS OF MEASURES OF FIT

Statistical models may be compared through a measure of fit such as residual sum of squares or likelihood. As the complexity of the model increases, these measures typically decrease. This section presents a display for the comparison of the measures of fit resulting from fits of models with varying numbers of terms. The development is described in Section 9.2.1 for models involving up to two terms only and then in Section 9.2.2 for models involving more than two terms.

9.2.1 Models with up to two terms

Consider a model with two terms, a, b, fitted using least squares. The terms may involve several degrees of freedom: for example, for blocks, treatments or the block $\times$ treatment interaction terms of a designed experiment. Let RSS (all) and $RSS(all\ but\ a)$ denote the residual sum of squares after fitting all terms and all the terms except a.

Then RSS (all) − RSS $(all\ but\ a)$, denoted by $RSS(-a)$, is a measure of the effect of the term a. Begin the display by plotting a line segment from the origin with length $[RSS(-a)]^{1/2}$. Construct an orthogonal line segment from the origin with length $[RSS(-b)]^{1/2}$. These two segments define three vertices of a rectangle. This rectangle will be used to give the direction in which $RSS(-a, -b)$, i.e.

$$RSS(all) - RSS(all\ but\ a\ and\ b),$$

will be represented.

Consider the diagonal of this rectangle and a point along the diagonal a distance $[RSS(-a, -b)]^{1/2}$ from the origin, the distance reflecting the combined effect of terms a and b. This fourth point completes the description of a four-sided figure. If the two terms, a, b, are 'orthogonal' their effects on the

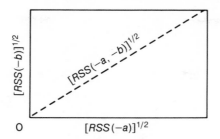

Figure 9.1 A plot showing the effects of two terms a and b with additive contributions to the residual sum of squares

residual sum of squares are additive,

$$RSS(-a, -b) = RSS(-a) + RSS(-b),$$

and the figure will be a rectangle as in Figure 9.1. If a is associated with a greater reduction in the residual sum of squares, the sides of the figure in the a direction will be longer. If the effects of a and b are highly correlated, typically their individual effects on the residual sum of squares is much smaller then their combined effect as is shown in Figure 9.2.

The projection of the diagonal onto the a axis contains the same information. The projection in Figure 9.1 overlaps the initial line segment exactly. In Figure 9.2 the projection is much longer. Thus the extent to which the effects of a are aliased with those of b may be seen from the one-dimensional a axis.

9.2.2 Models with more than two terms

The two-dimensional configuration described above may be extended to exhibit more terms $t_1, t_2, \ldots, t_p$. For each term t_i define the basis vector $\mathbf{b}_i$ with

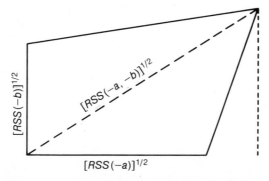

Figure 9.2 A plot showing two terms a and b whose effects are partially aliased with each other

coordinates

$$b_{ij} = \begin{cases} [RSS(-t_i)]^{1/2}, & j = i \\ 0, & j \neq i. \end{cases}$$

For each collection of terms $I = i_1, \ldots, i_k$ let $\mathbf{v}_I$ be the vertex

$$\mathbf{v}_I = \sum_{i \in I} \mathbf{b}_i \cdot [RSS(-t_{i_1}, \ldots, t_{i_k})]^{1/2} \sum \{[RSS(-t_i)]^{-1/2}\}.$$

The 2^p vertices define a p-dimensional 'box'. Any two-dimensional projection of this box on the plane $\mathbf{b}_i$, $\mathbf{b}_j$ shows:

(1) the relative importance of terms t_i and t_j;
(2) the extent to which other terms can account for the effects of these terms.

Rotations permit the appreciation of more than two dimensions of the structure. Such characteristics are difficult to infer from strictly two-dimensional representations.

9.2.3 An example of measure display

Blood samples were analysed for 194 patients. Of these, 67 measurements were from known carriers of Duchenne muscular dystrophy and 127 measurements were from people known not to be carriers. For each blood sample, four enzymes were measured: CK, H, PK and L. To study the relative importance of these four separately or in combination, logistic regressions were run using $GLIM$ to fit the 0–1 variable indicating disease. Table 9.1 presents the

Table 9.1   Deviances for example in Section 9.2.3

Fitted terms	Deviance
	250.1
L	165.9
P	183.6
PL	145.2
H	212.8
HL	148.5
HP	157.1
HPL	130.7
C	155.1
CL	131.3
CP	138.6
CPL	122.1
CH	113.5
CHL	104.6
CHP	105.9
CHPL	99.8

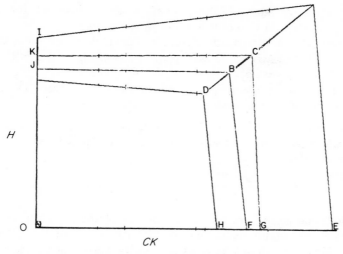

Figure 9.3   A plot showing the effects of *CK* and *H* by themselves (inner box) and with combinations of *PK* and *L* (outer
boxes)

deviances obtained from running the 16 possible fits to these four variables.
Figure 9.3 displays the projection on the *CK*, *H* plane of the 4-dimensional
configuration. Figure 9.4 displays the *PK*, *L* projection. From these displays it
is easy to note:

(1)   *CK* and *H* have larger effects on the deviance than *PK* and *L* (the
projection in Figure 9.3 is larger than that in Figure 9.4);

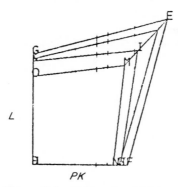

Figure 9.4   A plot showing the
effects of *PK* and *L* by themselves (inner box) and with
combinations of *CK* and *H*
(outer boxes)

(2)   *CK* and *H* are relatively independent in their effects on the deviance
      (the projection in Figure 9.3 is almost rectangular);
(3)   *PK* and *L* do not markedly change the deviance when these terms are
      added to the *CK*, *H* model (the projections in Figure 9.3 of the 'hyper-
      cube' almost overlap);
(4)   *CK* and *H* contain some of the information represented in *PK* and *L*
      (the remaining projections *CK*, *L*, ... are skew).

These assessments of relative size of effects are much more intuitively
achieved when the figure is considered as a four-dimensional structure and
rotated in real time.

9.3 DISPLAYS OF FITS

When additional terms are fitted in a linear model by least squares the
residual sum of squares decreases and the variability of the fitted values
increases. Sometimes these changes occur with the same degree for all observations; sometimes the effects may occur predominantly for only a few observations. This distribution of influence cannot be ascertained from aggregate
summaries such as the residual sum of squares.

   This section describes a display of both residuals and precision of fitted
values. The display is designed to exhibit the differences between models.

   The common residual plot, Figure 9.5, is a scatter plot of residuals *r* versus
fitted values $\hat{y}$. If this display is rotated by $\pi/4$ radians (see Figure 9.6) the
new axes become y and $2\hat{y} - y$. This rotated display contains the same information as the residual display, namely:

(1)   the size of each residual; distance from the line $r = 0$ in the original
      display, becomes distance from the 'diagononal' line $y = 2\hat{y} - y$ in the
      rotated display, and
(2)   patterns and trends in the original display are unchanged by rotation.

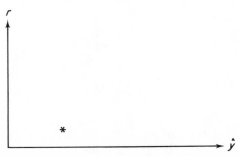

Figure 9.5   A common plot of residual versus fitted value for one observation

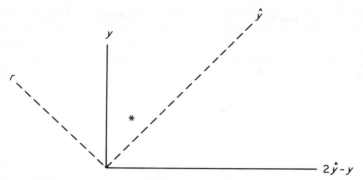

Figure 9.6   The plot of Figure 9.5 rotated, showing the new axes

The variability of fitted values may be added to this display. Under the assumption that the observations are independent, with the same variance, the variance of the fitted value $\hat{y}_i$ is just m_{ii} the corresponding element of the least-squares projection matrix $\mathbf{M}$, in the relationship

$$\hat{\mathbf{y}} = \mathbf{M}\mathbf{y}.$$

Let $s_i = s(m_{ii})^{1/2}$ and plot the line segments joining

$$\mathbf{l} = (2\hat{y} - y - 2s, y) \qquad \text{and} \qquad \mathbf{u} = (2\hat{y} - y + 2s, y)$$

(where s is an estimate of scale, perhaps the root error mean square) as shown in Figure 9.7

To compare the fits of *several* (p) models calculate the lower and upper ends of the line segment for each model and consider the line segments as segments in $\mathbb{R}^{p+1}$. The projection of this configuration onto two dimensions may be displayed.

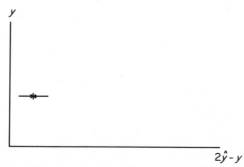

Figure 9.7   The plot of Figure 9.6 with the
variability of fitted values added

Rotating the configuration displays the differences, as one fit rotates to another. The user's attention is attracted to those aspects that change. The advantage of this particular parametrization of the plot lies with the possibility of comparing very different sorts of models. It is necessary only to calculate the upper and lower limits of the fitted values in the same units. Thus for example it is possible to compare the models fitted to both transformed and untransformed data.

9.3.1 Examples

Box and Cox (1964) illustrated a method for selecting a data transformation with a factorial experiment with 4 poisons and 3 treatments. Four observations were made for each situation. The response measured was survival time.

Box and Cox proposed a numerical procedure to select a transformation of the data. They suggested rate(time^{-1}) as a more suitable form of the response for analysis. Figure 9.8 is a display of an additive model fitted to the original data. Note the systematic departures of the data from the line with slope 1. Figure 9.9 is the corresponding display obtained by

(1) transforming to rates,
(2) calculating quantities used in the display,
(3) transforming back and displaying in units of time.

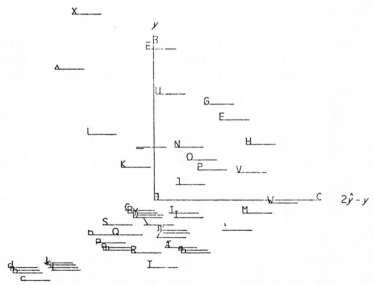

Figure 9.8 Plot of residuals showing variablity of fitted values for Box and Cox example using an additive model

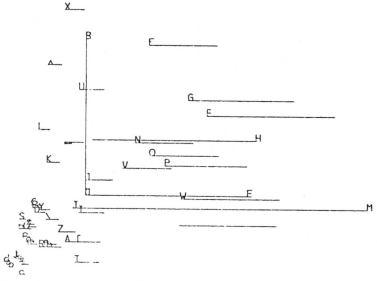

Figure 9.9   The display of Figure 9.8 but based on fitting the response
$$y = (\text{time})^{-1}$$

Note here that the departures are less systematic and that the size of departure from the line with slope 1 is related to the variability of the predicted values.

For some observations the variability of the predicted values has increased, for others it has decreased. It seems reasonable here to expect large variability with large times. (This is an effect of both the transformation and the design.) The two plots are projections of a three-dimensional structure. Rotations display the smooth transition from one to the other.

Figure 9.10 displays the projection of the data structure in the plane of the two models. Each observation is represented by a line segment. The distances of the centres of the segments from the diagonal line exhibit the systematic changes in the fitted values. The slope of each segment represents the relative precision of the fitted values under the two models. Here the systematic differences are clearly evident. Note that this is not a different type of display but a different projection of the same data structure.

This display has been useful in assessing different log-linear models of a multiway table. The display constructed with $(\text{count})^{1/2}$ as the dependent variable shows the *practical* significance of the differences among models. Changes and inadequacies in fitted values may be readily assessed.

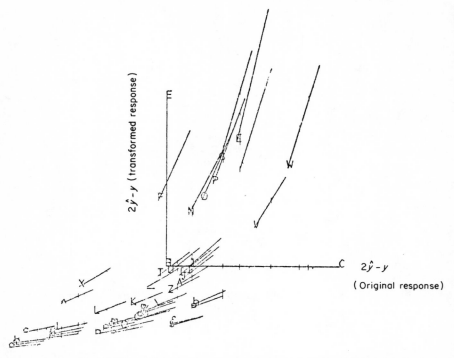

Figure 9.10 Variability of fitted values under the two models of Figures 9.8 and 9.9

9.4 QUICK ROTATIONS

The simulation of motion requires the display of 10–20 frames or pictures per second. The unpredictable response rate of time-sharing computers rules out their use for simulated rotations. Many inexpensive processors can produce such displays locally. However these processors typically perform floating-point operations rather slowly.

To simulate rotation the following procedure rotates points with considerable precision. It is sufficient to calculate $x \sin \theta$ and $x \cos \theta$ for some small angle θ. Setting $\theta = 1/32 \approx 2\pi/200$ and expanding yields $\sin \theta$ and $\cos \theta$ in the forms,

$$\sin \theta = \theta + o(2^{-16})$$

$$\cos \theta = 1 - \frac{\theta^2}{2} + o(2^{-22}).$$

Thus using terms up to θ^2

(1)   involves only shift operations (divisions by 2^n) which are fast on most machines, and

(2)   produces results with relative error of less than 2^{-16}.

Since the display precision is rarely greater than 2^{-10}, this procedure is accurate enough for display purposes. Since rotation by $\pi/2$ is trivial and exact, the accumulation of round-off error may be eliminated. We have not found this necessary. The choice of $\theta = 1/32$ rather than another power of $1/2$ was made with a view to obtaining acceptable accuracy and producing rotations which were fast enough to appear to move and slow enough for the viewer to absorb detail.

This procedure has been used both on expensive and on very inexpensive terminals.

REFERENCES

Box, G. E. P. and Cox, D. R. (1964) An analysis of transformations. *J. Roy. Statist. Soc. B*, **26**, 211–52.
Mallows, C. L. (1973) Some comments on C_p. *Technometrics*, **15**, 661–75.

PART III

Graphical Display of Data Sets in 3 or more Dimensions*

*Prepared in part in connection with research at Princeton University supported by the U.S. Army Research Office (Durham). Based in part on an earlier account supported by the U.S. Energy Research and Development Administration (Tukey and Tukey, 1977)

CHAPTER 10

Preparation; Prechosen Sequences of Views

P. A. Tukey, *Bell Laboratories, Murray Hill, New Jersey, U.S.A.*
J. W. Tukey, *Princeton University, Princeton, New Jersey, U.S.A.*
and *Bell Laboratories, Murray Hill, New Jersey, U.S.A.*

10.1 INTRODUCTION

10.1.1 The opportunity and the challenge

A data set, for our purposes, will usually be a cloud of points in p-dimensional space (where $p \geq 3$), and we shall want to learn things about the configuration of points by making, and looking at, a variety of graphical displays. Pictures are particularly valuable in an exploratory setting because not only can they confirm or contradict what we thought we knew in advance about the data, but they can also reveal in a dramatic way things that we did not even suspect. Moreover, a single picture can show us a number of things. This is the opportunity. The challenge lies in the fact that we will be trying mentally to visualize point clouds in ≥ 3 dimensions, but the world we are familiar with is 3-dimensional and ultimately our displays are all 2-dimensional. (Binocular vision might get us as far as 2.5 dimensions!) Thus, we must constantly make careful decisions about which aspects of our data to display and how to display them effectively in 2 dimensions. These choices will depend on our knowledge of what graphical techniques are available and work well, but they will also depend on our objectives in particular applications. Both aims and techniques are quite diverse; separating them can be vital. We begin by making some of these distinctions in broad terms. Many of these issues are further developed later in this chapter or in Chapters 11 or 12.

Uses of scatter diagrams and plots: individually versus merging

The simple scatter diagram, which shows a set of discrete points plotted in a two-dimensional rectangular coordinate system, is a basic tool for looking at data. To make an effective scatter diagram, or two-view, we have to be *keenly aware* of what it is supposed to do for us. If the number of points is small and there are meaningful labels associated with them, there can be uses for scatter diagrams which involve identifying individual points, either to read off their locations or to compare their locations with those of others. These are far rarer than uses in which the points—often all, but sometimes only most—are being asked to merge into a broad collective impression. We will want to aid this as much as we can, which will require quite different display techniques.

Impact graphics versus archival graphics

By concentrating on the objective of the display rather than on the nature of the eye/picture interaction, we are led to an alternative way to make this important distinction. We can ask, 'Is the purpose of the plot to store away information about the points in a compact way for later use?' (an archival function), or 'Is it to make an immediate overall impact?' The material which follows will be essentially confined to impact graphics.

Locations, characters, and backgrounds

Information about a single data 'point' can be given in three quite different ways in a plot, all of which are important:

* by the location of a symbol;
* by the symbol or character used to mark the point (dots, circles, letters or digits, glyphs and faces are some possibilities);

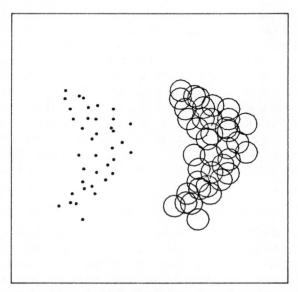

Figure 10.1   A single pattern of centres plotted first
as dots, then as circles to aid merging

* by the background around the point, which may involve: (1) shadings using parallel rulings with different spacings, line types, slants, and intensities, (2) contours, alone or supplemented, and—for lectures at least but more widely if technology permits—(3) different colours of background tint or shading.

Merging, separating, alternating

Although our interest is in impact graphics, we may still, at different times, be trying to do quite different things, particularly:

* merging, as when we use moderately large circles instead of points to encourage blending together into overall impressions;
* separating, as when we use different characters for points that belong to different subgroups, in the hope that we can 'see' those of a selected subgroup when we wish;
* alternating, as when we use quite definite points against a background of gentle contours, planned so we can look at either at will.

Figures 10.1, 10.2 and 10.3 show examples of these three ideas.

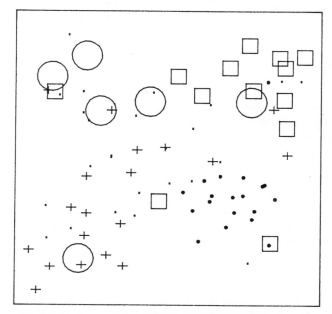

Figure 10.2   A scatter of points with subgroups coded by
different characters to allow separating

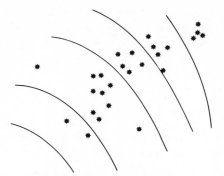

Figure 10.3   Points plotted against a
background of contours

The computer

Should we rely on the eye to merge? Or should we rely on the computer to do calculations so that what we display merges more easily or more effectively? Experience shows that using the computer makes effective impact graphics easier to design, so, in making displays, we plan to use it as much as possible, both to help us determine what is to be placed where and, whenever we can, to drive devices preparing the display (in whole or in part).

Mental combination

A possibility we need to consider carefully is how well we can do—and how we can arrange to do well—in presenting two or more views side-by-side and mentally combining them.

Kinematic display

Much can be gained by showing motion, although this can hardly be done *on paper*. In kinematic displays, a three-fold separation into *front variables* (the two overtly before us), *middle variables* (those having effect on changes in view position by simulated rotations or vibrations) and *back variables* (those not currently affecting position) becomes important.

We shall not have time to deal with kinematic displays. For static displays, the concept of middle variable is not as meaningful, but a two-fold separation into front and back variables will be crucial in all modes of display for three- or higher-dimensional data.

Static displays

A little reflection convinces us that in static displays nothing does even nearly as well as right–left position and up–down position for (a) producing impact, (b) facilitating synthesis of impressions from groups of points, and (c) making fine distinctions both possible and easy. Nothing is comparable, but what comes closest?

In order, from stronger to weaker, we feel that the prominent representatives are

(1) colour (where the establishment of synthesis-prone sequences deserves attention, as emphasized to us by W. J. Dixon);
(2) shape (of characters or symbols);
(3) size (as in pseudo-perspective displays);
(4) contrast (e.g. more gray corresponds to more distant).

Colour deserves much more attention than the others, especially in view of the hope for synthesis. Unfortunately, the limitations of current printing technology prevent us from showing here any examples in colour.

New choices of variables

Were we restricted to only the initial variables, we would be badly constrained. Techniques for identifying and computing useful new combinations (not necessarily linear) of original variables as a basis for our displays are often vital.

High-density problems

Once we have many points, regions of high density fail to get their fair importance, both because of reproduction phenomena (current technology is all too likely to make the very black come out light) and visual processes (with lots of points almost all of us look too hard at the fringes). Also, beyond a certain density, no further density increase can be perceived.

Balloon densities

A number of useful display techniques are guided by measures of the local density of data points. Empirical densities must be of the form (*count/ volume*). If we try to be classical by counting observations in fixed cells, we quickly have too many cells as the dimension increases. We do considerably better to hold count constant, and take

$$density = k/[(constant)(radius\ to\ k^{th}\ nearest)^p].$$

Think of this as blowing up a balloon until it includes k neighbours and call it a balloon density—the k-balloon density. We return to this idea and to properties of balloon densities (which are also called *nearest-neighbour density estimates*) in Section 11.3.2.

10.1.2 Scales for important quantities

We need to pay attention both to how many points we have and to how many dimensions they are in, since both will have major influence on our choice of effective displays. To this end, coding schemes, probably both literal and verbal, seem important.

Scales of numerosity

To describe the number of points in a data set, we suggest (a) a letter, (b) a modifier of 'data set', (c) a modifier of 'data', and (d) a modifier of 'points' as a rough scale of *numerosity* (Table 10.1). (Other people with other experience might have different feelings about where the class boundaries should fall.)

We will often find it helpful to reduce the number of points we have to display to B, C or possibly D. Profitable reductions to A seem quite unlikely. F is only likely to be worth displaying as such in very special circumstances, while E is questionable. Agglomeration (see Section 11.3.1) is one way to make effective reductions in numbers of points.

Scales of dimensionality

To describe the number of dimensions in a data set, we suggest (a) a letter, (b) a modifier of 'dimensions' and (c) a modifier of 'dimensional' (Table 10.2). We expect experience to lead to some modification of the class boundaries.

Table 10.1   Scales of numerosity

Number of data points	Letter	data set	data	points
1–3				
4–8	A	minuscule	skinny	few
8–25	B	small	moderate amount of	small number of
25–80	C	modest		modest number of
80–250	D	medium-sized		intermediate number of
250–800	E	substantial	copious	many
800–2500	F			
2500–8000	G	burdensome	extensive	crowds of
>8000				

Table 10.2 Scales of dimensionality

Number of dimensions	Letter	dimensions	-dimensional
2–5	A	few	low-
6–10	B	several	several-
11–20	C	many	many-
21–40	D	lots of	
41–up	E	high	high-

10.1.3 General outline of material in Chapters 10–12

We begin, in Section 10.2, by considering some ways for making initial adjustments to raw data before it is in a form suitable for effective graphical display.

Then Sections 10.3 and 11.1.1 will cover what can be done with sets of prechosen direct views (i.e., sets of views whose choice is not affected by the data) to look at point clouds in three, four, or more dimensions. The conclusion is 'we can do something but usually not enough'.

The next step, in the remainder of Section 11.1 and in Section 11.2, is to have the data—and our best judgement—help to select the views. The result is 'better but usually not enough better.'

Then, in Section 11.3, we consider changing the data in ways that make it easier to look at. Agglomeration, sharpening, and blunting all help. Sometimes the result is adequate, but often still more is needed.

Going further means, so far as we can see, giving up any idea of treating all variables alike. In any single view, the two front, or view, variables—horizontal and vertical, say—are treated very differently from all the others or back variables. Nothing we know how to do can change this. What we can do (and what we discuss in Chapter 12) is to treat the back variables still more differently, summarizing or smoothing them, and trying to display only their summarized or smoothed behaviour.

When we do this, we have scatter plots of the two view variables, possibly improved (by sharpening or blunting), supplemented by summarized and/or smoothed information about the back variables. This may be good enough; if not, we must wait for further developments.

Chapter 12 closes with a brief indication of some relevant things we will not have talked about.

10.2 PREPARATION

If we are to display data vectors satisfactorily, we need to begin by adjusting the raw variables in various ways. It is only after such adjustment or *re-*

expression that we will have our 'initial' variables for plotting. There are several important aspects to consider.

10.2.1 Centring and scaling

Frequently our raw variables come to us measured on scales that are convenient or customary for the subject-matter area, but incommensurable (e.g., temperature, currency, time), arbitrary from the point of view of the data (degrees Celsius or Fahrenheit? pounds or dollars? days or hours?), and falling in inconvenient or vastly different numerical ranges. Even when the physical units are the same, large differences in ranges can cause trouble. Very often we will want to *rescale* individual coordinates by dividing by suitable constants, and, when the origin is arbitrary, to *centre* them as well by subtracting constants.

How should we choose the constants to adjust individual coordinates? Do we use classical (over-Utopian) measures like sample means and standard deviations? Do we replace these by (preferably polyefficient, i.e., efficient in many situations) robust/resistant analogues like the biweight and s_{bi}, respectively (Mosteller and Tukey, 1977, Chapter 10)? Or do we use highly forgiving quantities such as the median or midmean and the interquartile range (*hingespread*) or the median absolute deviation? These questions are all far from trivial. No one seems to have an obvious generally defensible answer, but in most circumstances any robust/resistant choice is far better than the classical measures.

What is clear is that we should do *something* to bring our raw coordinates to reasonably useful—and usually comparable—ranges.

10.2.2 Sphering

For many purposes it is not enough to scale individual coordinates, especially when some of the coordinates are highly correlated so that they are measuring very similar things in the data, and when it is not those correlations *per se* that are of interest. Rather one wants to *sphere* the system of coordinates as a whole, creating new coordinates that are linear re-expressions of the old, that all measure substantially different aspects of the data. Such a re-expression maps an initially elliptically shaped cloud into a spherical cloud.

How chosen?

Again we can be classical (over-Utopian) and seek a set of new coordinates, all of whose sample variances are 1 and covariances 0, or we can be robust/resistant (perhaps along the lines leading to *cobs* and *bars* in Chapter 10 of Mosteller and Tukey, 1977), or forgiving (where the choice of an analogue to 'zero covariance' deserves more thought). Beyond this there is a choice of approach to the given coordinate list. Should we rearrange it in order of interest or importance and then use successive orthogonalization? Should we go to some form of principal (or other automatic) components? Or what?

Grinding off '5%'

One way to 'robustify' the sphering process begins by setting aside one point at a time, as long as the deviation of that point from the remaining point-cloud mean, as measured using the remaining point-cloud covariance matrix, is large. Then we sphere using the covariance matrix of the points *not* set aside. Here the numerical criterion for largeness can reasonably be chosen to set aside, on average, about 5% of the points from a Gaussian sample. (See also Gnanadesikan and Kettenring, 1972.)

Sphering as a way of forcing insight

The real value of graphical displays in exploratory work is not to demonstrate the obvious or well-understood (and multivariate ellipsoidal structure is often best understood by looking at a covariance matrix or its eigenstructure), but to highlight deviations from understood structure. Even if we are only going to look at a collection of scatters or one-views, sphering the data before display forces us to examine only aspects of our collection of data vectors other than its general ellipsoidal nature.

We will find it useful, as we will see in later sections, to sphere our point clouds or identifiable parts thereof before almost any direct or analysed display procedure. Thus we will often need to employ some or all of the kinds of techniques just sketched.

10.2.3 Curvature reduction

Curved configurations of points in pictures should always suggest (nonlinear) re-expression or transformation, and replotting in terms of re-expressed coordinates. If the initial display does not suggest a definite form of re-expression, as happens more often than not, we should probably begin by re-expressing the coordinates separately and plan to try several alternatives. Among them we should probably include, as a matter of course, the *'first-aid'* re-expressions of Mosteller and Tukey (1977, Chapter 5). They suggest logs for counts or amounts, logits for counted fractions, and the related transformation $\log[(3i - 1)/(n - 3i + 2)]$ for ranks i out of n.

We do not yet have quite enough insight to suggest further automatic techniques—especially techniques that choose good re-expression involving two or more coordinates at a time. But if we find certain kinds of distinctive appearances in plots of one coordinate against another, a nonlinear coordinate change is very nearly mandatory. Thus, points hugging a circle scream for polar coordinates, while points concentrating near a monotone curved arc call for a suitable simpler choice of at least one new simpler coordinate—simpler, that is, in the sense that the configuration of points will be simpler in terms of the new coordinates.

10.2.4 Looking at shape

If the point cloud, or a well-identified part of it, seems to show no really distinctive character after sphering, we may be reduced to studying the shape of its globular blur. After sphering, the sphere is the null or reference configuration from which deviations are to be studied, so we will often do well to convert to (generalized) spherical coordinates before making plots.

Radius and angle coordinates

Introduced by Andrews, Gnanadesikan, and Warner (1973) and emphasized by Gnanadesikan (1977), *radius and angle plots* are constructed, coordinate by coordinate, in a new set of generalized spherical coordinates that are derived from the original Cartesian coordinates as follows. First, the origin is set at a robust centroid of the data. (We could use the centroid of the data remaining after sharpening; see Section 11.3.3.) The first new coordinate is the radius; the rest of the information regarding a point is contained in the position of its radial projection on the $(p - k)$-dimensional sphere, where k initially equals 1. We are now ready for an iteration over k.

Once we pick a pair of opposite points on the $(p - k)$-dimensional sphere to serve as poles, we may take the angle to the north pole (a generalized colatitude) as our next new coordinate, projecting our directions from the $(p - k)$-sphere onto the locus of directions at right angles to the poles, that is, onto the generalized equator, which is a $(p - k - 1)$-sphere. We repeat this process until the equator is a circle, whereupon we take (generalized) longitude as the last coordinate.

Assuming the origin shift to have been done in advance, if the poles are chosen to line up, in turn, with the x_1 axis, the x_2 axis, etc., then the equations for the conversion to generalized spherical coordinates are:

$$r = \| \tilde{x} \|$$
$$\theta_1 = \cos^{-1}(x_1/r)$$
$$\theta_2 = \cos^{-1}[x_2/(r \sin \theta_1)]$$
$$\theta_3 = \cos^{-1}[x_3/(r \sin \theta_1 \sin \theta_2)]$$
$$\vdots$$
$$\theta_{p-1} = \cos^{-1}[x_{p-1}/(r \sin \theta_1 \cdots \sin \theta_{p-2})]$$

Further re-expression based on spherical symmetry

If the angular distribution of the points is spherically symmetrical around the origin, the successive spherical coordinates will be independent with fixed, simple densities. Then we can go one re-expression step further and work with the following expressions, which will be independently and uniformly distributed (Goldman, 1976):

$$t_1 = F_1(\theta_1), \qquad t_2 = F_2(\theta_2), \quad \ldots, \quad t_{p-1} = F_{p-1}(\theta_{p-1}),$$

where

$$F_k(\theta) = \int_0^\theta (\sin \theta)^{p-k-1} \, d\theta$$

We can re-express the radius with a similar objective, getting constant density from initially spherical Gaussian data by letting t_0 be an inverse chi-square cumulative of $(r/R)^2$, where R is a fitted constant. (Alternatively, we may wish to rank the radii and use $t_0^* = (i - \tfrac{1}{3})/(n + \tfrac{1}{3})$.)

Radius and angle plots

We now naturally plot (a) t_0 alone, probably as a *rootogram* if there are many data points (a 'rootogram' is a histogram with cell counts plotted on a square-root scale in order to stabilize variance), (b) t_0 against each of $t_1, t_2, \ldots, t_{p-1}$ (as scatters), (c) t_1 against t_2, t_2 against t_3, and so on (as scatters) and hope to see something interesting.

We should not ask any display to show us that which can be more simply dealt with otherwise. In particular, we should not ask radius and angle plots to show us ellipsoidal behaviour. Rather it is important to apply robust/resistant sphering to the data, as we have indicated, before beginning with radius and angles.

Which poles?

In the conversion to spherical coordinates, we are free to choose the poles. Equivalently, we are free to apply any orthogonal transformation (rigid rotation) to the $x_1, \ldots, x_p$ before calculating spherical coordinates. Were our interest along the lines of significance testing, we might reasonably select the poles at random, since if we allow data-guiding we change the chance distributions in ways that may not be easy to allow for. But if we want to make our displays as revealing as possible, we must make the selection of poles as data-guided as possible. At least eight $(=2^3)$ guidance schemes seem reasonable, any or all of which may need to be tried: namely, all combinations of

  guidance by choosing poles to extremize a local average of t_0 (or r)—single-ended or double-ended—maximizing or minimizing

guidance by choosing poles to extremize a broad density—single-ended or double-ended—maximizing or minimizing.

Single-ended guidance uses $\theta = \cos^{-1}(scalar\ product\ between\ directions)$; double-ended uses $\phi = \min\{\theta, \pi - \theta\}$. Guidance by t_0 or r involves extremizing the average of t_0 or r over, say, the $n/4$ data-point directions nearest the trial pole. Guidance by density should probably be based on $(n/4)$-balloon densities of points near a trial pole, where nearness is based on angular distance using θ or ϕ.

It might be desirable to develop a technique for trying all of these guidance schemes and then using the 'strongest' of the results to choose the next pair of poles, allowing different guidance at different stages of the iteration.

We have yet to gain extensive enough experience with this technique to allow us to comment on its usefulness and fine tuning.

Another approach

If we are only concerned with an omnibus (somewhat significance-like) approach, we could look at the distributions of angles (of the θ or ϕ variety) to the jth nearest neighbours, for $j \leq k$. For each j, these quantities could be 'binned' by partitioning the range of possible values into disjoint intervals and making counts of the numbers of observed jth-neighbour distances falling within each interval. Then the counts could be compared with those anticipated for a spherical distribution. The comparison should probably be done after re-expressing the counts on a scale which makes them behave roughly like observations from a unit Gaussian distribution, e.g., by computing and plotting the quantities

$$\sqrt{2 + 4\ (actual\ count)} - \sqrt{1 + 4\ (anticipated\ count)}.$$

(Use 1 for the the first term when *actual count* $= 0$; see Mosteller and Tukey, 1977, p. 235.) To get the anticipated counts, we observe that the hyper-area of a random cap (Section 11.1.1) extending out to the jth nearest neighbour follows the same general uniform-order-statistic distribution as the reciprocal of a balloon density (Section 11.3.2).

Yet another approach

An approach sensitive to multiple 'noses' (that is, bumps on the periphery of the data cloud which might sometimes also be described as overlapping ellipsoids, jack-shaped contours, or hyper-cross structures) though not in itself identifying their location, would be to plot r or t_0 against the logarithm of the balloon density (in θ or ϕ), with trends being the most plausible diagnostic result to look for.

10.3 PRECHOSEN DIRECT VIEWS

The most elementary two-dimensional displays of data in more than two dimensions are those in which we make one or more pictures, each showing every data vector as a point, using two front variables (horizontal and vertical in the picture) which are (orthogonal) linear combinations of the initial variables, chosen in some automatic way before looking at the data.

Many people are in the habit of thinking of this kind of view as a projection onto a view plane. However, we feel that if we are to do a good job of understanding the geometry of multiple views it will often pay to recognize that a view is a many-to-one mapping, and to focus attention not only on what is mapped onto, but also on the loci of points in the data space that correspond to single points in the view. Thus, for instance, a view of three-dimensional data is defined by a family of parallel lines, which we can call *isolines*. (They are, in fact, all the lines perpendicular to the 'view plane.') This is depicted by Figure 10.4. For four-dimensional data, since we must collapse along two dimensions to produce a two-view, the loci are a stack of parallel planes—*isoplanes*, or generalized Venetian blinds! In p dimensions, they are parallel $(p - 2)$-dimensional linear manifolds, or *isoflats*.

There are several advantages to this approach. Not only does it emphasize the nature and especially the dimension of what a single point in the view may represent, but it allows us to use the same framework to think about many other kinds of views: the isolines do not have to be perpendicular to the view plane (e.g., as in rescaled coordinates, or sphered rectangular coordinates), nor parallel to each other (e.g., as in perspective views, or in plots of θ_i versus θ_j or t_i versus t_j above), nor even straight lines or flat subspaces (e.g., in a rootogram of r in Section 10.2.4 the *isoloci* would be concentric spherical shells). One further advantage is that, having obtained a view, we can present

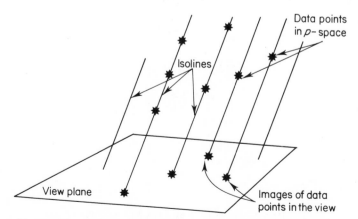

Figure 10.4   Sketch of a two-view and its family of isolines

it in many ways, perhaps even transforming it nonlinearly if that seems useful, but the isoloci remain the same.

10.3.1 Prechosen direct views of three-dimensional point clouds

We discuss prechosen direct views in terms of three cases distinguished by dimensionality, starting with the simplest case of three-dimensional data.

Collections of regularly-spaced views

We can restrict ourselves to the conventional three views defined by the three families of lines parallel to a coordinate axis. The isolines form a 'three-way brush', as in Figure 10.5, and the three views are often called the *coordinate plane views*. If we do this, we still have a choice of presentation of the views, which we illustrate with a series of exhibits showing the first three coordinates out of four of the well-known Anderson iris data—often attributed errone-ously to Fisher (Anderson, 1935, 1936, Fisher 1936). There are observations on 150 specimens of iris: the first two coordinates are the sepal length and width, the others the petal length and width. The 150 specimens include 50 each of three different varieties of iris, which are coded in these exhibits as A, B and C. (We would prefer colour coding instead of or in addition to letters, and would encourage hand tracing with colour when a colour plotter is not available.)

Our choices of view presentation include:

(1)   A draughtsman's three views (front, top and side), as in Figure 10.6. Adjacent views are arranged to have an axis in common.
(2)   A perspective view of the projections onto the faces of a cube, which can in turn be viewed 'face on' as in Figure 10.7, or perhaps along a diagonal

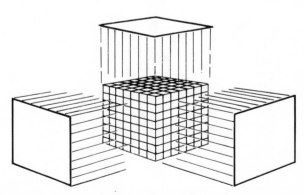

Figure 10.5   The three-way brush of isolines corresponding to the three coordinate-plane views

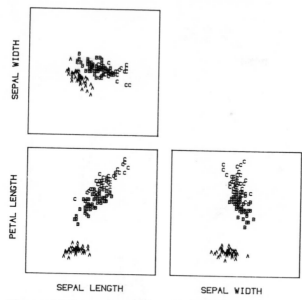

Figure 10.6 A draughtsman's three views of the
Anderson iris data (first three variables) (*A* = iris setosa,
B = iris virginica, *C* = iris versicolor)

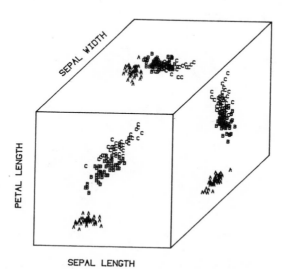

Figure 10.7 A perspective view of a cube with
two-views of the iris data 'pasted' on its faces
(Cleveland, Kettenring and McGill, 1976)

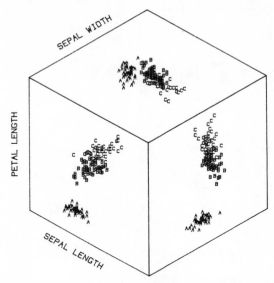

Figure 10.8   The cube of Figure 10.7 viewed
along a major diagonal

of the cube as in Figure 10.8. The latter has the slight advantage of
distorting all views equally.

(3)   Three squares with a common vertex, as in Figure 10.9, which does not
distort any of the views.

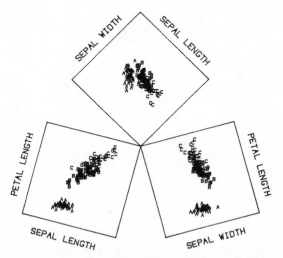

Figure 10.9   The cube of Figure 10.7 cut along its
edges and 'flattened'

Dodecahedral views, etc.

The three views described above correspond to three faces of a cube surrounding the data cloud, but we need not restrict ourselves to a cube. We can, for instance, conceptually project the data onto six of the 12 faces of a pentagonal dodecahedron, cut along several edges, and flatten it out. This gives the six *dodeca-views* shown in Figure 10.10, which are angularly well-separated. (The other six faces give the same views, since they are parallel to the first six.) If we orient the dodecahedron inside the unit cube as shown in Figure 10.11, then none of the six views coincides with any of the three coordinate-plane views, and each one involves linear combinations of all three coordinates. In practice, of course, we write a computer program to do all this, and we need formulae for the faces of the dodecahedron. (See, for instance, Sommerville 1929 or Coxeter, 1961, 1963.)

Any regular polytope can replace the dodecahedron. For instance, we could add to the three coordinate-plane views a set of views defined by families of isolines that form equal angles with the coordinate axes (both positive and negative). This is equivalent to using a 14-faced polytope that is a cube with its corners bevelled by planes orthogonal to the body diagonals. Another possibility is an icosahedron (20 faces) or even a dodecahedron bevelled by an icosahedron (32 faces).

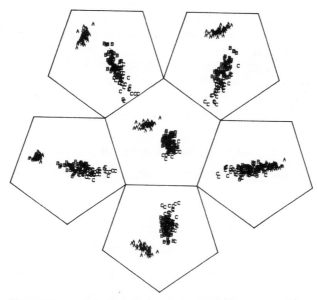

Figure 10.10   Dodeca-views of three variables of the
Anderson iris data

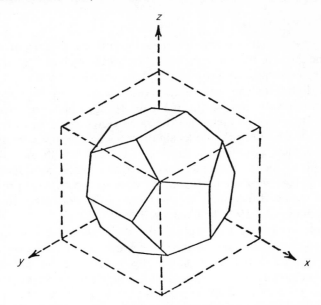

Figure 10.11   Canonical orientation of a dodecahedron
inside the unit cube

Denser systems of views; selection

If we take denser sets of isoline directions, which though not regular may be
either (a) carefully packed, as in certain types of codes (see Section 10.3.3
below) or (b) the results of random sampling, we soon come to the point
where we do *not* want to see all the views, only the more interesting ones.
Automatic techniques for selection, discussed later, now become of considerable importance. We want to push as much down into the computer as we can.

10.3.2 Prechosen direct views of four-dimensional point clouds

When the data are four-dimensional, matters are somewhat more complicated.

Collections of regularly-spaced views

The elementary approach is one in which the families of planes parallel to a
coordinate plane are taken as the isoplanes of views. Since there are $\binom{4}{2} = 6$
coordinate planes, there will be 6 such views. These views can then be
presented in a lower-triangular configuration, which is a generalization of the

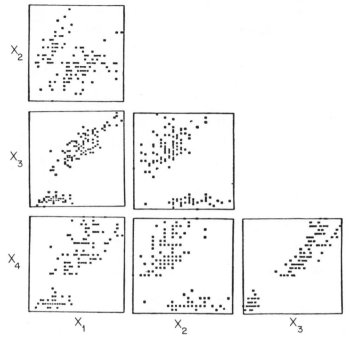

Figure 10.12 Generalized draughtsman's views of the four-dimensional Anderson iris data

draughtsman's views, since every adjacent pair of plots share a coordinate axis. Figure 10.12 shows a collection of six views for the full four-dimensional Anderson iris data. Alternatively, we can make the complete 4 × 4 array of plots, so that all the plots involving a particular coordinate line up. One penalty for doing this is that on fixed-size paper the plots must all be smaller to accommodate the extra row and column required. Hartigan (1975) suggests using the diagonal positions in such an array for histograms of single variables. The present authors would probably prefer rootograms or 'rootagons' in the diagonal positions tilted by 45°, much as in multiwindow displays (see Section 11.3.1 below).

Six views are clearly insufficient for four-dimensional data, so we seek larger sets of views 'regularly' spaced in four dimensions. As before, we can begin with a regular polytope and use a maximal set of nonparallel two-dimensional boundaries. The '600-cell', for instance, has 1200 two-dimensional faces. (It also has 120 vertices and 600 three-dimensional boundary cells—see Sommerville, 1929, or Coxeter, 1963.) If formulae are available for the vertices but not for the faces, we can run through pairs of vertices and select a set of maximally separated pairs.

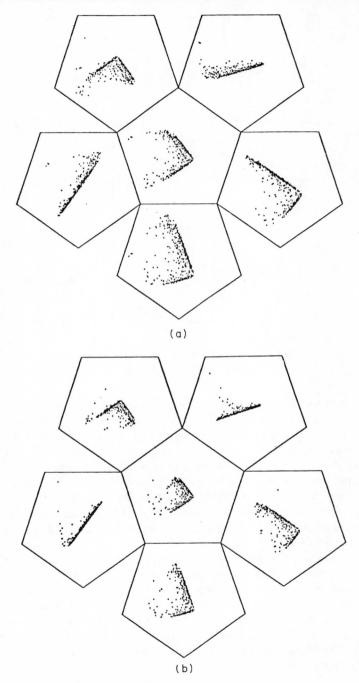

(a)

(b)

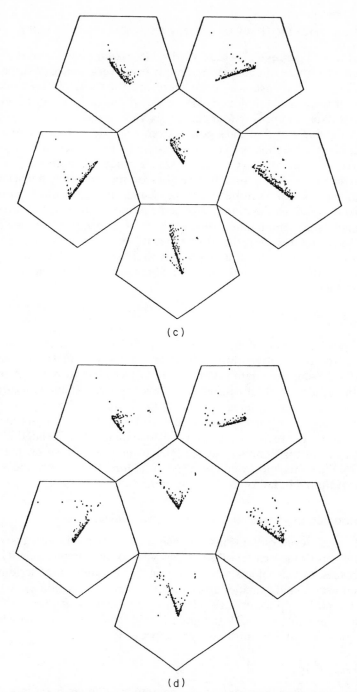

(c)

(d)

Figure 10.13 Dodeca-views of four-dimensional particle physics data (500 points); (a) coordinates 1, 2 and 3; (b) coordinates 1, 2 and 4; (c) coordinates 1, 3 and 4; (d) coordinates 2, 3 and 4

Another way to get regularly separated views in four dimensions is to take a good scheme for three dimensions and apply it to every choice of three out of four coordinates. For instance, since there are four ways to leave out one coordinate if we work with dodeca-views, we will have 24 views of our four-dimensional data, comprising four sets of six views each. Figure 10.13 shows such a set of views of 500 data points from a particle-physics experiment. Each data point corresponds to a single instance of a particular kind of collision between two elementary particles which produces three new particles. For each reaction, the momentum vectors of the resulting particles were measured, and a set of identities based on symmetries and conservation laws were applied to reduce the nine components of momentum to four quantities or coordinates that completely describe the event. The apparently two distinct arms in these pictures correspond to types of reactions well understood by particle physicists; it is the straying points that are of greater interest, since they suggest rarer events whose explanations might lead to refinements in the underlying theory.

Linked views

A type of presentation usefully possible only for four-dimensional data arises when we place two scatter plots, one of (x, y) and one of (u, v) near each other and represent each data vector (x, y, u, v) as a line from (x, y) in one to (u, v) in the other. Whether confusion will ever by overridden by indication is not very clear. There is some reason to think that connecting (x, y) to a 'centre' of the (u, v)s corresponding to (x, y) and its neighbours may have promise. Clearly the reciprocal display will also be needed. Related ideas and other approaches for thinning out the lines to be drawn have been explored recently by Diaconis and Friedman (1980). Figure 10.14 reproduces one of their thinned plots based on a study of human diabetes.

10.3.3 Automatic view selection in still higher dimensions

For data in several dimensions we can make triangular arrays of two-coordinates-at-a-time scatter plots. However, as the dimensionality of the data increases, two problems arise, one minor, the other more serious. First, the plots must be made smaller and smaller if they are to fit on a single page; second, and more importantly, they become less and less representative of the totality of all possible views. With increasing dimensionality the need for good methods of selection becomes ever more pressing.

Random selection

In dimensions higher than four, only the simplest regular polytopes exist, so we look elsewhere for additional collections of candidate views.

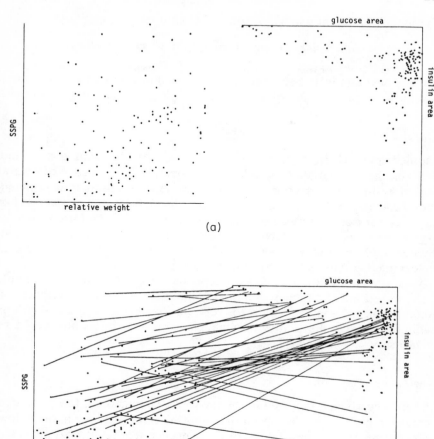

Figure 10.14 (a) Four-dimensional diabetes data—two variables in each plot; (b) linked views (From Diaconis and Friedman, 1980. Reproduced by permission of the authors)

One approach is just to generate random views, and select those that differ enough from each other in direction. Here we would, presumably, measure the greatest angle between each new possibility and all those already accepted, and accept this possibility if the minimum of these greatest angles is large enough. In p dimensions, the isoflats for a two-dimensional view will be $(p - 2)$-dimensional, so we would need $p - 2$ vectors to define an isoflat directly. However, we will likely take the easier route and define an isoflat in terms of its orthogonal two-space by choosing two vectors. The natural criterion for 'different enough' is probably based on

$$minimum \; \{largest \; angle \; (new \; isoflat, \; previous \; isoflat)\}$$
(previous isoflats)

with any new candidate being accepted if this minimum exceeds a prechosen constant, or a percentage point in the distribution of angles between views.

Codes

Another approach is to start with a code (e.g., MacWilliams and Sloane, 1977) on the appropriate hypersphere. As usually defined, a code consists of a set of well-packed directions, or points, on the $(p-1)$-sphere in p dimensions. From such a set of directions, we can form all pairs, and proceed as just suggested for isoflats defined by pairs of random vectors. Unfortunately, for large p and even a moderately large code, this search becomes computationally burdensome. It may prove desirable to confine our attention to pairs of vectors making fairly large angles with one another.

A stack of parallel $(p-2)$-flats corresponds to a point on the unit manifold of the $(p-2)$nd Grassmann manifold (Jenner 1963) over the p sphere. It would be nice if someone were to work out 'codes' directly on such unit manifolds so that the search through pairs of code directions would be unnecessary.

How far have we come?

All this suggests that the need for 'many views examined but few presented' increases rapidly as the dimension rises. Indeed, as we shall see in the following two chapters, the possibilities of using even carefully selected individual views as candidates become rapidly more and more constricted. Our conclusions at this point are: (a) if we are to deal with point clouds in more than three dimensions, prechosen sets of direct views seem unlikely to show us what we would like to see, and (b) even in three dimensions where we can surely do the simplest cases, it is uncertain how well we can treat complicated ones with prechosen direct views.

REFERENCES

Anderson, E. (1935) The irises of the Gaspe Peninsula. *Bull. Amer. Iris Soc.*, **59**, 2–5.
Anderson, E. (1936) The species problem in Iris. *Ann. Mo. bot. Gdn.*, **23**, 511–25.
Andrews, D. F., Gnanadesikan, R., and Warner, J. L. (1973) Methods for assessing multivariate normality. In Krishnaiah, P. R. (ed.) (1973), *Multivariate Analysis III*. New York: Academic Press.
Cleveland, W. S., Kettenring, J. R. and McGill, R. (1976) Graphical methods in multivariate analysis and regression. Talk presented at meeting of Am. Pub. Health Assoc.

Coxeter, H. S. M. (1961) *Introduction to Geometry*. (pp. 289–290, stereographic projection). New York: Wiley.

Coxeter, H. S. M. (1963). *Regular Polytopes* (2nd edn). New York: Macmillan.

Diaconis, P. and Friedman, J. H. (1980) *M* and *N* plots. *Standford Linear Accelerator Center Report PUB-2495*.

Fisher, R. A. (1936) The use of multiple measurements in taxonomic problems. *Ann. Eugen.*, **7**, 179–88. Reprinted in Fisher, R. A. (1950). *Contributions to Mathematical Statistics*. New York: Wiley.

Gnanadesikan, R. and Kettenring, J. R. (1972) Robust estimates, residuals, and outlier detection with multiresponse data. *Biometrics*, **28**, 81–124.

Gnanadesikan, R. (1977) *Methods for Statistical Data Analysis of Multivariate Observations*. New York: Wiley.

Goldman, J. (1976) Detection in the presence of spherically symmetric random vectors. *IEEE Trans. Inf. Th.*, **IT-22**, 52–9.

Hartigan, J. A. (1975) Printer graphics for clustering. *J. Statist. Comput. Simul.*, **4**, 187–213.

Jenner, W. E. (1963) *Rudiments of Algebraic Geometry*. (Chapter VI: Plücker Coordinates and Grassmann varieties.) Oxford: Oxford University Press.

MacWilliams, F. J. and Sloane, N. J. A. (1977) *The Theory of Error-correcting Codes*. (Chapter 2 for simple codes.) Amsterdam: North Holland.

Mosteller, F. and Tukey, J. W. (1977) *Data Analysis and Regression*. Reading, Mass.: Addison-Wesley.

Sommerville, D. M. Y. (1929, republished in 1958 edition) *An Introduction to the Geometry of N Dimensions*. (Chapter 10 for regular polytopes.) New York: Dover Publications.

Tukey, J. W. and Tukey, P. A. (1977) Aide-memoire for: Methods for direct and indirect graphic display for data sets in 3 and more dimensions. University of Western Ontario, November, 1977.

CHAPTER 11

Data-Driven View Selection; Agglomeration and Sharpening

P. A. Tukey, *Bell Laboratories, Murray Hill, New Jersey, U.S.A.*
J. W. Tukey, *Princeton University, Princeton, New Jersey, U.S.A.*
and *Bell Laboratories, Murray Hill, New Jersey, U.S.A.*

11.1 THE NEED FOR CAREFUL SELECTION

11.1.1. Cap sizes

We have stressed that to obtain a comprehensive collection of prechosen direct views of a data cloud, the number of views that we require increases dramatically with the number of dimensions. The reason for this is closely connected with the fact that the hypersurface area of a unit hypersphere increases rapidly with dimension. To explore this quantitatively, let us suppose that there exists a two-view of our data cloud that we would like to look at if we knew in advance everything about the data—a view that would reveal whatever interesting structure is there—but in our ignorance we look at a different view. Let us call the angle between the two views the *squint angle*. A good collection of prechosen views is one which insures at least one small squint angle to the (arbitrary) 'correct' view. It is natural to ask, then, what fraction of all possible views come close to a given fixed view (in terms of squint angles)?

We are interested in two-views, of course, but to approach this question we first consider the simpler case of one-views. A fixed one-view corresponds to a unit vector or a point on the unit sphere, and all the views that make a squint angle of $\theta°$ or less with it constitute a circular cap of half-angle $\theta°$. What fraction of a sphere is contained in a cap covering all directions within $\theta°$ of a specified direction? Table 11.1 gives some illustrative values. Table 11.2 gives some angles for illustrative fractions.

Suppose that we are able to do a good job of spreading 100-odd directions over the two-sphere in three-space so that all directions are within an angle A of at least one of the 100-odd directions. The corresponding caps will overlap by amounts that will depend on our ingenuity in spreading out the directions. Suppose that the average number of the 100-odd directions within angle A of

Table 11.1 Fraction of a full $(p - 1)$-sphere within θ of any specified direction (denominators to nearest integer)

	$\theta = 5°$	$\theta = 10°$	$\theta = 15°$	$\theta = 30°$	$\theta = 45°$
$p = 3$	1/526	1/132	1/59	1/15	1/7
$p = 5$	1/92 196	1/5 806	1/1 162	1/78	1/17
$p = 7$	1/14 560 051	1/230 773	1/20 748	1/369	1/40
$p = 9$	1/2 190 180 925	1/8 739 840	1/353 362	1/1 673	1/90

Table 11.2 Cap (half) angles to give specified fractions of the $(p - 1)$-sphere

	1/100 000	1/10 000	1/1 000	1/100	1/50	1/20	1/10	1/5
$p = 3$	0.26°	0.8°	2.6°	8.1°	16.3°	28.8°	36.9°	53.1°
$p = 5$	4.9°	8.7°	15.6°	28.1°	33.7°	43.2°	52.5°	64.8°
$p = 7$	11.5°	17.0°	25.2°	37.9°	43.2°	51.6°	59.6°	69.7°
$p = 9$	17.5°	23.7°	32.1°	44.3°	49.1°	56.7°	63.7°	72.6°

a random point is $1 + \delta$, so that δ measures the average overlap. Then

$$area\ of\ sphere = \frac{100\text{-}odd}{1 + \delta}\ (area\ of\ cap\ of\ \tfrac{1}{2}\text{-}angle\ A)$$

and we see from Table 11.2 that if $100\text{-}odd = 100(1 + \delta)$, then we can make A about 8°.

To do as well on the four-sphere in five dimensions would require 10 000-odd points, on the six-sphere in seven dimensions would require 800 000-odd points, and on the eight-sphere in nine dimensions we would require 50 000 000-odd points to come within 8.1° of all directions. We can hardly afford to come very close in higher dimensions!

These calculations are for one-views; our original problem was for two-dimensional views. How many planes will it take to get within $A°$ of all planes? For $p = 3$ the answer is the same as for directions, since there is a one-to-one correspondence between planes and vectors. For larger p, this does not happen, and the situation worsens even faster. To get within $A°$, the cap fractions are proportional to A^{p-1} for directions, but proportional to A^{2p-4} for planes.

11.12 Ways out

We now recognize that getting close to a desired view in higher dimensions with a prechosen sequence of views will require more trial views than we are likely to be able to afford to make or would care to look at. What are other possible strategies? Four kinds of alternatives will be discussed; some of them may need to be used in combination. We can either:

* Find a data-driven view-hunting technique that does well when started from a moderate or perhaps reasonably large squint angle. Some methods that iteratively 'extremize' a criterion have a reasonable hope of doing well from a relatively remote start. We will discuss 'projection pursuit' shortly.

* Find special starting views (determined from the data) that are especially likely to give small squint angles. These include some of the more familiar classical techniques, but they are of surprisingly limited usefulness.

* Modify the data cloud so that wider squint angles will show us as much or more. Two possibilities, both to be discussed under 'sharpening' below, are to clear away, or weaken, low-density areas, and to move points toward regions of higher apparent density.

* Find an effective way to display more aspects simultaneously. This will be the major thrust of Chapter 12.

If we are to be effective in 'looking' at higher-dimensional data sets, we will need to employ some or all of these kinds of techniques.

11.2 SELECTING DIRECT VIEWS

We now turn to various techniques that are available to help us select views. Some are based on judgment, others are automatic.

11.2.1 Composites, coordinates, etc.

To select a view means to select two functions of our data to use as x and y coordinates for a display. Our first task will nearly always be to consider what linear combinations of our initial coordinates are suitable to use as display variables.

It is usually far from obvious that the various numerical aspects of the data (i.e., coordinates of the data points) we consider are equivalent—whether or not their units of measurement are the same, and whether they are of equal importance. (The doctrine of the 'unthinking statistician' is here, as always, very dangerous.) If there is a general rule, we suspect it is that 'coordinates come with at least a rough order of priority'. If so, our display practices should take advantage of this, for instance in the choice of front and back variables in Section 10.3, or in the assignment of aspects in trees in Chapter 12.

When trying to decide what our displays are supposed to do, we need to be clear about which changes of coordinate system are thought to produce equally appropriate descriptions. It is from the appropriate views that we wish to select. On the one hand, we may conclude that

(1)   nothing else is equally appropriate ('This is it!'),

or we may decide to allow

(2)   only location and scale changes on the given coordinates ('These are *the* aspects, well-measured.')
(3)   only monotone re-expressions of the given coordinates ('These are *the* aspects, at least ordinally measured.')
(4)   orthogonal rotations of the given coordinates ('There really is a Euclidean metric that is meaningful.')
(5)   orthogonal rotations of (linearly) adjusted coordinates (adjusted individually, perhaps to constant variance—or globally, perhaps to variance one and covariance zero). Here orthogonality's excuse is that it preserves adjustment, at least approximately.
(6)   affine transformations of the given coordinates, that is, arbitrary linear transformations, including origin shifts ('Any linear combination is as good as any other.')
(7)   affine transformations of monotonically re-expressed coordinates. (This needs to be developed further.)

We note that principal components analysis fits into category (4). It will be discussed briefly below, along with some similar techniques.

We will not elaborate on these alternatives here except to say that choice among them is important, depends on the circumstances of a particular application, and deserves much more attention than it usually gets!

11.2.2 Judgment composites and residuals

As is so often the case in multiresponse analysis, we should be prepared to begin by using judgment, based at this early stage on the names of the initial variables and our general knowledge about them. Only when judgment does not help us enough should we turn to automatic choices.

If, for instance, four of the variables seem likely to be highly correlated with the Gross National Product, we almost certainly ought to replace these four by (a) a linear combination of the four with coefficients chosen by judgment, and (b), (c), and (d) three (or possibly all four) of the residual variables arising from (robust/resistant) regression of the original variables on this composite.

11.2.3 Pursuing a criterion

When we have exhausted our judgment for forming composites and we turn to automatic view-selection algorithms, the simplest approach to *think* about is to define a criterion or index or objective function that measures some appropriate kind of interesting structure in a view, and then to pursue views that correspond to the extremes of the criterion. (Other kinds of algorithms *might* do even better.)

If we think of the criterion function as defining a curved surface over the space of possible views, then this process can be carried out by choosing one or a number of starting points (initial views) and moving 'uphill' by modifying each initial view step by step until no further reasonable amount of improvement is attainable. 'Finding good hill-climbing directions might exploit special characteristics of the criterion function or the data cloud, or might be done by a general-purpose optimization program. In either case, the calculations will almost certainly be done by computer.

Except in the cases of certain simple and rather uninteresting criterion functions (e.g. maximum variance in a projection, which leads to principal components), we will want to try a number of starting views with the hope of finding and exploring local maxima of the criterion function. One simple route based on random starts involves (a) the highest criterion value encountered to date in the process, (b) a discount factor (maybe 88%), (c) choosing random views as candidates for new starts, (d) forgetting those with criterion value below (*highest to date*) × (*discount factor*), (e) hill-climbing from those not forgotten.

11.2.4   The Friedman–Tukey projection-pursuit algorithm

Friedman and Tukey (1974) have proposed and implemented a *projection-pursuit* algorithm involving general hill climbing. The index of interesting structure that they use is one which is intended to measure *clottedness*, and they employ a general-optimization computer program to change a trial projection into one which locally maximizes the index of interest. The algorithm can work with one- or two- (or in principle higher-) dimensional projections.

Careful choice of the index is crucial. For a one-view defined by a vector $\mathbf{v}$, they use

$$I(\mathbf{v}) = s(\mathbf{v})d(\mathbf{v}).$$

The first factor $s(\mathbf{v})$ measures overall spread and is taken to be an $\alpha\%$ trimmed standard deviation. The second factor $d(\mathbf{v})$ describes 'average local density', and is defined as

$$d(\mathbf{v}) = \sum_{|r_{ij}|<R} f(r_{ij})$$

where r_{ij} is the distance between the ith and jth points in the view, R is a constant, and f is a symmetric function that decreases smoothly to zero at $\pm R$. A typical f is sketched in Figure 11.1. Properly tuned, the index is a smooth enough function of $\mathbf{v}$ to make the optimization program work well.

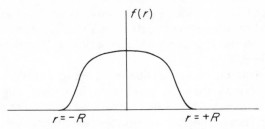

Figure 11.1   A typical f for measuring average
local density in projection-pursuit

The index $I(\mathbf{v})$ is a measure of clottedness in the sense that it describes the degree to which the data points in the view are concentrated locally [$d(\mathbf{v})$ large] while at the same time expanded globally [$s(\mathbf{v})$ large]. Experience suggests that such projections tend to be unusually interesting to researchers. (Kruskal, 1969 and 1972, describes another algorithm with similar objectives but a different index, one that he calls an *index of condensation* which is essentially the coefficient of variation of the interpoint distances in the view.)

The function $I(\mathbf{v})$ can be generalized in several obvious ways to a clotted-ness index $I(\mathbf{u}, \mathbf{v})$ for the two-view corresponding to the plane spanned by $\mathbf{u}$ and $\mathbf{v}$. (See Friedman and Tukey, 1974, for details.)

The projection index $I(\mathbf{v})$ can have several local maxima. In some optimiza-tion applications, multiplicity of local maxima is considered a nuisance, since only the global maximum is sought. However, in this application where we are

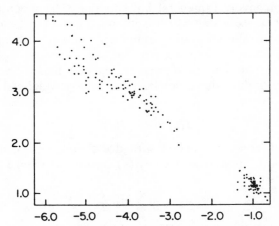

Figure 11.2   Projection pursuit two-view of the 150 points of four-dimensional iris data (From Friedman and Tukey, 1974. Reproduced by permission of The Institute of Electrical and Electronic Engineers, Inc. © 1974 IEEE)

studying data with complex structure, several local maxima may correspond to potentially interesting views, and their multiplicity can be an advantage. We will certainly want to start the algorithm at several different trial views to try to find several local maxima.

Every pair of solutions from the one-dimensional version of the algorithm, or every single solution from the two-dimensional version, provides a scatter plot or two-view of the data cloud for inspection and interpretation. When clumps of points with identifiable substructure are found, it is usually wise to split the data into parts for separate study by projection-pursuit. This process can be iterated until no further structure is found.

Iris data example

It is not surprising that, when applied to the full 150 points of Anderson's four-dimensional iris data, projection-pursuit produced the view shown in Figure 11.2, in which one species of iris is clearly separated from the other two. In fact, that species is so well separated in the four-dimensional space that it will be isolated by any reasonable method.

When applied separately to the 100 points of the two species that are hard to separate, projection-pursuit produced Figure 11.3. There may not seem to be much visible clottedness here, but when species identifiers are put on the points in Figure 11.4 it becomes clear that projection-pursuit—*using no species information at all*—has produced a view that separates the two species nearly as well as the first two Fisher linear discriminant coordinates, which are

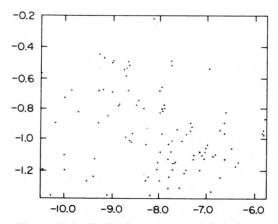

Figure 11.3   Projection-pursuit two-view of 100 points for two iris species (From Friedman and Tukey, 1974. Reproduced by permission of The Institute of Electrical and Electronic Engineers, Inc. © 1974 IEEE)

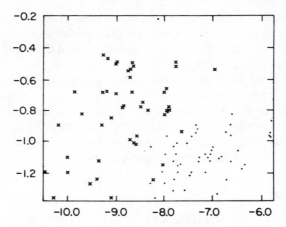

Figure 11.4 Copy of Figure 11.3 with iris species identified by plotting character (From Friedman and Tukey, 1974. Reproduced by permission of The Institute of Electrical and Electronic Engineers, Inc. © 1974 IEEE)

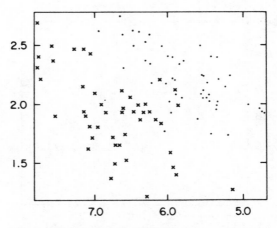

Figure 11.5 Linear discriminant two-view of 100 iris data points (From Friedman and Tukey, 1974. Reproduced by permission of The Institute of Electrical and Electronic Engineers, Inc. © 1974 IEEE)

plotted in Figure 11.5, even though the Fisher procedure uses the full species information.

Gaussian simplex example

Another example where conventional approaches do not succeed follows a pattern suggested by Sammon (1969) where samples of size 65 from a spherical Gaussian distribution are centred at the vertices of a regular 15-vertex simplex in 14 dimensions. As Friedman and Tukey show, principal components are of no help whatsoever here. The histogram in Figure 11.6 of the projections of the 975 points onto the largest principal axis does not reveal the clustering.

However, even one-dimensional projection-pursuit takes the example apart step-by-step. Figure 11.7a is a histogram along the one-view of a projection-pursuit solution, and following it are the first few in a series of histograms that show the results of applying projection-pursuit to successively smaller clusters isolated in earlier plots in the sequence. See Figures 11.7(b)–(e).

Particle physics example

To show a more substantial real-data application, we reproduce one more of Friedman and Tukey's examples which analyses a set of 500 data-points from a particle-physics experiment. The data are similar to those described above in Section 10.3.2, except that we now consider collisions which yield four resultant particles having 12 components of momentum reducing to a set of seven-dimensional data.

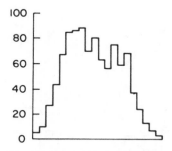

Figure 11.6 Histogram of first principal coordinate of 14-dimensional simplex data (975 points) (From Friedman and Tukey, 1974. Reproduced by permission of The Institute of Electrical and Electronic Engineers, Inc. © 1974 IEEE)

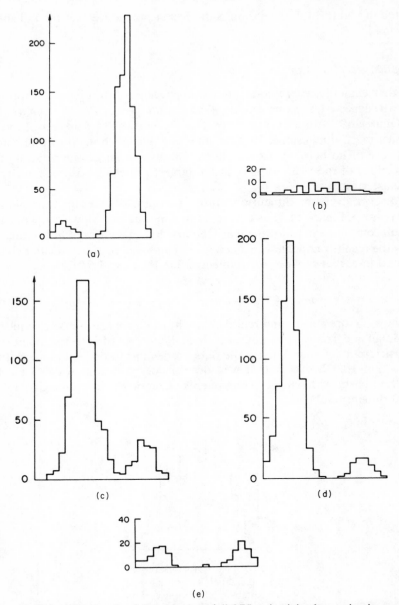

Figure 11.7(a)   Histogram of simplex data (all 975 points) in the projection-pursuit one-view; (b) projection-pursuit one-view of the left-hand cluster of 65 points from Figure 11.7(a); (c) projection-pursuit one-view of the right-hand cluster of 910 points from Figure 11.7(a); (d) projection-pursuit one-view of the left-hand cluster of 780 points from Figure 11.7(c); (e) projection-pursuit one-view of the right-hand cluster of 130 points from Figure 11.7(c) (From Friedman and Tukey, 1974. Reproduced by permission of The Institute of Electrical and Electronic Engineers, Inc. © 1974 IEEE)

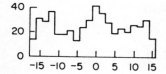

Figure 11.8 First principal component one-view of 500 points of seven-dimensional particle-physics data (From Friedman and Tukey, 1974. Reproduced by permission of The Institute of Electrical and Electronic Engineers, Inc. © 1974 IEEE)

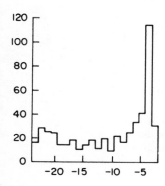

Figure 11.9 One-dimensional projection-pursuit view of data from Figure 11.8 (From Friedman and Tukey, 1974. Reproduced by permission of The Institute of Electrical and Electronic Engineers, Inc. © 1974 IEEE)

Figures 11.8 and 11.9 show the one-dimensional principal components solution and a one-dimensional projection-pursuit solution, respectively, and Figures 11.10 and 11.11 show the two-dimensional solutions. In both cases it is clear the projection-pursuit is the approach that has uncovered substantially more structure.

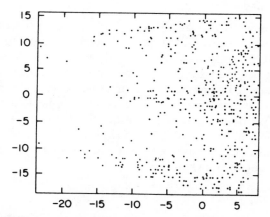

Figure 11.10 Two-view of particle-physics data defined by first two principal components (From Friedman and Tukey, 1974. Reproduced by permission of The Institute of Electrical and Electronic Engineers, Inc. © 1974 IEEE)

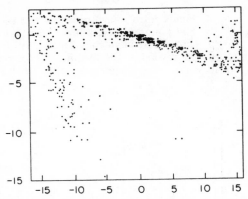

Figure 11.11   Projection-pursuit two-view of particle-physics data (From Friedman and Tukey, 1974. Reproduced by permission of The Institute of Electrical and Electronic Engineers, Inc. © 1974 IEEE)

11.2.5 Quadratic criterion approaches

If we pursue a criterion that is a quadratic function of the data, we may be able to find the linear combination of our variables that maximizes it by solving a problem in linear algebra. This can often be done using commonly available computer software.

Principal coordinates—Princos

The classical thought is to take the sample variance in the one-view as the criterion and to seek a series of solution directions, constraining each to be orthogonal to all previous ones. The result is ordinary principal components and the solution is given by the eigenanalysis of the variance–covariance matrix of the data. This has been known to work, in the sense that taking pairs of the first few principal components as the coordinates of views has been revealing. We doubt, however, whether this happens very often, for the reasons mentioned in Section 10.2.2. In fact, if the data have been sphered in advance, the covariance matrix is a multiple of the identity matrix and principal components gets us nowhere.

Dendral components

At least one other sort of approach seems promising, when modified to gain enough robustness/resistance. We describe it here both incompletely and in a non-robust form. Suppose the initial variables, $y_1, y_2, \ldots, y_p$, have been converted to zero average and unit variance. Let y_i and y_j be the most highly correlated pair. Replace them by suitable multiples of $y_i + y_j$ and $y_i - y_j$ (keeping track of the divisors required to preserve unit variance). Repeat until the largest correlation (which is also the largest covariance, since all the variances are 1) is smaller than a chosen stopping value. Tag each final variable with the product of the divisors used in its construction, order the final variables in accordance with these products, and use the first few of them as coordinates for views.

Simplified components—Simcos

For better interpretability of views and other analyses, there is often value in modifying otherwise plausible linear combinations so that they have simple coefficients (0, +1 and −1, for instance), but there is no reason to expect this to improve what we can see in the display.

Canonical analysis

When we are lucky enough to have a meaningful classification of the data points and we can calculate variance–covariance matrices both within and among classes, the corresponding eigenvectors, those associated with the determinantal equation

$$\left| \begin{pmatrix} among \\ var\text{–}cov \end{pmatrix} - \lambda \begin{pmatrix} within \\ var\text{–}cov \end{pmatrix} \right| = 0,$$

often lead to revealing views. (It is often desirable to sphere the pooled within-class components, e.g., Aston, Healy and Lipton, 1957, Delaney and Healy, 1964). A view using, say, the 1st and 2nd components is often made considerably more revealing by a slight rotation. These ideas are really a refinement and extension of Fisher's linear discriminant analysis. Gains from using robust/resistant analogues of *var* and *cov* seem likely. (See Mosteller and Tukey, 1977, for *cobs* and *bars*, or Gnanadesikan and Kettenring, 1972.)

Moral

It doesn't seem easy to find a *quadratic* criterion that does a good job of identifying those characteristics of a view that make it interesting. (In particular, the sensitivity of second moments to outliers can only leave us fearful.)

11.2.6 Other components

A number of other methods have been proposed over the years for selecting useful components, or linear combinations, of the variables. Although they have generally not been conceived as graphical methods, any process which selects and orders components provides a source of two-views. We briefly mention a few of them.

With p-dimensional data having rank less than p, many factor analysts would recommend seeking out 'simple structure' (e.g. Thurstone, 1947). They do this mainly to search for interpretable components, but we can always try plotting the ith factor against the jth, again for the first few values of i and j. We guess this would work slightly more often than principal components do.

For problems with many coordinates, it seems slightly more promising to use forms of factor analysis that focus on finding clusters of coordinates, a process which can be called *cluster factor analysis* (e.g. Hunter, 1981).

If one likes more classical factor-analysis techniques, then either varimax or quartimax rotations can be considered.

Robust/resistant versions of principal components have received some recent attention. It is true that in the presence of serious outliers they will come closer to achieving the objective of ordinary principal components (to describe the general ellipsoidal shape of the point cloud) and in the absence of outliers the two approaches should lead to similar results. But again we assert that such an objective does not generally produce the most useful plots.

An alternate approach to studying the shape of a cloud of points would begin by seeking one or more linear combinations of the original coordinates that appear to be highly non-Gaussian (Gnanadesikan, 1977, p. 142). Before using such an approach, it will be wise (a) to examine pictures like those in Day (1969), who warns of finding spurious structure, and (b) to conduct some experimental sampling studies on pure-Gaussian data to see what sorts of patterns turn up and how often, under the null hypothesis of no structure.

11.3 AGGLOMERATION AND SHARPENING

We now turn to ways of so altering the collection of points we are to display that we are more likely to see the underlying structure even with wide squint angles. We are driven to such actions by the limitations of both prechosen views and data-dependent views as we currently judge them. We expect these techniques to be used in conjunction with view-selection techniques.

11.3.1 Agglomerated views and agglomerated clouds

Instead of plotting each data point individually, we may decide to plot 'points' of different 'sizes', each one representing a different number of original data points, displayed by a character of suitable intensity, and plotted at the centre of gravity of the original points that it represents. This process of *agglomeration* is related to certain kinds of population-density maps made by geographers.

Numerosity as driving agglomeration

If we have 'too many' points, no picture can do a good job of showing us how they lie. More than 250 points (numerosity E or greater, cf. Section 10.1.2) is almost sure to be too many; more than 80 (numerosity D or greater) is quite likely to be too many. If we are willing to have, for instance, *large points* (each corresponding to about k^2 original points), *medium points* (each corresponding to k), and *small points* (each corresponding to a single point), we can usually choose k and an algorithm for agglomeration that will bring us down to a reasonable number of plotted points (C, or a low D). We may then use distinctive characters of suitably graded impact for large, medium, and small points to produce a useful picture.

Agglomeration in the view

One way to use agglomeration is to consider only the two front, or view, variables, combining points in accordance with their inter-point distances in the view. As long as a single view, well enough selected, meets our needs, this is likely to be the agglomeration of choice.

Figure 11.12 shows the 500 points of four-body final-state particle-physics data discussed earlier under projection-pursuit. Here we have re-expressed

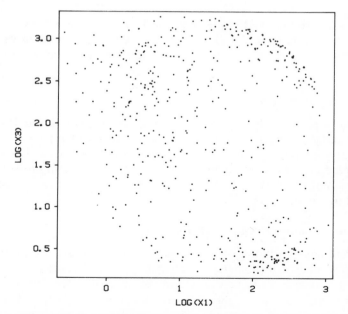

Figure 11.12   A two-view defined by ($\log x_1$, $\log x_3$) of the 500 points of seven-dimensional particle-physics data

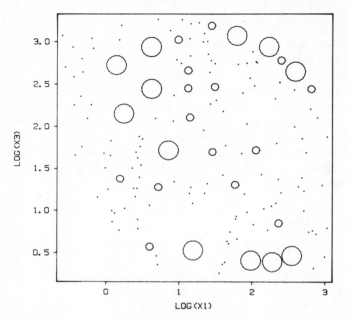

Figure 11.13   An agglomerated view of Figure 11.12 (circles
represent 5 and 25 points)

the data as logarithms, and plotted the third variable (out of seven) against
the first. The companion plot (Figure 11.13) is an agglomerated version in
which the large circles represent 25 points and the smaller circles represent 5
points each.

Agglomeration in the cloud

Alternatively, particularly if we plan to look at two or more selected views, we
can use distances in the p-dimensional cloud (involving all of $y_1, y_2, \ldots y_p$) as a
basis for agglomeration. This gives an agglomeration wholly independent of
view. Instead of circles, we might choose to plot ellipses and crosses of suitable shape and orientation to suggest the ellipticity and orientation of the
groups of points being agglomerated.

Cellulations, contour-driven subdivisions, etc.

Rather than agglomerating on a distance-controlled basis, we might try to
divide a view-plane (or perhaps a three-space) into cells, and give a summary
character for each cell. As before, we would make the impact value of each
character relate suitably to the number of points replaced, and we might
locate this character at or near the centre of gravity of those points within the

cell. (Cellulation in three dimensions requires many points; cellulation in four or more would require more points than we are likely to have.)

We could use a rectangular cellulation with cells of equal size, particularly if the data cloud has been sphered, but for the simpler patterns of distribution we should be able to do better. If we could approximately contour the (smoothed) apparent density of the points in a view, we might do very well by using a selected sequence of density contours and a selection of trajectories (approximately) orthogonal to these contours to define a contour-driven cellulation. Alternatively, we could base the contours on a smoothed version of a back variable (cf. Section 12.1.2 for smoothing).

Multiwindow displays

Another way to use a cellulation is to place a *window* in each cell, and through it to view some other aspect or aspects of the points that fall within the cell. if x and y are the variables which determine the cellulation, and z and w are two back variables, each window can show, for instance:

* the corresponding local distribution of z, perhaps as a rootagon, or
* a two-view or (z, w) scatterplot.

Figure 11.14 is a multiwindow display of the 500 four-body data points

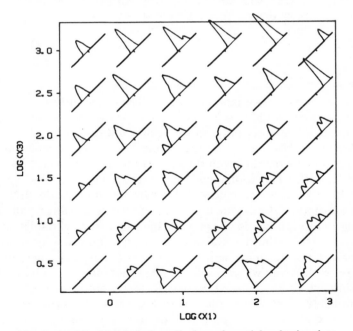

Figure 11.14 Multiwindow display of particle-physics data showing rootagons of log x_7 windowed by (log x_1, log x_3)

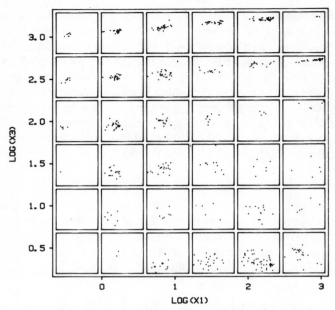

Figure 11.15   Multiwindow display of particle-physics data
showing $(\log x_4, \log x_7)$ windowed by $(\log x_1, \log x_3)$

with the same two front variables as before. The distributions of the values of
$\log x_7$ for the points within each (x, x_3) cell are shown as rootagons. (A rootagon is simply a frequency polygon with cell count re-expressed on a square-
root scale, thus stabilizing the variance of the counts. A frequency polygon, in
turn, is like a histogram but with the tops of the bars connected by lines and
the bars left off.) The rootagons have been tilted to enable easy visual
scanning from window to window both vertically and horizontally.

The multiwindow display in Figure 11.15 shows a scatter plot of $\log x_4$
versus $\log x_7$ in each window, again for the same front variables (x_1, x_3). It
reveals many interesting facts about the relationships among these 4 variables. For instance, scanning across the top row (where x_3 is high) we see that
x_4 increases with x_1, but when x_3 is low, x_4 does not increase with x_1. There is a
relationship among these variables that is clearly not linear! (Of course, we
would probably want to see plots with the variables permuted in several
ways.) This quite effective portrayal of four-dimensional data has been
achieved by giving up precise position in the two front variables in order to
accommodate information on two of the back variables.

11.3.2 Balloon densities

One of the most prominent and useful characteristics of point clouds is their pattern of variation in 'density' from place to place. The notion of density can be regarded as graphical in its own right, but in addition, as we shall show, measures of density can be useful for guiding the construction of certain displays.

In terms of observed data, density in a neighbourhood is necessarily thought of as some form of the ratio (*count/volume*). In one dimension we tend to count contents of bins or cells of fixed size; in two dimensions we often simply make scatter plots and rely on the eye to merge the points into density patterns where possible (usually losing any useful distinction among regions of extremely high density). What should we do in more dimensions? And indeed, how could we do better in two or one?

The number of potential combinations of subdivisions of the coordinates rises so fast with the number of dimensions that we cannot stick to 'counts in bins'. In fact it is difficult to do well with bins in so few as two dimensions. Clearly, bins are for the birds! There are several ways out, including methods based on Fourier techniques (Tarter and Raman, 1972), and kernel density estimation. We prefer a computationally efficient approach based on nearest neighbours.

Expanding spheres

We need not discard the notion of (*count/volume*) if we adopt the device of holding *count* fixed and varying *volume*, as depicted in Figure 11.16. Sitting at a data vector x, we can think of x as the centre of a sequence of expanding 'spheres' or balloons of any reasonable shape. Three possibilities for defining the distance from x to y are

(1) $r = [\sum (x_i - y_i)^2]^{1/2}$
(2) $r = \sum |x_i - y_i|$
(3) $r = \max |x_i - y_i|$.

according to which the 'spheres' of constant r are ordinary spheres (generalized to a suitable number of dimensions), generalized octahedra, and generalized cubes, respectively. We need not be as restricted as these examples suggest. There is no need in principle for a triangle axiom, so we could take, for instance,

(4) $r = \sum_i (1 - e^{-(x_i - y_i)^2})$

which, roughly, counts coordinates that are different, and thus, complementarily, focuses on how many aspects two data vectors share, completely or nearly.

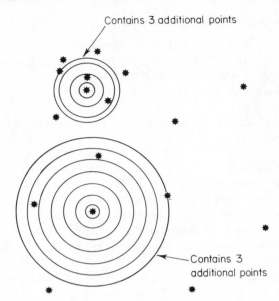

Contains 3 additional points

Contains 3 additional points

Figure 11.16   Using 'expanding balloons' to find
the three-balloon density at each of two points;
different 'volumes' but same count

The computational algorithm

If expanding spheres are to be of practical value, we need to be able to obtain
a list of the k nearest neighbours of each of our data vectors. Can we do this at
affordable cost? Since the publication of the KD-tree nearest-neighbour
algorithm by Friedman, Bentley, and Finkel (1975, 1977), the answer has
been 'yes'. The cost of computation need not increase as n^2 for n data vectors,
but only as a multiple of $n \log n$.

The algorithm that uses 'expanding spheres' or 'k nearest neighbours' to
obtain a density estimate then has the following form:

(1)   choose a reference point (which can be, but does not have to be, one of
       the data points)
(2)   find the kth nearest neighbouring data point
(3)   calculate the volume of the corresponding sphere
(4)   take k times the reciprocal of the volume as the estimated density or
       balloon density at the reference point. (Determination of densities up to
       a constant factor is adequate for most purposes.)

Such procedures suffer only from the inevitable problems with steep (or
rapidly changing) gradients of density; otherwise they work well over a wide

variety of circumstances (see, for instance, Loftsgaarden and Quesenberry, 1965).

One of the main competitors to balloon densities is the class of *kernel-density estimates* in which each data point is 'smeared' over a small range (preferably with a smooth smearing function which decreases to zero) and the smears are added together. (Going even further, one may want (a) to have a scale factor in the smearing function, (b) to adjust this at each test point to make the total equal some constant, and (c) to take the appropriate negative power of the scale factor as a *kernel-balloon density*, thus 'combining all the known principles of witchcraft'.)

To give some idea of the behaviour of balloon densities, Figure 11.17 shows a set of one-dimensional data and two density profiles: one a histogram

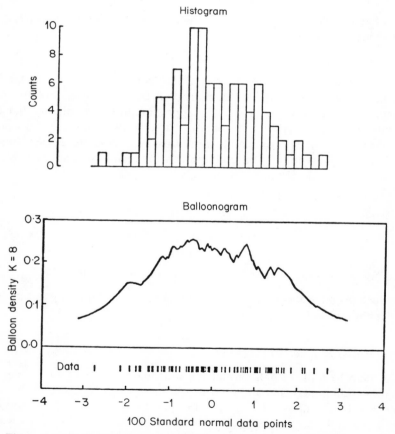

Figure 11.17   A histogram and a balloonogram as density profiles for a set of 100 data points

and the other a plot of 8-balloon densities, which we might call a *balloono-gram*. Although the real advantages of balloon densities are for higher-dimensional calculations, the balloonogram can be used as an alternative to the frequency polygon in certain applications (e.g. Sections 11.3.1 and 12.2.2). For these purposes we might want to smooth it further and to re-express it on a square-root vertical scale.

Distributional facts

If the data vectors are indeed a sample from some (continuous and smooth) multivariate distribution dF, we can label a set of spheres surrounding the reference point with values of V^*, where

$$V^* = volume \text{ (according to } dF \text{) within the given sphere.}$$

In repeated sampling, drawing n data vectors independently from dF each time, the joint distribution of

$$V_1^*, V_2^*, \ldots, V_n^*$$

is that of a constant times the order statistics from the unit rectangular distribution. (If dF is not continuous, there will be granularity, but the unit rectangular is still likely to be a good approximation.) It follows that the distribution of V_k^* is a multiple of a beta-distribution, which, for usefully large n and moderate k, is approximately a multiple of a chi-squared distribution with $2k$ degrees of freedom. Thus balloon densities can be expected to behave rather like reciprocals of multiples of χ_{2k}^2 values (Tukey, 1947).

Simplification

This of course means that if we look at logarithms of balloon densities we have

$$\log balloon\ density \approx constant - \log \chi_{2k}^2 \approx constant - \log (2k - \tfrac{1}{3}),$$

where the constant depends on the true sampling density at that point, but the term depending on k does not.

Looking across k; local dimensionality

We can plan to look at balloon-density information at a point for various values of k simultaneously, and thereby obtain a rough measure of the local dimensionality of our point cloud. If the point cloud is locally reasonably uniform in q dimensions—and quite thin in the others, the volumes V_k^* will be q-dimensional volumes, proportional to the qth power of the kth radius. Thus we expect

$$\log k\text{th } radius \approx constant + \frac{1}{q}\log(2k - \tfrac{1}{3}).$$

Fitting of this for several nearby points (with different constants) offers a way to determine the local effective q. (Whether extrapolation to log $(2k - 1/3) = 0$ gives us a more helpful measure of local density is not yet clear.)

Variations

It may be, in approaches like those of the last section, that looking at *annular densities*—apparent densities of spherical annuli (which are differences of consecutive expanding spheres)—will prove more useful than densities based on the spheres themselves.

We may wish to smooth our balloon densities somewhat. One way is to compute *cascade densities* which would entail first obtaining an ordinary balloon density at each data point, and then using sums of balloon densities of several nearest neighbours in place of a simple count in the formula (*count/volume*).

Instead of taking the reciprocal of a single value of V_k^*/k, we can combine over several k in many ways (maximum, high hinge, etc.), or we might do better to combine the values of $V_k^* - V_{k-1}^*$ similarly. If we combine these values by using something like the maximum or the high hinge (third quartile), then we will obtain *low-side* densities which may give more effective ways of assessing loneliness or isolation.

On the other hand, if we use the minimum or the low hinge we will have *high-side densities*. Both high-side and low-side densities may be more useful than ordinary balloon densities for application in sharpening, described below.

11.3.3 Sharpening

We should never feel that our displays must be 'formally true' to the data we represent. We want 'true messages' from our displays, which often means displaying an altered form of the data. (If this seems like a radical idea, consider the removal of outliers, or the smoothing of time-series data, or the plotting of a fitted function instead of raw data.) One natural kind of alteration is to *sharpen* the data, increasing contrast between dense regions and thinly occupied regions. We present various ways to do this, using balloon densities in each case. The computation can be done either in the original p-space or in the one- or two-dimensional view space.

Sharpening by excision

Simply by deleting points in regions of low density, we can make patterns stand out more clearly. A basic approach is to

(1) assign a weight to each data point,
(2) order the data points in a list according to weight, from largest to smallest,
(3) delete points from the end of the list until some criterion is satisfied.

The assigned weight at a point might be a balloon density (for some choice of k). Deletion could continue until a fixed fraction of the points remain, or until a fixed fraction of the total assigned weight remains. Also, the whole process can be iterated. Short of completely removing such points, we might choose to display their 'shadows' by plotting small dots instead of asterisks.

Such algorithms for *sharpening by excision* bear some relationship to the idea of removing outliers. As with outlier removal, the goal is to understand the behaviour of the bulk of typical data. The removed points are not necessarily to be forgotten; indeed, they may deserve special but separate attention.

Figures 11.18 and 11.19 show an example based on a bivariate Gaussian point cloud. In the first plot, the 'deletion' of 30% of the points has brought

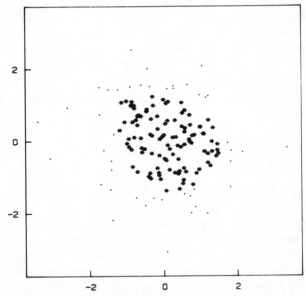

Figure 11.18 One Gaussian cloud sharpened by excision to remove 30% of the points

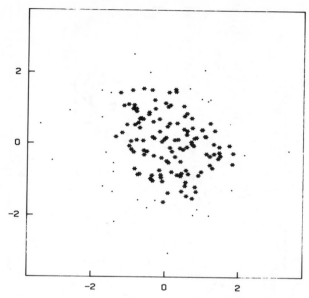

Figure 11.19   The same cloud sharpened by removing
30% of the total balloon-density weight

out the disc-like contour of the cloud. In the second, additional points were
deleted until 30% of the total balloon-density weight was removed; one
might argue that too many points were deleted in this case. Figure 11.20 is an
example in which sharpening by excision makes two overlapping Gaussian
clouds (with separation of $\sqrt{2}\sigma$) visually quite distinct. Figure 11.21 shows the
100 points of the iris data in the projection-pursuit view similarly sharpened.

One unfortunate consequence of the algorithm as described is that a tight
but small cluster (one with fewer than $k + 1$ points) might be entirely
removed. An appropriate modification might be to rank each point among its
neighbours according to balloon densities, and then delete only points with
low local ranks. This would lead to *local sharpening*.

Sharpening by displacement

Alternatively, we may allow points to drift toward regions of higher density.
We can replace each point by an (appropriately weighted) average of it and its
nearest neighbours, and iterate. Clumps will coalesce and debris will be swept
up; a primordial cloud of raw data may evolve into a structured collection of
galaxies, etc. Friedman, Tukey, and Tukey (1980) use this idea of *sharpening by displacement* as one step in a procedure for exploring data which lie

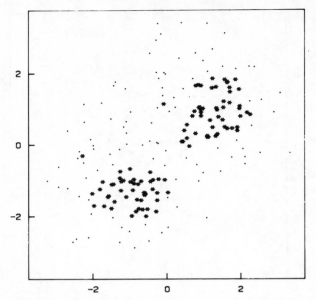

Figure 11.20   Two overlapping clouds sharpened by
removing 30% of total balloon-density weight

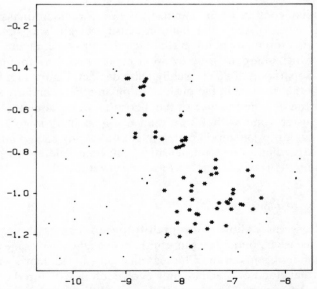

Figure 11.21   The projection-pursuit view of the 100 iris
data points sharpened by excision (cf. Figure 11.3)

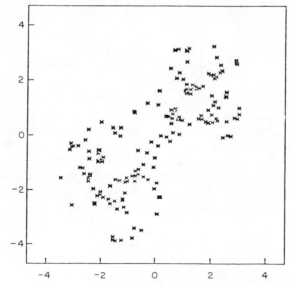

Figure 11.22 Two overlapping clouds sharpened
by (uphill) displacement of points

near curved manifolds in high dimensions. Also, in recent unpublished work,
A. F. Siegel has exploited the gravitational analogy.

Continuing the previous example, Figure 11.22 shows two bivariate Gaussian clusters sharpened by displacement. Further refinements of the algorithm
can reduce the characteristic string-like appearance and alleviate the incidence of exact 'overstrikes' which lead to false visual impressions of density.

Sharpening and blunting by Russian roulette

Many other schemes are possible. We might, for instance, give each point a
probability of retention that increases with density, conceivably taking

$$prob(retention) = 1 - e^{-(c)(balloon\ density)}$$

where c is some suitable constant, and then play 'Russian roulette' to see if
each point is retained or not.

In some applications we may want a clearer visual presentation of the
density of a point cloud in regions of quite high density. If so, we may profit
from the reverse process, *blunting*, in which Russian roulette is used to slow
down the increase of density, thereby thinning out the dense regions to man-

ageable density. For instance, we might take

$$prob(retention) = \begin{cases} 1, & \text{if } density \leq c \\ \dfrac{(c)(\log density)}{(\log c)(density)}, & \text{otherwise,} \end{cases}$$

thus making the increase of displayed density logarithmic beyond a certain point. (The advantages of such techniques are related to the advantages of rootograms). If we had the great luxury of kinematic display, we could design a blinking display and try making *fraction of time visible* differ from point to point in the way just proposed for the probability of retention.

In other applications, we may well want to sharpen the low densities and blunt the high ones at the same time. This can be done in a single step by taking the probability of survival equal to, for instance,

$$\frac{2\sqrt{d_0}\sqrt{\max(0, d - d_0)}}{d}$$

which has a maximum of 1 at $d = 2d_0$. (The probability exceeds 0.5 from about $1.1d_0$ to $17d_0$ and exceeds 0.75 from about $1.2d_0$ to $7d_0$.)

How far have we come?

Our general conclusions at this point are that:

* data-driven selection of views can be of help,
* so far nothing else seems as effective as projection pursuit, although there is ample room for new development,
* agglomeration needs to be actively pursued and refined,
* sharpening should also be a standard tool,
* if we are trying to deal with a point cloud in more than three (or perhaps more than four) dimensions, these techniques may help a fair amount, but are not likely to help enough.

Therefore, we still need to look further.

REFERENCES

Ashton, E. H., Healy, M. J. R., and Lipton, S. (1957) The descriptive use of discriminant functions in physical anthropology. *Proc. Roy. Soc. B*, **146**, 552–72.

Day, N. E. (1969) Estimating the components of a mixture of normal distributions. *Biometrika*, **56**, 463–74.

Delaney, M. J. and Healy, M. J. R. (1964) Variation in the long-tailed field-mouse (*Apodemus Sylvaticus* (*l*)) in northwest Scotland II. Simultaneous examination of all characters. *Proc. Roy. Soc. B*, **161**, 200–7.

Friedman, J. H., Bentley, J. L. and Finkel, R. A. (1975) An algorithm for finding best matches in logarithmic time. *Technical Report STAN-CS-75-482*, Stanford University.

Friedman, J. H., Bentley, J. L., and Finkel, R. A. (1977) An algorithm for finding best matches in logarithmic time. *ACM Trans. on Math. Software*, **3**, 209–26.

Friedman, J. H. and Tukey, J. W. (1974) A projection pursuit algorithm for exploratory data analysis. *IEEE Trans. Comp.* **C-23**, 881–90.

Friedman, J. H., Tukey, J. W., and Tukey, P. A. (1980) Approaches to analysis of data that concentrate near intermediate-dimensional manifolds. In Diday, E. *et al.* (eds.) (1980) *Data Analysis and Informatics*. Amsterdam and New York: North-Holland.

Gnanadesikan, R. (1977) *Methods for Statistical Data Analysis of Multivariate Observations*. New York: Wiley.

Gnanadesikan, R. and Kettenring, J. R. (1972) Robust estimates, residuals, and outlier detection with multiresponse data. *Biometrics*, **28**, 81–124.

Hunter, J. E. (1981) Chapter on factor analysis in Monge, P. R. and Capella, J. N. (eds.) (1981) *Multivariate Techniques in Human Communications Research*. New York: Academic Press (to appear).

Kruskal, J. B. (1969). Toward a practical method which helps uncover the structure of a set of multivariate observations by finding the linear transformation which optimises a new 'index of condensation'. In Milton, R. C. and Nelder, J. A. (eds.) (1969) *Statistical Computation*. New York: Academic Press.

Kruskal, J. B. (1972). Linear transformation of multivariate data to reveal clustering. In Shepard, R. N., Romney, R. K. and Nerlove, S. B. (eds.) (1972) *Multidimensional Scaling: Theory and Applications in the Behavioural Sciences, Vol. 1, Theory*. New York: Seminar Press.

Loftsgaarden, D. O. and Quesenberry, C. P. (1965) A nonparametric estimate of a multivariate density function. *Ann. math. Statist.*, **36**, 1049–51.

Mosteller, F. and Tukey, J. W. (1977) *Data Analysis and Regression*. Reading, Mass.: Addison-Wesley.

Sammon, J. W. Jr. (1969) A nonlinear mapping for data-structure analysis. *IEEE Trans. Comp.* **C-18**, 401–7.

Tarter, M. and Raman, S. (1972) A systematic approach to graphical methods in biometry. In Le Cam, L. M., Neyman, J., and Scott, E. L. (eds.) (1972) *Proc. 6th Berk. Symp. on Math. Statist. and Prob.* Vol. IV, University of California Press, pp. 199–222.

Thurstone, L. L. (1947, 2nd edn. 1957) *Multiple-factor Analysis*. Chicago: University of Chicago Press.

Tukey, J. W. (1947) Non-parametric estimation II. Statistically equivalent blocks and tolerance regions—the continuous case. *Ann. Math. Statist.*, **18**, 529–39.

CHAPTER 12

Summarization; Smoothing; Supplemented Views

P. A. Tukey, *Bell Laboratories, Murray Hill, New Jersey, U.S.A.*
J. W. Tukey, *Princeton University, Princeton, New Jersey, U.S.A.*
        and *Bell Laboratories, Murray Hill, New Jersey, U.S.A.*

12.1 SUMMARIZATION

12.1.1 Kinds of summarization of back variables

In foregoing chapters, we have considered ways of selecting two-views of point clouds in higher dimensions and ways of altering the cloud to make the selected views more revealing. If we want to go further and try simultaneously to display additional aspects or coordinates, it is clear that we are not likely to be able to see *in detail* what goes on in all coordinates. We must learn to do as well as we can by looking at two front or view coordinates in detail, and at the remaining back coordinates in some smoothed or summarized way.

In this chapter we begin by indicating some aspects of a back variable z that we might wish to summarize across the (x, y) view plane, given a collection of (x, y, z) points. We must then devise ways of portraying the summary values. We also briefly consider ways to summarize the (x, y) cloud itself.

Summarization of z-level

Only in cases with very low numerosity in which the z-values are already quite smooth will we want to display the exact z-values themselves. We most often want to show typical z-values (e.g., averages, or, more likely, medians) at the individual (x, y) points or in small neighbourhoods. We will ordinarily want to give up precision (or accuracy) in favour of smoothness. Thus the 'median of z for the k nearest neighbours in the (x, y) view' may be a good start, but we expect it to need—and to receive—some further form of smoothing.

Summarization of z-width

We may also wish to summarize the local *width* of z (i.e., spread or scatter) as a smooth function of (x, y), and we will usually want to do this quite

245

separately from the display of z level. A robust width of z for the k nearest neighbours in (x, y) might well be a good start but it also will almost certainly need further smoothing.

Indicating z-foliation

One or more additional kinds of graphical summary may be needed to reveal foliation or layering at quite different levels of z. (In a sense, this is a way of thinking about one kind of multimodality.) We have not yet thought this through adequately, but one plausible route is to choose some procedure for locating 'the most imposing gap' in the collection of z-values for nearby (x, y) points, and follow this by smoothing. Then, to study the foliated structure, we may make one of several kinds of plots: we can plot the smoothed gap location values, or we can display the original points coded in some way to indicate which layer they are in, or we can make separate displays for the points in each layer.

12.1.2 Smoothing, mainly in the view-plane

Since our smoothing ordinarily takes place over the view, and our views are generally two-dimensional, we will require algorithms for smoothing over a plane. Two quite different kinds of smoothing are possible: smoothing by *excision* or *suppression*, and smoothing by *change of value*. For instance, if we have a few 75s to 99s at points scattered across a field of many points with values in the range 11–17, we can smooth matters considerably by either forgetting the high values, or changing the high values to values in the teens.

Suppression in the view

We have not had sufficient experience to be specific about suppression algorithms, but generally we want to 'forget' a high value if there are either many low values or one very low value in some clearly specified small vicinity, and to treat low values in an analogous way. This type of smoothing seems most likely to be appropriate when we plan to indicate the value of z by the character or glyph used to represent a given point in an (x, y) view. Short of completely removing unusual points, we can choose to add a low noticeability character, to be read 'confused', to our list of characters, and use it whenever our algorithm asks us to forget the z-value at the point in question.

Figure 12.1 gives two examples of discrete graded character scales that might help. One is a single five-point scale, and the other is a double three-point scale for coding two aspects or back variables simultaneously. In both cases, a small circle can be used as the 'confused' character.

In Figure 12.2 we apply the idea to three variables from a demographic

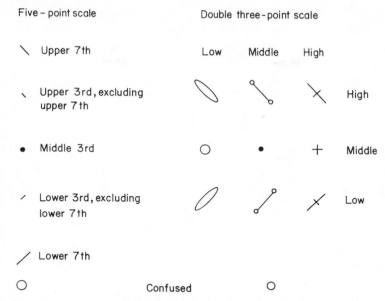

Figure 12.1   Two discrete character scales with confusion character

study of a set of Swiss counties in 1888 (Mosteller and Tukey, 1977). Figure 12.2(a) shows a back variable quantized and coded with the digits 1 to 9. Both the lack of smoothness and the failure of the coding scheme to provide a graded visual scale make it difficult to perceive the increase in z from lower-left to upper-right which is effectively brought out by Figure 12.2(b) using the graded five-point scale with confusion character. The latter picture includes a hand-drawn contour showing roughly the separation between high and low z values.

For another kind of suppression, see Figure 12.7 later.

Smoothing by change of value—head-banging

The problem of smoothing data over one dimension by change of value has received considerable attention, particularly in the analysis of time series, but the problem of smoothing over two dimensions is relatively unexplored. A basic, simple and highly robust/resistant smoothing device for z as a function of a single variable x is the moving median of three values: the z value at each point is compared to the z values at its left and right neighbours in x, and it is moved in if it falls outside their range.

This idea cannot be applied directly to smooth a z given at irregularly spaced points in the (x, y) view, because there is no immediate analogue of 'left' and 'right' neighbours. So far, the most satisfactory basis found for doing

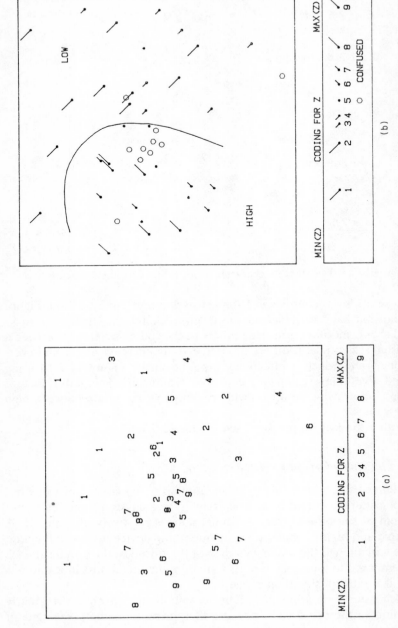

Figure 12.2(a) Scatter plot of 47 Swiss counties in 1888. The front variables are derived from (percent of draftees with highest exam mark) and (percent of population with education beyond primary level). The back variable is fertility; (b) the Swiss data plotted with a different coding for the back variable, including one neutral contour

median-based smoothing over the plane appears to be the identification of *triples*, or ordered sets of three points where the central point in the order is roughly at the midpoint of the other two in the (x, y) view. We will look for several triples with a given point as centre, and we can tolerate triples that are moderately bent and rather more than moderately unbalanced.

Picking such triples out by hand and eye presents no great difficulty. Clearly, however, if we are to deal with many points we want a computer procedure. Relatively simple approaches seem to work. One possibility, for instance, is to make a list of the k nearest neighbours to a given centre point and look for pairs of end points that form triples which minimize an index such as

$$(\log d_1 - \log d_2)^2 + c \cdot \sin^2\theta,$$

where c is a constant, d_1 and d_2 are the lengths of the arms, and θ is the angle between them. (We exclude triples for which $|\theta| < \pi/2$.) Another approach (which in its simplest form produces less satisfactory triples) is to use opposite pairs of 'natural' or Voronoi neighbours, based on the Voronoi diagram of the (x, y) point configuration (see Section 2.3 above). Figure 12.3 shows a typical set of points and the criterion-selected triples for several of them ($c = 25$.).

It is natural to classify points as *body* if they are centre points of two or more triples, as *edge* if they are centre points exactly once, and as *corner* if they are never centre points. One natural smoothing step for body points operates as follows: Convert each triple with the given point as centre into a

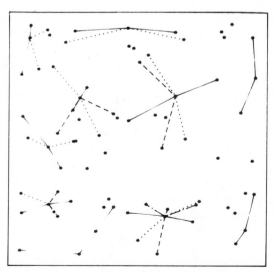

Figure 12.3 A scatter of data points with several sets of triples for smoothing

pair (low_i, $high_i$) where low_i and $high_i$ are the present working z-values at the end points of the ith triple, ordered so that $low_i \leq high_i$. Now compute

$$low\ screen = \underset{i}{median}\{low_i\}$$

$$high\ screen = \underset{i}{median}\{high_i\}$$

and take, for the new value at the centre point,

$$new\ working\ z\text{-}value = median\ \{low\ screen,\ Z,\ high\ screen\},$$

where Z can be, alternatively, (a) the present working z-value at the centre point, or (b) the original z-value at the centre point.

In the case of an edge or corner point z^*, we can augment the list of triples centred at z^* by finding triples for which z^* is an end point, and extrapolating the working z-values of the other two points in the triple to an artificial point beyond z^*. (Such 'end rules' are often used in one-dimensional smoothing as well.)

Carrying out one step of smoothing at each data point is likely to 'bang down' most of those that stick out, but it might make others 'pop up', (think of repairing a wall in which the heads of some of the nails have popped out!), so we will want to repeat this *head-banging* process, perhaps until some stopping criterion is met. We will also want to *twice* the repetition, which means applying the whole process again to the *rough* (i.e., the residuals) from the first application, forming as the final *smooth*,

smooth PLUS *smooth of rough*.

We note that 'twicing' is especially important since the operation is very nonlinear.

There are, of course, many other possible ways to smooth z over a plane. This is an area that requires considerable research. One approach might be to work more directly with the Voronoi diagram (see Section 2.3 above).

12.1.3 Traces and delineations in the view

We can sometimes aid our perceptions by graphically summarizing the (x, y) points themselves using *traces* and *delineations*. (A scatter diagram without middle traces might often be considered at best a lost opportunity!)

Traces and delineations can be constructed by generalizing the *letter values* for scalar batches. In terms of *depth* of an order statistic, which is its order counting in from the nearest end, the median has depth $d_M = \frac{1}{2}(n + 1)$; hinges (fourths) have depths $d_H = d_F = \frac{1}{2}([d_m] + 1)$, eighths have depths $d_E = \frac{1}{2}([d_F] + 1)$, sixteenths have depths $d_D = \frac{1}{2}([d_E] + 1)$, and so on, where '[ ]' means 'the greatest integer not exceeding'.

Chapter 8 of Tukey (1977) explains some ways to draw smoothish traces that try to follow local ('moving') hinges, eighths, etc., of y as a function of x. (To discuss other techniques would take us too far afield. See, for instance, Cleveland and Kleiner, 1975, and Cleveland, 1979.)

Chapter 9 of Tukey (1977) explains some ways to use two sets of traces—one for y against x, the other for x against y—to delineate the pattern of variation of an (x, y) point cloud. Figure 12.4 is an example in which, over most of the range of the data, the middle trace of y as a function of x is horizontal and the middle trace of x over y is vertical—showing no dependence between x and y—but in the lower left, some dependence is seen.

In order to help see the 'shape' of a clump of (x, y) points, Alan Gross (personal communication, 1977) has suggested the usefulness of placing a polar coordinate origin at or near a (robustly computed) 'centre', of the clump and tracing a smoothed radius, r, as a function of angle, θ. If we choose to trace a single letter value in the local distribution of r over θ, it will probably be a median or upper hinge, or something in between. (We may wish to make several traces based on different letter values.) The three *polar traces* in Figure 12.5(a) have been further smoothed by hand to produce Figure 12.5(b).

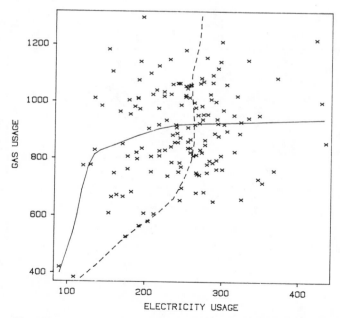

Figure 12.4   A plot of gas usage versus electricity usage, delineated by a smooth of x as a function of y, and of y as a function of x

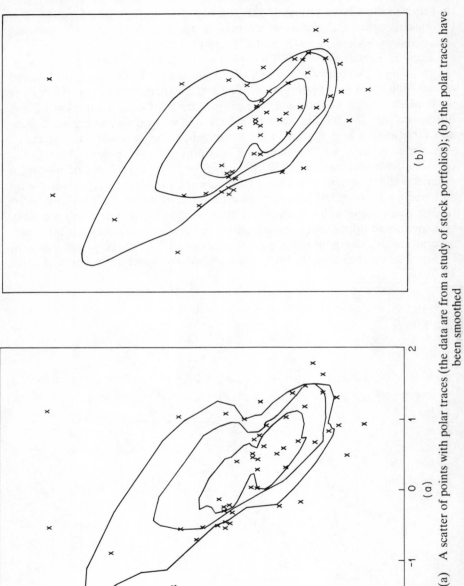

Figure 12.5(a)   A scatter of points with polar traces (the data are from a study of stock portfolios); (b) the polar traces have been smoothed

To conclude this section, we emphasize that in tracing and delineation, as in other uses of smoothing, it is important that the computational processes be quite nonlinear and twiced. Only by well-chosen nonlinearity can we protect against the effects of exotic points. By twicing we can conveniently avoid 'wearing down the hills and filling up the valleys'.

12.2 SUPPLEMENTED VIEWS

We are now ready to turn our attention to the key graphical tools that we can use to supplement the (x, y) location of points, raw or agglomerated, possibly sharpened, and to consider some presently preferred ways to use these tools.

12.2.1 Characters and glyphs

We look first at the various kinds of symbols we can place at (x, y) to describe the local behaviour of the back variables. With fairly few points (up to numerosity B, maybe C) symbols may show individual values of back variables, although smoothing by change of value may often be required to enable value merging. As numerosity increases to C, maybe D, suppression will often be useful. Larger data sets will probably require considerable agglomeration and display of only summarized values for the agglomerated points. As the number of points increases even further, the usefulness of collective representation (Section 12.2.2) also increases.

Some distinctions

To help organize our thinking about the range of possibilities, we offer several ways that plotting 'characters' can be classified in terms both of their construction and of their graphical impact and intended use:

* *individual-value* versus *collective summary* characters—Does the character convey a value for a single data point, or does it show a range of summary information regarding the local distribution of a back variable?

* *simple* versus *compound* characters—Is there information coded into the character on one or on several back coordinates?

* *1-code* versus *2-code* versus *3-code* etc.—How many numerical values are coded into the character?

* *qualitative* versus *ordinal* character scales—Are the characters merely qualitatively distinct, or do they form a sequence with graded visual impact?

* *single-ended* versus *double-ended* versus *circular* scales—Are the characters suitable for cases with *neutrality* (i.e., indifference, or 'zero') at one end (as perhaps for values that are only positive), or in the middle (as perhaps for values that are positive and negative), or for values on a cyclical scale (such as wind direction, or months, or time of day)?

* *single-aspect* versus *double-aspect* versus *multi-aspect* characters—If several values are coded into a character, are they coded in terms of similar or different graphical aspects of the symbol? (See comments below on *multi-aspect characters.*)

* *separable (alternable)* or not—Can we easily concentrate on the separate codes or aspects, one at a time? Or can we concentrate on the points in each of several classifications according to z-level?

* *value mergeable* or not—Can we let our visual impression shift from individual points to a broadly merged synthesis, not just of where the points are, but indeed a synthesis of the z-values of nearby points?

The following sections list a number of possible character scales in three of these categories, and Section 12.2.2 deals with collective summary characters in more detail. The lists are certainly not complete. Suitable choices will depend on the details of particular applications and user's preferences. More experience and careful thought will be necessary before any clear recommendations can be made.

One fruitful source of ideas is the set of techniques used by geographers, since we are in a sense devising ways to code additional information into 'maps'. (See especially Monkhouse and Wilkinson, 1963, and Bertin, 1973, 1977, 1980.)

Individual-value simple characters

We deal first with situations in which a single numerical value is to be coded into a simple character. Several of these are illustrated in Figure 12.6.

* Qualitatively distinct characters, such as crosses and polygons, for use when z is a categorical or classification variable. Figure 10.3 gave an example of this. We note that coding by letters, as in Figures 10.6–10.9, is usually unsatisfactory (except for archival purposes), since letters do not usually have sufficiently distinct visual impacts.

* Whisker directions, where the value is shown by the direction of a light line (*a whisker*) of fixed length emanating from a small circle, probably restricted to a range of 120°. (Think of a voltmeter or speedometer.)

* Whisker length, with two discrete directions to distinguish positive and negative. (Figure 12.1 gave an example of this.)

* Heaviness of line, using some fixed character. This gives a single-ended scale.

* Size of character, again for characters of some fixed shape. This also gives a single-ended scale.

* The five-point size scale used in Tukey (1977), with +'s for positive values and ○'s for negative. This scale is useful for displaying residuals.

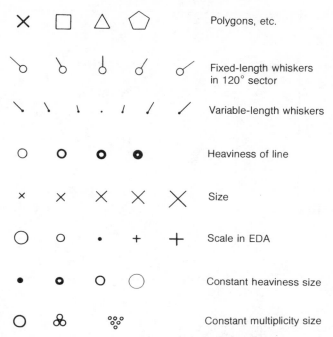

Figure 12.6   Several possible individual-value simple character scales

* A scale of, say, circles of increasing size but decreasing heaviness of line, so
  that overall 'blackness' is constant.
* A scale of multiple circles in patterns, with size balanced against multiplicity (a size-adjusted 'domino', or 'cannonball-pile' scale?)
* Colour, using a fixed character. This is effective as a qualitative scale, but
  requires considerable care if used as a quantitative scale.

  Grey level. This is not very different in visual impact from heaviness of
  line.

Some of these are explicitly short discrete scales, but this is rarely a disadvantage, since subtle differences are very difficult to perceive in most character
scales. This is one of the reasons that we must give up detail in representing
back variables.

Figure 12.7 shows the four-body particle-physics data again. This time the
points in the ($\log x_1$, $\log x_3$) view have been 'sliced' into ninths on a back
variable, x_2. The first, fifth and last of the ninths have been coded with
qualitatively distinct symbols (colour is much more effective, but is not available to us in this written account), and the other ninths have been suppressed.

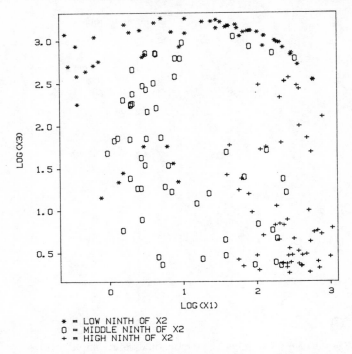

Figure 12.7   Four-body particle-physics data showing top,
middle, and bottom slices on x_2

The result is a display which shows a clear nonlinear dependence of x_2 on log
x_1 and log x_3. This illustrates the effectiveness of a three-point character scale
as well as another form of smoothing by suppression.

Individual-value compound characters

Next, we consider coding single values of two or more back variables into one
compound character. There are more possibilities here, and less available
guidance from existing comparative studies. Some of the following are illustrated in Figure 12.8:

* weathervane symbols, as on weather maps;
* stars or polygons (e.g., Friedman *et al*. 1972), in which the angles are fixed
  and the lengths of radii to the vertices carry the message;
* glyphs, in particular Anderson's (1957, 1960) style of metroglyph—a circle
  with 1–7 variable-length whiskers at the top;
* circle-based glyphs with water level and, say, 2 whiskers emanating right
  and left from the equator with values coded into their angular positions;

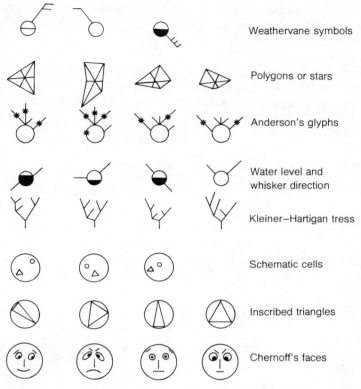

Weathervane symbols

Polygons or stars

Anderson's glyphs

Water level and
whisker direction

Kleiner–Hartigan tress

Schematic cells

Inscribed triangles

Chernoff's faces

Figure 12.8   Several possible individual-value compound character
scales

* trees, castles, and related symbols (Kleiner and Hartigan, 1981);
* schematic cells—round or triangular enclosures with distinctive inclusions
  distinctively placed (the size of the enclosure may also be a code);
* inscribed triangles—circles containing triangles, with values coded into the
  shapes and/or orientations of the triangles;
* multi-aspect characters (see below);
* cartoon faces (Chernoff, 1973).

When designing or choosing compound character scales, one must consider
whether the scales are separable (that is, whether one can easily shift attention from one coded aspect to another), and whether the coded aspects are
individually value-mergeable into impressions of regional trends. Furthermore, most of these scales will produce displays that are very sensitive to the
order of coupling of back variables to graphical aspects of the characters.

Finally, it will clearly be easier to use such displays to study the relationship of each back variable to the front variables, than to study relationships among the back variables.

Figure 12.9 uses Chernoff's faces to display several air-pollution and meteorological variables along a single front variable, time. It shows hourly observations for one 24-hour period at a monitoring station in Bayone, N.J., with a deliberately suggestive assignment of variables to facial features. One

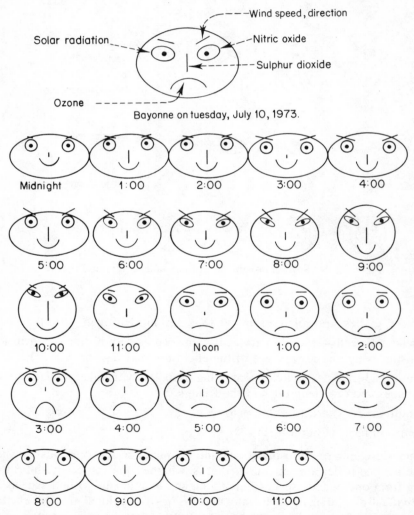

Figure 12.9   Faces used to code air-quality data from Bayonne N.J. on July 10, 1973

difficulty with faces, which is shared to varying degrees by other types of compound characters, is that the coded visual aspects can interact with each other in undesirable ways. For instance, if ellipticity and orientation of eyes are both used, then a low value of ellipticity will make orientation hard to perceive. We have tried to avoid such combinations here. In the figure it is quite easy to perceive the diurnal increase and decrease of most variables and the lags among the peaks, etc. The smoothness of the variables over time enables us to see this structure and makes this example more effective than most applications of faces that we have seen. This underscores the need for smoothness in character-coded displays in general. If the data had not been this smooth initially, then smoothing before display would have been in order.

An example of Kleiner–Hartigan trees is shown in Figure 12.10. The values of the variables are coded into the lengths of the terminal branches, and the internal branches have lengths that depend on the sums of the terminal

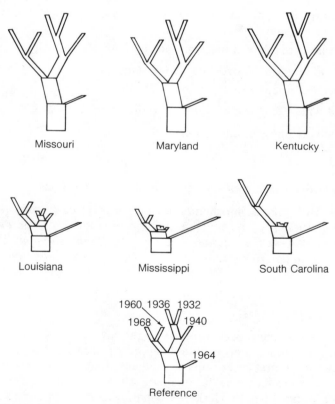

Figure 12.10   Kleiner–Hartigan trees to show percent Republican vote in several U.S. elections for several states

branches that they support. One important feature of these trees that distinguishes them from most other compound characters is that an attempt has been made to remove the arbitrariness of assignment of variables to branches by doing a hierarchical clustering of the variables and using the dendrogram as the basic tree. This helps matters, though it may in some senses have put the arbitrariness at a different level.

Multi-aspect characters

One of the distinctions made at the beginning of this section was whether one or several graphical aspects of the character will be used to display, in coded form, the several numerical aspects involved. Available aspects include, but are not limited to, shape, orientation, size, intensity, and colour. We need to gain experience to judge which combinations work well together, but some possibilities are:

* aspect ratio of ellipses and crosses for one variable, and orientation for
* another, as in Figure 12.1;

* size for one variable, but blackness for another;

* size and orientation of arrow or wedge symbols;

* blackness and orientation of arrow symbols;

* length of whiskers (for magnitude) and direction (for sign).

This is relatively unexplored territory.

12.2.2 Collective characters and other special considerations

To display distributional information for one or more back variables—either for agglomerations, for rectangular (etc.) cellulations, or for overlapping neighbourhoods—we must design *collective* or *collective summary* characters. Both the information to be transferred and the characters are obviously more complicated.

Collective simple characters

When we have a single back variable to display, we seek *collective simple characters*. One immediately profitable approach seems to be *k-number fans*, wherein two or more letter values (medians, hinges, etc.) from the local distribution of z are shown by the angular positions, constrained to lie within a 120° sector, of fixed-length whiskers emanating from a point or a small circle. A two-number fan will probably show the hinges (quartiles), a three-number fan will show the median and (using shorter rays) the hinges, a five-number

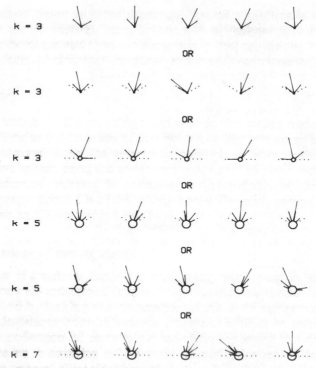

Figure 12.11 *k*-number fans as collective simple
characters

fan the median and hinges along with the extremes (shown with still shorter
rays), and so on. This is illustrated in Figure 12.11.

We can go further and try to show the whole distribution of *z* using *large
collective simple characters*. Two possibilities for displaying a smoothed profile of the local *z* density are the rootagon (Section 11.3.1) and the balloonogram (Section 11.3.2). The multiwindow display of Figure 11.14 is really an
example of this, although we could have defined neighbourhoods by agglomeration instead of cellulation.

Collective compound characters

If we seek *collective compound characters* for showing distributional information on two or more back variables simultaneously, there is the possibility of
double *k*-number fans, desirably in 120° sectors above and below a point. If
colour is available, triple *k*-number fans might be separable/alternable.

A *large collective compound character* for showing two density profiles can be constructed by putting two rootagons or two balloonograms back to back. (Colour would certainly help here, too.)

In a sense, the scatter plots in the multiwindow display of Figure 11.15 are really large collective compound characters showing entire bivariate (u, v) distributions of points in (x, y) neighbourhoods.

Standard symbol technology, anyone?

Several questions of symbol technology need to be explored, involving both psychological and operational considerations. Should, for instance, standard symbol sizes be in logarithmic steps—unit *decigalts* (steps of 0.1 in logs of base 10) in area, or perhaps in linear dimension? Note that a continuous scale of sizes offers no serious advantage. If there are to be standard discrete symbol sizes, can they be made available in the form of a self-stick medium that is transferred by burnishing or peeling? Current technology might make it easy to have them computer produced and photo-reduced.

Special considerations for cellulations

Both *arrowhead* and *wedge* symbols should work especially well as two-aspect characters in a rectangular cellulation, using direction and size as the aspects. (We are likely to use up one aspect, probably size, on the number of points in the cell.) Figure 12.12 shows the four-body particle-physics data displayed in this way. Circular discs divided into two colours by a line of varying orientation and varying position are another interesting possibility. Tints and shadings could be done on a cell-by-cell basis, but this seems less encouraging.

12.2.3 Backgrounds

The final graphical element that we have at our disposal is the background against which we plot points. At this time, we see three major possibilities: colour, shading with parallel rulings, and contours. We cannot expect background to give us very detailed visual information, so we will nearly always use background to show only the level or typical value of a back variable, and we will plan to do a considerable amount of smoothing. In all three cases, we will also want to keep the background elements light enough that they do not obscure the plotted points.

The possibilities of moiré patterns of varying density do not seem to have been examined.

Steps of background tint

While a smooth gradation of *background tint* between two extreme colours is conceivable, it is not achievable with most currently available technologies.

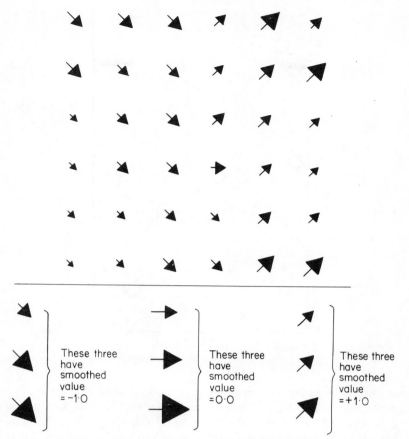

Figure 12.12 Particle-physics data in a cellulated ($\log x_1$, $\log x_3$) display, where symbol area shows cell count, and symbol direction shows smoothed values of x_7

We can do as well, perhaps better, with discrete steps of tint in regions bounded by contour lines of the 'surface' being represented.

Computer technology, even to produce plots with discrete steps of background tint, is not widely available at present, but hand enhancement of black-and-white computer plots can go a long way.

Steps of shading

An alternative to tint is the use of *shading* by light parallel rulings. This idea actually offers more diverse possibilities than colour, since we can control spacing, direction, and breaking. One attractive shading code, illustrated by Figure 12.13, shows values by closeness of lines using solid lines for positive

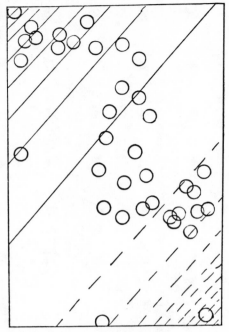

Figure 12.13   A SE to NW gradation of
z shown by spacing of shading lines

regions and broken lines for negative regions, so that neutral areas are nearly empty. In Figure 12.13 it is important to realize that the shading lines are *not* to be thought of as contour lines with equal z-spacings; it is the density of shading that shows z value; the surface depicted here is actually linear.

If the surface to be portrayed does not have linear contours, we cannot use rulings that extend across the whole plot. Instead, we will probably break them at the edges of regions defined by a set of z-contour lines (perhaps corresponding to equal z-spacings), and use different patterns of rulings in different regions, as illustrated in Figure 12.14.

Contours

The great advantages of contours for showing values of a back variable are clear in their many appearances in topographic maps. In the present context, we need to contour at least moderately smoothed versions of back variables. The detail of what is shown can increase with the number of points, but the amount of smoothing required is likely to remain nearly the same, since it should focus on appropriate neighbourhoods containing about the same numbers of points.

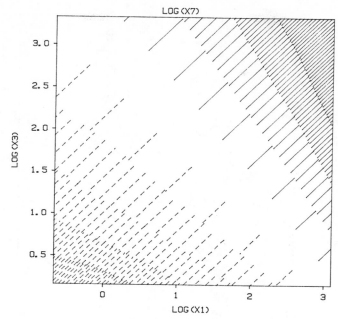

Figure 12.14   Shading within zones defined by contour lines

Since we wish to make contoured results visible without eliminating our ability to look at other things, particularly point location, we want to use light lines for our contours. This leaves us an opportunity to go beyond simple contouring, labelling hill tops with scattered + signs and valley bottoms with scattered ○'s, in an effort to alleviate one of the inherent difficulties with contours, that of distinguishing hills from valleys. (It may be useful to show one neutral contour with alternating +'s and ○'s.) Another way to tackle this difficulty is to use solid contour lines for high z-values and broken lines for low z-values.

Figure 12.15 shows the by now familiar (log x_1, log x_3) view of the four-body particle-physics data, here plotted against a background of smooth contours of $z = \log x_5$ constructed by hand from tabulations of ordered z observations within cells of an (x, y) cellulation. Figure 12.16 is a similar plot showing log x_7 contours, this time entirely computer produced. The log x_7 values were smoothed by head-banging (Section 12.1.2) and passed along to an existing contouring program. Clearly some further smoothing would be helpful, as well as some refinement of the contouring algorithm.

An alternative possibility for a single z is to add a set of orthogonal trajectories (gradient or hill-climbing paths) to a system of contours. This is easy to do by eye, but we are unaware of any existing computer software to accomplish the task. The merits of this approach remain to be explored.

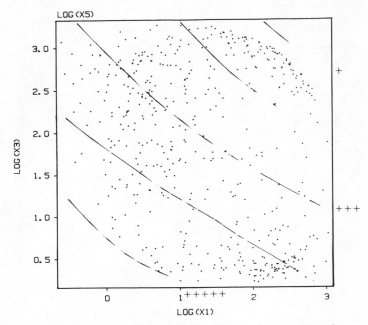

Figure 12.15   Four-body physics data as a ($\log x_1$, $\log x_3$)
scatter, with smoothed contours of one back variable

12.2.4 Deployment of tools

We give a brief indication of how these various display techniques might be chosen for use and combined, depending on increasing dimensionality and numerosity.

Three-dimensional data

With one back variable and few points, we want more detail for the back variable; with more points, we can tolerate less. The following approaches are roughly in order of increasing numerosity.

With few enough points we can show, usually with some discretization (quantization), the back-variable value of each point. All the styles of simple one-code characters are feasible, but whisker direction seems attractive—and preferred by us to whisker length as more mergeable. As the numerosity grows, suppression is an important adjunct to the use of one-code characters; then gradually agglomeration becomes attractive, still using one-code characters to show collective local z-level, possibly with some additional smoothing. Eventually the need to merge back values dominates. We can then also consider pure background representations, either by tints, by shading, or by

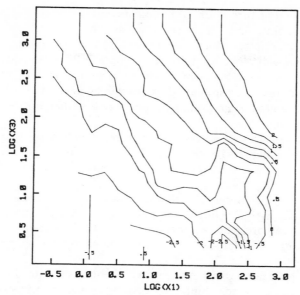

Figure 12.16 Four-body physics data. Contours of log x_7 as a function of $(\log x_1, \log x_3)$, smoothed by computer using head-banging

contours, as a reasonable possibility; we expect to have to smooth in most cases.

At some point in this sequence of situations, depending on our needs and the complexity of the point configuration, we will want to introduce more detail about the local z-distribution for (x, y) neighbourhoods. The natural first step is the use of two-number fans, probably based on some form of cellulation, and smoothed. Only with fairly high numerosity will we have sufficient information to make sensible use of three-number fans and other collective summary characters.

In most cases, effective display of an (x, y, z) data cloud as a supplemented (x, y) plot ought to be possible.

Four-dimensional data, and beyond

One way to handle two back variables is to show two side-by-side pictures, one for each back variable, using the same front variables and any of the styles of display just discussed. The numerosity considerations are largely the same. Any of the one-code characters or backgrounds should work well, but it will probably be harder to make effective visual comparisons between pairs of displays of collective-summary characters.

A superimposed picture offers some real advantages as long as separability and clarity are maintained. Of course, if we are showing two (or more) back variables with characters alone, we cannot superimpose simple one-code characters, so we will move to multicode or perhaps multi-aspect characters. Raw values of back variables can be shown if points are few to modest in number, but suppressed or smoothed values will be needed as the numerosity rises. A greater degree of smoothing may be required than for the display of a single back variable.

Much the same is to be said about displaying summary values of two back variables for agglomerates or for cells. Multiwindow displays (Section 11.3.1 and Figure 11.15) are often a very effective approach to the four-dimensional case.

Combining a good mergeable character with an alternable background offers real possibilities. We might like to consider several types of characters with or without suppression, against any of the backgrounds described. For larger numerosities we would certainly base the characters on agglomeration or cellulation.

Toward the high numerosity side, we will want to consider the use of two superimposed backgrounds. Since the psychological colour space is, in a sense, three-dimensional, it has been proposed to represent two or even three variables by suitable mixing of colours. We doubt, however, whether this works well, partly because the two or three colour scales so far tried are not sufficiently separable. (See Fienberg, 1979, for examples and discussion.)

On the other hand, there is certainly the possibility of using shadings with rulings in different directions to represent two (or even three) back variables simultaneously, especially if colour is available to code the rulings to improve separability. We expect this to work better than mixing of background tints, but we have not yet had adequate experience with either individual or combined use of shading to make strong recommendations.

We may also consider the possibility of portraying two (or more) back variables simultaneously with superimposed contours. This is most likely to work if the represented 'surfaces' are smooth enough, and, in the black and white case, if the sets of contour lines are sufficiently noncollinear. Here also, separation is enhanced by using different colours or line styles to code the sets of contours. (Hand tracing with colour onto a transparency is cheap and easy.)

Other schemes deserve trial. For instance, we might try to combine two types of backgrounds (contours for one back variable, say, and shading for another) especially if colour is used to aid separation. We do not yet know how difficult it is mentally to assimilate such a picture.

Generally speaking, with experience, we should be able to do a moderately good job of displaying 4 variables. As we move to more coordinates, our possible choices become more diverse, but our sensible choices become more constrained.

We can consider for instance, using multicode Anderson glyphs, circle-based glyphs, stars, or trees if we do not have too many points. The use of first suppression and then agglomeration or cellulation along with smoothing is more important than ever as the numerosity increases. The more aspects that are displayed, the more difficult it is to separate and mentally merge any single aspect.

Character representations can be combined in various ways with background representation of up to three additional aspects (perhaps four in some cases). If shadings are used, the rulings can be drawn at $120°$ to each other and possibly distinguished by line styles; with shadings or contours, colour distinctions, if available, will be helpful. Generally we feel that (a) if more aspects are displayed, more detail must be sacrificed in favour of greater smoothing, (b) it will be wise to gain experience with lower-dimensional cases before tackling the higher-dimensional ones, and (c) eventually we will want to combine many of these tools with kinematics.

Examples

We offer two examples of these tools used in combination both based on the particle-physics data. In Figure 12.17 the agglomerated view of Figure 11.13

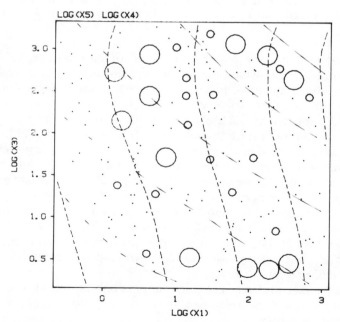

Figure 12.17   Agglomerated four-body physics data with
smoothed contours of two back variables

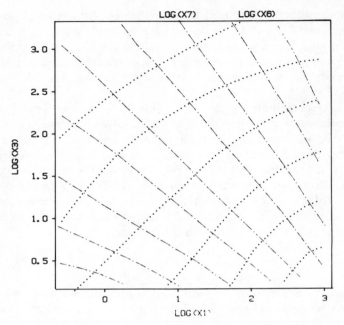

Figure 12.18   Contours of two more back variables that can
be traced onto a transparency and overlaid on Figure 12.17

is combined with (heavily smoothed) contours of $\log x_1$ and $\log x_3$. Although all drawn in black-and-white, the sets of contours are easily separable since they are nearly orthogonal. Figure 12.18 gives contours of two more back variables over the same two-view.

A useful approach to such complex plots is to hand trace each set of contours onto a different transparency with a distinct colour and to tape the transparencies at different edges onto the basic two-view. Then they may be flipped over at will and viewed in different combinations. (In full colour and with all contour lines shown at once, this example looks rather like new-year's eve confetti and streamers!)

Figure 12.19 shows a cellulated version of the same two-view, augmented by two sets of contours (and further augmentable by the contours of Figure 12.18). In this view, the size of the square conveys the number of points in the cell, and the values of two back variables are coded into the left and right wings, as indicated in the key.

These examples illustrate not only the possibilities, but also some of the dangers of trying to code many aspects into a single plot. Careful work needs to be done in this area.

We remark in passing that the choice of the log re-expression and the

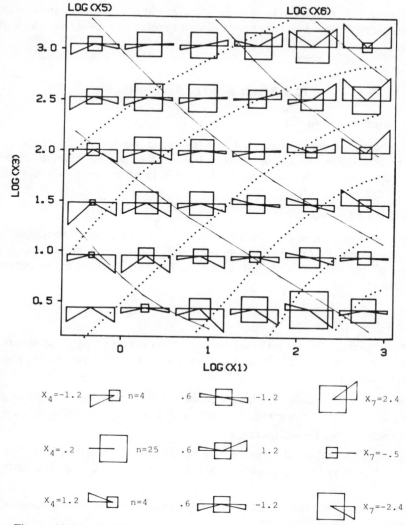

Figure 12.19 Cellulated view of the four-body physics data. Area of squares shows cell count, wings show median of x_4 and of x_7 in cells, and contours of x_5 and x_6 are drawn

choice of (x_1, x_3) as the main view variables for the particle-physics data were both made after trying a variety of possibilities. These choices did a good job of spreading the data out over the view, but they are otherwise fairly arbitrary from the point of view of the subject matter. Clearly there is some advantage to retaining one pair of view variables for a sequence of pictures, since this allows us to build up a mental framework for thinking about the data. On the other hand, a thorough study of these data would not be complete without studying pictures based on other permutations and re-expressions of the variables.

12.3 TOPICS NOT COVERED

12.3.1 Some omissions

We conclude by listing, for reference, a few topics we feel are interesting or relevant but which we did not cover above. Many would require actively driven computer graphics or movies. The list is in no sense complete.

Macrokinematic displays

A *macrokinematic display* is a real-time display that shows smooth transitions among two-views that may be widely separated in p-space, with at least moderately flexible control of the motion, as in PRIM-9 (Tukey, Friedman and Fisherkeller, 1976).

Microkinematic displays

A *microkinematic display* takes advantage of parallax, but only parallax corresponding to small (local) changes of view orientation. We may want to have the picture:

* rock smoothly back and forth between two two-views with a small angular separation, probably showing the motion horizontally (*gimbling*)
* go around a small cone (*gyring*)
* or do both together, the gyring at a faster rate (*wabing*, all three terms inspired by 'gyring and gimbling in the wabe in Lewis Carroll's *Jabberwocky*.)
* alternate between two static pictures (a special case of an *alternagraphic display*)
* be a static stereoscopic pair (We include this here because of its close connection to small-angle shifts.)

Moving bright zones

Points in a kinematic (x, y) view can be enhanced or brightened for $A(t) < z < A(t) + \delta$, where $A(t)$ may be taken as a cyclical function of viewing time. Then we will see a *bright zone* move repeatedly through the data in the z direction.

Andrews paths

Andrews's original idea (1972) was to imagine a time-varying one-view of a p-dimensional point cloud, where the direction of the one-view follows a compound sinusoidal curve on the $(p-1)$-sphere (a curve which repeats after $t = 2\pi$ in the original conception, but which is easily made non-repetitive and 'space filling'), and then to make a static plot of the one-view against a t axis. Each data point traces a curved trajectory in such a plot. The two-dimensional analogue (called a *ouija plot* in Tukey and Tukey, 1977), is a kinematic two-view in which t is represented by real time in the display, and each view coordinate is determined by a compound sinusoidal path. (The two together determine a path on a Grassmann manifold.) A further generalization would be to use such paths for four- or higher-dimensional microkinematic displays (gimbling or gyring or bright-zoning), with the back variable involved following an Andrews path on the space of *back* variables; or even wabing, with the two back variables following an Andrews path on the corresponding Grassmann manifold.

Other improvement devices

These would include (a) *pinching*, to bring nearby points close to manifolds of concentration (Friedman, Tukey and Tukey, 1980), and (b) *reflective regression*, in which z-location is related to (x, y) location.

In reflective regression, we follow these steps:

(1) develop a smooth trace in the x, y plane, parametrized by z_0, and guided by the (median x, median y) points for all (x, y) with z close to z_0,

(2) given a point (x_0, y_0), take a neighbourhood in the view, identify the z-values of data points in that neighbourhood, and use the trace to find a corresponding set of (x, y) points,

(3) find the *image point* for (x_0, y_0) as (median x, median y) where the medians are taken over the (x, y) pairs just found. We can now move the given point toward its image point, either in the view or in (x, y, z), (or, for our purposes, draw a ray in that point's direction, etc.).

Extension to two back variables would be easy; direct extension to three or more would require very high numerosities.

Minimal rising trees or forests

Instead of plotting discrete points, we may sometimes improve our perception of structure by connecting the points in various ways with line segments, as, for example, in a minimal spanning tree. We will obtain one kind of *minimal rising tree* if we connect each point to the nearest point with greater cascade density in p-space (Section 11.3.2). We could do the same, using the value of a back variable in place of the cascade density. Or we can omit links that do not run to one of the initial point's k nearest neighbours, and obtain a *minimal rising forest.*

Related topics

These might include (a) two-sample and multisample displays, (b) graphical methods for presenting eigenvalues (for studying elipsoidal shapes, canonical correlations, etc., Tukey and Tukey, 1977), (c) Tarter's techniques (Tarter and Raman, 1972), (d) graphics for studying regression residuals (Daniel and Wood, 1971), (e) pictures of relative lack of fit, (f) graphics for studying the structure of identified clusters in the data cloud (Gnanadesikan, Kettenring, and Landwehr, 1977 and 1981).

Multidimensional scaling, and its extensions to complete mappings

Multidimensional scaling (Carroll and Kruskal, 1978, Kruskal and Wish, 1978, and Carroll and Arabie, 1980) is usually presented as a computational algorithm for analysing (possible high-dimensional) data that comes not in the form of coordinate values, but as interpoint 'distances'. In practice, however, it is usually used to produce two-views of point clouds in 'reconstructed' coordinate systems for subjective study and interpretation. Thus, it deserves to be mentioned here as a graphical tool. It can also be adapted as a device for studying some interesting kinds of nonlinear structure, even in data that are initially given in a coordinate system (Shepard and Carroll, 1966, Gnanadesikan, 1977, p. 38).

REFERENCES

Anderson, E. (1957) A semigraphical method for the analysis of complex problems. *Proc. of the Nat. Academy of Sciences*, **13**, 923–27 (reprinted in *Technometrics* (1960), **2**, 387–91).

Andrews, D. F. (1972) Plots of high-dimensional data. *Biometrics*, **28**, 125–36.

Bertin, J. (1973) *Semiologie Graphique* (2nd edn., in French). Paris and The Hague: Mouton.

Bertin, J. (1977) *La Graphique et le Traitement Graphique de l'Information.* Paris: Flammarion.

Bertin, J. (1980) *Graphics and the Graphical Analysis of Data.* (Translated by W. Berg). Berlin: DeGruyter.

Carroll, J. D. and Arabie, P. (1980) Multidimensional Scaling. *Ann. Rev. Psychol.*, **31**, 607–49.

Carroll, J. D. and Kruskal, J. B. (1978) Multidimensional scaling of two-way and three-way arrays. In *The Encyclopedia of Statistics*, Kruskal, W. H. and Tanur, J. M. (eds.) (1978). New York: Free Press.

Chernoff, H. (1973) The use of faces to represent points in k-dimensional space graphically. *J. Amer. Statist. Assn.*, **68**, 361–8.

Cleveland, W. S. (1979) Robust locally weighted regression and smoothing scatterplots. *J. Amer. Statist. Assn.*, **74**, 829–36.

Cleveland, W. S. and Kleiner, B. (1975) A graphical technique for enhancing scatterplots with moving statistics. *Technometrics*, **17**, 447–54.

Daniel, C. and Wood, F. S. (1971) *Fitting Equations to Data*. New York: Wiley. (There is an enlarged 2nd edn., 1980)

Fienberg, S. E. (1979). Graphical methods in statistics. *The American Statistician*, **33**, 165–78.

Friedman, H. P., Farrell, E. S., Goldwyn, R. M., Miller, M., and Sigel, J. H. (1972) A graphic way of describing changing multivariate patterns. *Proc. of the Sixth Interface Symposium on Computer Science and Statistics*, Oct. 16–17, 1972, pp. 56–9. Univ. of California, Berkeley.

Friedman, J. H., Tukey, J. W., and Tukey, P. A. (1980) Approaches to analysis of data that concentrate near intermediate-dimensional manifolds. In Diday, E. *et al.* (eds.) (1980). *Data Analysis and Informatics*. Amsterdam and New York: North-Holland.

Gnanadesikan, R. (1977) *Methods for Statistical Data Analysis of Multivariate Observations*. New York: Wiley.

Gnanadesikan, R., Kettenring, J. R., and Landwehr, J. M. (1977) Interpreting and assessing the results of cluster analyses. *Bull. Int. Statist. Inst.* **47**, 451–63.

Gnanadesikan, R., Kettenring, J. R., and Landwehr, J. M. (1981) Projection plots for displaying clusters. To appear in Kallianpur, G., Krishnaiah, P. R. and Ghosh, J. K. (eds.) (1981) *Statistics and Probability*: *Essays in Honor of C. R. Rao*. Amsterdam: North-Holland.

Kleiner, B. and Hartigan, J. A. (1981) Representing points in many dimensions by trees and castles. *J. Amer. Statist. Assn.* **76**, 260–9.

Kruskal, J. B. and Wish, M. (1978) *Multidimensional Scaling*. London: Sage Publications.

Monkhouse, F. J. and Wilkinson, H. R. (1963) *Maps and Diagrams*. London: Methuen; New York: Harper & Row.

Mosteller, F. and Tukey, J. W. (1977) *Data Analysis and Regression*. Reading, Mass.: Addision-Wesley.

Shepard, R. N. and Carroll, J. D. (1966) Parametric representation of nonlinear data in structures. In Krishnaiah, P. R. (ed.) (1966) *Multivariate Analysis*. pp. 561–92. New York: Academic Press.

Tarter, M. (1975) Implementation and applications of bivariate Gaussian mixture decomposition. *J. Amer. Statist. Assn.*, **70**, 47–55.

Tarter, M. and Raman, S. (1972) A systematic approach to graphical methods in biometry. In Le Cam, L. M., Neyman, J. and Scott, E. L. (eds.) (1972) *Proc. 6th Berk. Symp. on Math. Statist. and Prob. Vol. IV*, pp. 199–222. University of California Press.

Tukey, J. W. (1977) *Exploratory Data Analysis*. Reading: Addison-Wesley.

Tukey, J. W., Friedman, J. H., and Fisherkeller, M. A. (1976) PRIM-9, an interactive multidimensional data display and analysis system. *Proc. 4th International Congress for Stereology*, Sept. 4–9, 1975, Gaithersburg: Maryland.

Tukey, J. W. and Tukey, P. A. (1977) Aide-memoire for: Methods for direct and indirect graphic display for data sets in 3 and more dimensions. Presented at University of Western Ontario, November, 1977.

PART IV

Specific Methods and Practical Applications

Plotting the Optimum Positions of an Array of Cortical Electrical Phosphenes

B. S. Everitt, *University of London, U.K.*

J. C. Gower, *Rothamsted Experimental Station, U.K.*

The data involved in this investigation were collected as part of a project concerned with the substitution of vision in blind people. One approach to this problem has been the *cortical visual prosthesis* (Brindley and Lewin, 1968). This device is an implanted electrical stimulator, with an array of electrodes laid on the surface of the area of the brain concerned with vision, namely the *visual cortex*. Stimulation at one or more electrodes can be applied under control from the exterior via inductive ('radio') links across the skin. When a train of electrical pulses is delivered at one of the electrodes, the patient reports the presence of a spot or patch of light sensation, termed a *phosphene*. Stimulation through different electrodes results in phosphenes in different positions in the visual field, and the characteristic positions of different phosphenes are largely consistent from test to test. The notion then is to combine phosphenes into more elaborate visual sensations which could be of practical use to the patient, by stimulation at more than one electrode at once. For example, ordinary print might be read using a camera suitably arranged to control the pattern of stimulation at different combinations of electrodes.

Before beginning to use the prosthesis in this way, the position of each phosphene in the visual field has first to be determined, and the result of this process is termed a *phosphene map*. Since the patient is blind, the positions of the phosphenes can only be observed relative to each other, so that the phosphene map must be built up from individual observations of the angle and separation between various different *phosphene pairs*, which are then fitted together to form the phosphene map. Such observations of phosphene pairs are conveniently made by stimulating the two phosphenes in sequence, and asking the subject to record the angle and distance of the centre of the second phosphene from the centre of the first, taking the first as if at the centre of a clock face; angles are therefore reported by the subject in 'clock minutes'. Distances are recorded in inches of separation at the apparent distance of the phosphenes from the eye. Since different observations of the same phosphene pair may vary somewhat from time to time—and it is often found that the observations of phosphene pairs do not fit together perfectly into a phosphene map—the maps have to be constructed in such a way as to minimize the discrepancy between individual observations and the fitted map. For early patients this was accomplished largely by 'hand-fitting' procedures. However, in one patient, observed over five years, some 6000 observations were made relating to 751 phosphene pairs amongst 90 phosphenes (not all pairs were observed); with such a quantity of data, fitting by hand would obviously be far too laborious and consequently several methods were developed which could be computerized. It is two of these which will be described below.

13.1 MINIMIZATION METHOD

In seeking a map of the phosphenes, we wish to obtain a set of two-dimensional coordinates for the positions of the phosphenes, such that the interphosphene distances and angles implied by these coordinates are, in some sense, the best fit to the observed distances and angles. One obvious way to achieve this is to choose the coordinates so that they minimize some function of the difference between the fitted and the observed angles and distances. The function chosen for this purpose was as follows:

$$S(\mathbf{X}) = S_1(\mathbf{X}) + wS_2(\mathbf{X}),$$

where

$$S_1(\mathbf{X}) = \sum_{i=1}^{N-1} \sum_{j=i+1}^{N} \sum_{k=1}^{n_{ij}} D_{ijk}^2; \qquad S_2(\mathbf{X}) = \sum_{i=1}^{N-1} \sum_{j=i+1}^{N} \sum_{k=1}^{n_{ij}} C_{ijk}^2,$$

with

$$D_{ijk} = d_{ijk} - d_{ij} \qquad \text{and} \qquad C_{ijk} = \sin \tfrac{1}{2}(a_{ijk} - a_{ij})$$

and

$$w = \sum_{\substack{i,j,k \\ i<j}} d_{ijk}^2 \bigg/ \sum_{\substack{i,j,k \\ i<j}} \sin^2 a_{ijk}.$$

In the above formulae, N is the number of phosphenes, n_{ij} is the number of observations (distances and angles) made on phosphene pair i and j (in some cases n_{ij} may be zero since there are not observations on every possible phosphene pair); d_{ijk} and a_{ijk}, $k = 1, \ldots, n_{ij}$, are the observations of distance and angle between phosphene pair i and j (the angles now having been converted from the original 'clock minutes' to radians). $\mathbf{X}$ is a $N \times 2$ matrix of co-ordinate values for the phosphenes, and d_{ij} and a_{ij} represent the distance and angle between phosphenes i and j defined by these coordinates; consequently they are of the form

$$d_{ij} = [(x_{i1} - x_{j1})^2 + (x_{i2} - x_{j2})^2]^{1/2},$$

$$a_{ij} = \frac{\pi}{2} - \tan^{-1}(x_{i2} - x_{j2})/(x_{i1} - x_{j1})$$

where $\mathbf{x}_i = (x_{i1}, x_{i2})$ and $\mathbf{x}_j = (x_{j1}, x_{j2})$ are the coordinates of phosphenes i and j.

For the distances the sum-of-squares criterion S_1 is an obvious choice; for the angles the choice of criterion is perhaps not so immediately clear but the choice was eventually made to give a maximum value when an observed angle and a fitted angle differed by π (or $-\pi$) radians. The weight, w, is chosen to make the 'distance' and 'angle' parts of S comparable.

S is a function of the $2N$ coordinate values, $\mathbf{X}$, and since $N = 90$ the minimization of S presents a formidable computational problem. Steepest descent was used incorporating Davidon's linear-search method to find the

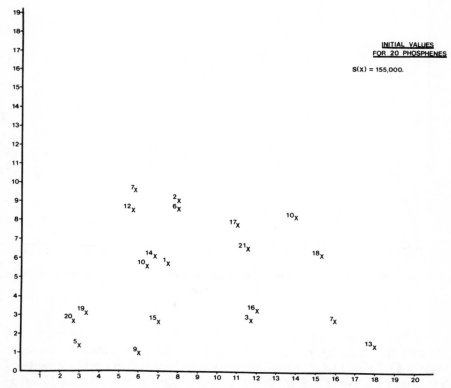

Figure 13.1   Part of initial configuration of phosphenes used in minimization procedure. (Positions of first 20 phosphenes are shown)

appropriate step size. Other more sophisticated minimization techniques might be considered but the computational problems would remain considerable. Since the solution obtained from the steepest-descent procedure proved satisfactory to the investigator involved, and the study was essentially undertaken to consider the feasibility of automated methods of fitting phosphene maps, little effort has been given to the possibility of using alternative minimization procedures, although these might be considered in the future.

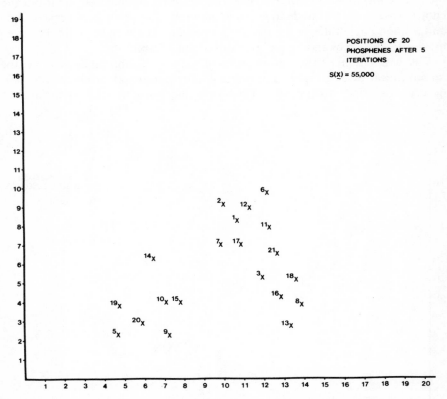

Figure 13.2 Positions of first 20 phosphenes after 5 iterations of the minimization procedure

As some indication of the operation of the minimization procedure, we can consider the changing positions of twenty of the phosphenes as shown in Figures 13.1 and 13.2. (The initial configuration was provided by a fairly *ad hoc* procedure which we shall not consider here; details can be found in Everitt and Rushton, 1978, where complete maps given by this minimization technique may also be found.)

13.2 WEIGHTED GENERALIZED PROCRUSTES METHOD

The second method used to analyse the phosphene data was derived from the generalized Procrustes procedure described by Gower (1975). In this procedure a number of $n \times p$ matrices, $\mathbf{X}_i, i = 1, \ldots, m$, are available whose jth row gives the coordinates of a point $P_j^{(i)}$ referred to p orthogonal axes. Typical practical situations are when each $\mathbf{X}_i$ is an observed data matrix or has been obtained as multidimensional scales of n stimuli or as factor loadings, or scores, etc. Problems are common where it is desired to study the relationships amongst the m sets and frequently some kind of combined analysis is desirable. Generalized Procrustes simultaneously translates, rotates and reflects all m data sets so that the fit is optimized according to a goodness-of-fit criterion. In brief, the method attempts to find orthogonal matrices $\mathbf{H}_i$ so that

$$S = \text{trace} \sum_{i=1}^{m} (\mathbf{X}_i\mathbf{H}_i - \mathbf{Y})^{\mathrm{T}}(\mathbf{X}_i\mathbf{H}_i - \mathbf{Y})$$

(the superscript ^{T} denotes a vector or matrix transpose) is minimized, where

$$\mathbf{Y} = \frac{1}{m} \sum_{i=1}^{m} \mathbf{X}_i\mathbf{H}_i.$$

Gower shows that $\mathbf{H}_i$ is given by

$$\mathbf{H}_i = \mathbf{U}_i^{\mathrm{T}}\mathbf{V}_i$$

where

$$\mathbf{X}_i^{\mathrm{T}}\mathbf{Y} = \mathbf{U}_i^{\mathrm{T}}\mathbf{\Gamma}\mathbf{V}_i,$$

the singular-value decomposition of the left-hand side.

Since the centroid matrix, $\mathbf{Y}$, is not known, this does not give an immediate method for calculating $\mathbf{H}_i$, but suggests the following simple iterative procedure

(1) Set $\mathbf{Y} = \mathbf{X}_1$; for $i = 2, \ldots, m$, rotate $\mathbf{X}_i$ to fit $\mathbf{Y}$ and re-evaluate $\mathbf{Y}$ as the mean of $\mathbf{X}_1, \ldots, \mathbf{X}_i$
(2) Rotate $\mathbf{X}_i, i = 1, \ldots, m$, to fit $\mathbf{Y}$; recompute $\mathbf{Y}$, evaluate S and repeat this step until some convergence criterion is satisfied.
(3) Refer $\mathbf{Y}$ and each $\mathbf{X}_i$ to principal axis of $\mathbf{Y}$, to give a unique average picture to be compared with each individual set of observations.

The adaptation of this method described below and applied to the phosphene data is what may be termed a *weighted generalized Procrustes analysis*. Associated with each $\mathbf{X}_i$ matrix is a diagonal matrix of 'weights', $\mathbf{N}_i$, one weight for each of the n points in $\mathbf{X}_i$, and we now wish to find orthogonal matrices $\mathbf{H}_i$ that minimize

$$S^* = \text{trace} \sum_{i=1}^{m} (\mathbf{X}_i\mathbf{H}_i - \mathbf{Y})^{\mathrm{T}}\mathbf{N}_i(\mathbf{X}_i\mathbf{H}_i - \mathbf{Y}),$$

where

$$Y = \left[\sum_{i=1}^{m} N_i \right]^{-1} \sum_{i=1}^{m} N_i X_i H_i.$$

In this case H_i is obtained from

$$H_i = U_i^T V_i,$$

where

$$X_i^T N_i Y = U_i^T \Gamma_i V_i,$$

The iterative algorithm for generalized Procrustes may easily be adapted for 'weighted' Procrustes as follows:

(1) Find an initial value for Y. (Here using any particular X_i matrix may not be possible.)
(2) Rotate $N_i^{1/2} X_i, i = 1, \ldots, m$, to fit $N_i^{1/2} Y$; recompute Y, evaluate S^*, and repeat until some convergence criterion is satisified.
(3) Refer Y and each X_i (if required) to the principal axis of Y.

(Both generalized and weighted Procrustes are easily implemented using GENSTAT; see Nelder et al., 1977.)

Let us now consider how this method may be applied to the phosphene data to obtain a phosphene map. In this case the matrices X_i arise from phosphene i as in Table 13.1.

Each observation of distance and angle may be converted to the corresponding Cartesian coordinates and these are averaged to give the coordinates of phosphenes $i_1, \ldots, i_{n_i}$ relative to phosphene i as the origin. These coordinates are stored in X_i, so here $n = N, p = 2$, and $m = N$. (Some rows of X_i will contain no entries since phosphene i is not observed relative to all other phosphenes.)

Table 13.1 Phosphene i—observations relative to phosphenes $i_1, \ldots, i_{n_i}$

Phosphene Pair	Observations		
$i - i_1$:	(d_{ii_11}, a_{ii_11})	$\cdots$	$(d_{ii_1n_{ii_1}}, a_{ii_1n_{ii_1}})$
$i - i_2$:			
$\vdots$			
$i - i_{n_i}$:	$(d_{ii_{n_i}1}, a_{ii_{n_i}1})$	$\cdots$	$(d_{ii_{n_i}n_{ii_{n_i}}}, a_{ii_{n_i}n_{ii_{n_i}}})$

The weight matrices, N_i, arise because of the differing numbers of observations made on each phosphene pair, and contain the n_{ij} values on the main diagonal, with $n_{ii} = \sum_{j=1, j \neq i}^{N} n_{ij}$, the number of times phosphene i is observed in matrix X_i.

To begin the interative algorithm for weighted Procrustes, we need an initial value of Y which contains an entry for each row, i.e. we need initial coordinate values for *all* phosphenes. None of the X_i matrices satisfy this requirement, and so we must look elsewhere. One possibility is to set $Y = X_i$; for $i = 2, \ldots, m$ rotate X_i to fit Y for rows that are not null in either X or Y and recompute Y as the (weighted) mean of the rotated X_i. A weighted form of pairwise Procrustes analysis can be used to find these rotations. However, with these data the solution obtained from the method described in the previous section was available, so it was used. Finally we must translate the X_i matrices in some sensible way before proceeding with the iterative procedure outlined above. One method would be to translate each so that a chosen phosphene was taken as positioned at the origin. Unfortunately, there was no

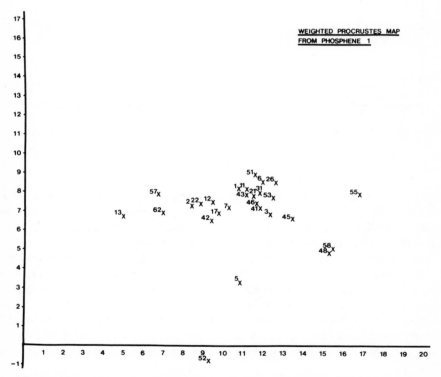

Figure 13.3   Weighted Procrustes map of phosphenes observed in relation to phosphene number 1

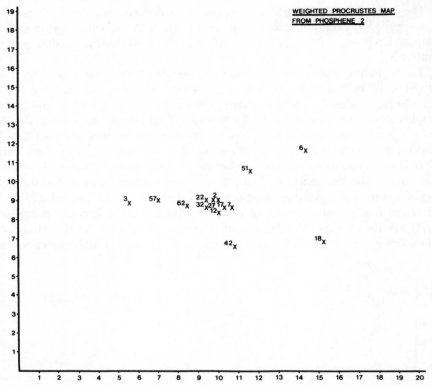

Figure 13.4   Weighted Procrustes map of phosphenes observed in relation to phosphene number 2

phosphene which had an entry in every X_i matrix. Another method is to place the weighted mean of each X_i matrix at the origin. The method used here was to translate X_i so that the coordinates of phosphene i were equal to those in the solution obtained from the previous minimization technique.

The weighted Procrustes algorithm took some 28 iterations to converge, the criterion value S being reduced from 7775.8 to 6799.4. The final map was very similar to that obtained by the previous method, although it was interesting to note that it had a slightly lower value of the criterion, $S(X)$, used in Section 13.1 and might be used to provide a new starting configuration for the minimization procedure, although this has, as yet, not been tried. For interest two of the final 'individual' phosphene maps are shown in Figures 13.3 and 13.4.

13.3 CONCLUSIONS

The rather elaborate methods described here for arriving at an overall 'best' phosphene map became necessary because of the degree of variability of, and conflict between, observations. Possible sources of such variation have been listed and discussed by Rushton and Brindley (1977). Some of the sources of variation (notably eye movement) could be substantially eliminated if two phosphenes or more could be presented at once. However, the form of the observations would be similar even when two phosphenes were presented simultaneously, so that the same methods might still be applicable; for these data both methods gave very similar solutions, and neither had obvious advantages computationally (both were very slow!). However, the weighted generalized Procrustes method is appealing because it avoids combining angles and distances in a single criterion and because it has possible applications in other areas.

REFERENCES

Brindley, G. S. and Lewin, W. S. (1968) The sensations produced by electrical stimulation of the visual cortex. *Journal of Physiology*, **196**, 479–93.

Everitt, B. S. and Rushton, D. N. (1978) A method for plotting the optimum positions of an array of cortical electrical phosphenes. *Biometrics*, **34**, 399–410.

Gower, J. C. (1975) Generalized Procrustes analysis. *Psychometrika*, **40**, 33–51.

Nelder, J. A. and Members of the Rothamsted Statistics Department (1977) *GENSTAT A General Statistical Programme*. Harpenden: Statistics Department, Rothamsted Experimental Station.

Rushton, D. N. and Brindley, G. S. (1977) Short- and long-term stability of cortical electrical phosphenes. In Rose, F. C. (ed.) (1977) *Physiological Aspects of Clinical Neurology*, pp. 123–53. Oxford: Blackwell.

CHAPTER 14

Analysing Data from Multivariate Directed Graphs: An Application to Social Networks*

S. E. Fienberg and M. M. Meyer, Carnegie-Mellon University, U.S.A.
S. S. Wasserman, University of Minnesota, U.S.A.

A multivariate directed graph consists of a set of g nodes, and a family of directed arcs (one for each relation) connecting pairs of nodes. Such multivariate directed graphs provide natural representations for social networks. In this chapter we consider methods to analyse a network of 73 organizations in a Midwest American community linked by three types of relations: information, money, and support. The resulting data set, described by Galaskiewicz and Marsden (1978), involves $3 \times 73 \times 72 = 15\ 768$ possible arcs or 'observations'. We describe a class of stochastic log-linear models for multivariate directed graphs, demonstrate how they can be fitted to the data using generalized iterative scaling as described by Darroch and Ratcliff (1972), and explain the connection between these models and variants on standard log-linear models for multidimensional contingency tables discussed by Bishop, Fienberg, and Holland (1975). We also consider a disaggregation of the organizations into sub-groups, and demonstrate how to adapt our models to explore the intra- and inter-group relationships. These methods generalize research of Holland and Leinhardt (1981), who develop a model for dyadic relationships in univariate directed-graph data. The chapter includes a detailed analysis of the Galaskiewicz–Marsden data.

14.1 INTRODUCTION

The main emphasis throughout this volume on interpreting multivariate data has been on the use of graphical methods. Despite the fact that the title of the present chapter contains the words 'data', 'multivariate', and 'graphs', we shall break step with the other authors and describe a class of multivariate network problems, in which we would have liked to use graphical methods

*The preparation of this chapter was supported in part by Grants SOC78–26075 and SES80–08573 from the National Science Foundation, and Contract N00014–78–C–0151 from the Office of Naval Research, to the University of Minnesota.

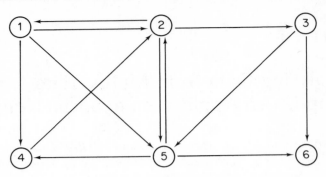

Figure 14.1   Example of a univariate directed graph involving $g = 6$ individuals

but, for the moment, have had to settle for a more traditional multivariate model-based approach. This may seem even more surprising since the network problems we address begin with data that correspond to a picture or graph.

Figure 14.1 contains an example of a *univariate directed graph*, a graphical representation of a network involving $g = 6$ individuals. There are $g(g - 1) = 30$ possible arrows or *directed arcs* linking these 6 individuals in pairs, only 12 of which are present in Figure 14.1. The information in a univariate graph for g individuals can be summarized by means of a $g \times g$ *adjacency matrix* $\mathbf{x}$, with elements

$$x_{ij} = \begin{cases} 1 & \text{if } i \text{ relates to } j \\ 0 & \text{otherwise,} \end{cases}$$

where, by convention, the diagonal terms, x_{ii}, are set equal to zero. The adjacency matrix for Figure 14.1 is:

$$\mathbf{x} = \begin{array}{c} \\ 1 \\ 2 \\ 3 \\ 4 \\ 5 \\ 6 \end{array} \begin{array}{c} \begin{array}{cccccc} 1 & 2 & 3 & 4 & 5 & 6 \end{array} \\ \left[\begin{array}{cccccc} 0 & 1 & 0 & 1 & 1 & 0 \\ 1 & 0 & 1 & 0 & 1 & 0 \\ 0 & 0 & 0 & 0 & 1 & 1 \\ 0 & 1 & 0 & 0 & 0 & 0 \\ 0 & 1 & 0 & 1 & 0 & 1 \\ 0 & 0 & 0 & 0 & 0 & 0 \end{array} \right] \end{array}$$

There are several approaches that we might adopt to model the data in the adjacency matrix, $\mathbf{x}$. For example, we might focus on the 6 individuals and assume that individual i makes 5 possible independent choices (corresponding to arrows), with some unknown Bernoulli parameter, $p_i (i = 1, 2, \ldots, 6)$.

Then a suitable data summary would be the row totals of **x**, i.e., (3, 3, 2, 1, 3, 0). The assumption of independence of choices is not likely to be satisfied in practice, however. Alternatively, we might focus on the $6 \times 5 = 30$ pairs of individuals, and assume that the data for the pairs are independent and identically distributed. In effect, then, we would choose to focus on relationships, and would observe three different types:

Null,

Asymmetric,

Mutual.

Thus the observed data could be summarized as shown in the following 2×2 table:

		Receive Choice		
		Yes	No	
Send Choice	Yes	4	8	12
	No	8	10	18
		12	18	30

Note that each pair has been counted twice, once for 'sending' and once for 'receiving', thus merging the asymmetric relationships.

The approach involving pairs essentially uses the $g(g - 1)$ permutations of the g individuals, two at a time, and thus leads to a double counting of each pair. By focusing on the $\binom{g}{2} = g(g - 1)/2$ combinations or *dyads*, we can eliminate the double counting and obtain the following summary:

No. of Dyads

5

8

2

We shall consider stochastic models of multivariate directed graphs, involving several types of arrows or relationships, that treat the $\binom{g}{2}$ dyads as independent random variables. We do this in the full knowledge that for most network problems dyads are constructs. We do not sample them. Rather, if we sample at all, we take a sample of individuals and we measure information on dyadic relationships. The independence of dyadic information is an assumption which in practice is in need of some verification. We do not address this issue here. For population directed-graph data, consisting of the dyad information for all of the individuals in a network, the use of stochastic models leans for support on (1) randomization arguments, (2) super-population ideas, or (3) simple convenience, in providing a framework for exploratory data analysis.

In Section 14.2 we describe a set of network data involving organizations and three types of organizational relations. Then, in Section 14.3, we describe a class of models and multivariate methods for the analysis of such data, which treats the organizations as a single group. After fitting these models to the data, in Section 14.4, we further develop the models in Section 14.5 to allow for disaggregation of the organizations into subgroups. We conclude by returning to the *graphical* theme and suggest some extensions of our modelling approach which might lead to interesting graphical summaries.

14.2 A SPECIFIC NETWORK: TOWERTOWN, U.S.A.

The data that have motivated our work on this topic come from a study of 109 formal organizations (each with more than 20 employees) in a small midwest U.S. community of 32 000 persons, referred to by the pseudonym 'Towertown'. Galaskiewicz (1979) described the survey of Towertown, Galaskiewicz and Marsden (1978) report on the data considered here, and we have described the data elsewhere in detail (Fienberg and Wasserman, 1981). For the present, it will suffice to note that we are concerned with the results of questionnaire data for a subset of 73 organizations, representing the ties between pairs of organizations for three types of relations: (1) information, (2) money, and (3) support. This data set can then be represented as a *multivariate directed graph*, summarized by three adjacency matrices (x_1, x_2, x_3) defined for the same 73 organizations. Each matrix is of dimension 73×73 and represents $73(73-1) = 5256$ possible directed arcs using 0s and 1s.* Given the size of these matrices, it should not be surprising that graphical representations of even the univariate links are too complex to comprehend.

Thus, we still need a way to look at and, perhaps more importantly, summarize the data. Table 14.1 contains one such summary of the data given by Galaskiewicz and Marsden (1978), in the form of a 2^6 table of counts of pairs of organizations. This table gives the direct multivariate generalization of the 2×2 representation for a single relation given in Section 14.1. Each pair of

---

*(Throughout this chapter we work with summaries of this data set. The full data set, consisting of three adjacency matrices and pseudonyms for the organizations, is available on request from the authors.)

Table 14.1 Observed distribution of inter-organizational transactions involving three relations and 73 organizations

	1. Information sent	−	−	−	−	−	−	−	−	+	+	+	+	+	+	+	+
	1′. Information received	−	−	−	−	+	+	+	+	−	−	−	−	+	+	+	+
	2. Money sent	−	−	+	+	−	−	+	+	−	−	+	+	−	−	+	+
	2′. Money received	−	+	−	+	−	+	−	+	−	+	−	+	−	+	−	+
3. Support sent	3′. Support received																
−	−	3042	100	100	20	145	15	11	7	145	11	15	7	322	47	47	16
−	+	111	18	12	3	20	9	3	4	32	20	2	1	77	38	15	25
+	−	111	12	18	3	32	2	20	1	20	3	9	4	77	15	38	25
+	+	116	14	14	4	15	4	6	0	15	6	4	0	100	50	50	28

Table total = 5256

'+' indicates that a directed flow is present, '−' indicates that a directed flow is absent. A somewhat different version of these data appeared in Galaskiewicz and Marsden (1978).

organizations is counted twice, once from the perspective of each member. Thus, the total of the counts in the table is 5256, twice the number of pairs, $\binom{73}{2} = 2628$. Henceforth, we refer to Table 14.1 as the w-table with entries $\{w_{ii'jj'kk'}\}$.

The 2^6 cells of Table 14.1 consist of (a) 8 cells whose counts are doubled, and (b) 28 cells whose counts are duplicated. If we eliminate the duplication and doubling of counts, we get an arrangement of 36 cells, whose counts correctly total 2628. In Table 14.2 we give one possible representation of these 36 cells in a form resembling a three-dimensional $4 \times 4 \times 4$ cross-classification, where the three 'variables' correspond to the three relations (1) information, (2) money, and (3) support.

Table 14.2   Structure for actual table of 36 counts

Information		Money		Support M	A		N
			M	z_{MMM} 14	z_{MMA} 25		z_{MMN} 8
	M	Money	A	z_{MAM} 50	z_{MAA} 38	$z_{MA\bar{A}}$ 15	z_{MAN} 47
			N	z_{MNM} 50	z_{MNA} 77		z_{MNN} 161
			M	z_{AMM} 0	z_{AMA} 4	$z_{AM\bar{A}}$ 1	z_{AMN} 7
Information	A	Money	A	z_{AAM} 4	z_{AAA} 9	$z_{AA\bar{A}}$ 2	z_{AAN} 15
				$z_{A\bar{A}M}$ 6	$z_{A\bar{A}A}$ 3	$z_{A\bar{A}\bar{A}}$ 20	$z_{A\bar{A}N}$ 11
			N	z_{ANM} 15	z_{ANA} 20	$z_{AN\bar{A}}$ 32	z_{ANN} 145
			M	z_{NMM} 2	z_{NMA} 3		$z_{A\bar{A}N}$ 10
	N	Money	A	z_{NAM} 14	z_{NAA} 18	$z_{NA\bar{A}}$ 12	z_{NAN} 10
			N	z_{NNM} 58	z_{NNA} 111		z_{NNN} 1521

When the dyadic structure for a single relation is asymmetric, the 'direction' of the corresponding arc does not matter. We use a single subscript, A, to denote the relation in such situations. When the dyadic links for two or more relations are both asymmetric, we need to distinguish between situations where the arcs for a pair of relations go in the same or different directions. Thus, to distinguish these situations, we use two different subscripts, A and $\bar{A}$, with identical subscripts for those relations whose asymmetric directed arcs go in the same direction. We arbitrarily assign the subscript A to the lowest-numbered asymmetric generator. (Note that interchanging the subscripts A and $\bar{A}$ yields the same dyadic structural relationship.) We denote the observed counts in Table 14.2 by z_{abc}, for $a, b, c = M, A, \bar{A}, N$ (for Mutual, Asymmetric, $\bar{A}$symmetric, and Null), where the convention for the use of the subscripts A and $\bar{A}$ is as described above. These observed counts can be thought of as realizations of a set of random variables, $\{Z_{abc}\}$, whose probability structure we wish to model.

14.3 LOG-LINEAR MODELS FOR MULTIVARIATE DIRECTED GRAPHS

We wish to model the probability p_{abc} that a randomly selected dyad would be assigned to cell (a, b, c) in Table 14.2, where

$$\sum_{\text{all cells}} p_{abc} = 1. \tag{14.1}$$

Although we might think of using log-linear models directly for the $\{p_{abc}\}$, such an approach leads to difficulties of interpretation (see Fienberg and Wasserman, 1980, for further details). Instead, we define

$$\xi_{abc} = \begin{cases} \log p_{abc} & \text{if } a, b, \text{and } c \text{ are each equal to } M \text{ or } N, \\ \log\left[\dfrac{p_{abc}}{2}\right] & \text{if one of } a, b, \text{ and } c \text{ equals } A. \end{cases} \tag{14.2}$$

Our plan is to develop a class of linear models for the $\{\xi_{abc}\}$, which for the $\{p_{abc}\}$ yields an affine translation of a class of log-linear models (see Chapter 9 of both Haberman, 1974 and Haberman, 1979). This approach

(1) treats dyads involving asymmetric ties as having been produced with an orientation and then pooled. (This also accounts for the divisor of 2 for counts involving asymmetric ties.)
(2) includes as a special case the model of independent individual choices (see the discussion of Section 14.1).
(3) is directly related to an approach of Holland and Leinhardt (1981) which allows for parameters associated with the individuals in the dyad (see also Fienberg and Wasserman, 1981).

We plan to consider models for the $\{\xi_{abc}\}$ which are linear in parameters that reflect the 13 distinct types of dyadic patterns depicted in Figure 14.2. Note that the patterns have a hierarchical structure. For example, the six-arrow full mutuality pattern, (xiii), contains all the other patterns as special cases, and the conditional multiplex mutuality pattern, (xii), contains all patterns from (i) to (xi) as special cases. We consider different levels (I, II, III, IV) in a class of increasingly complex log-linear models for the $\{\xi_{abc}\}$ with parameters based on the patterns in Figure 14.2.

(I) The null model corresponding to Figure 14.2 (i) depicts the probabilities $\{p_{abc}\}$ as being constant, and could be represented as

$$\xi_{abc} = \theta,$$

where $\theta = \log (1/36)$. This is an individual, independent Bernoulli choice, model. For subsequent models we use θ as a *normalizing constant*.

(II) At the next level, we add choice parameters, $\{\theta_1, \theta_2, \theta_3\}$ for the relations [Figure 14.2(ii)]: one for each directed arc. For example,

$$\xi_{MAN} = \theta + 2\theta_1 + \theta_2$$
$$\xi_{MAA} = \theta + 2\theta_1 + \theta_2 + \theta_3$$
$$\xi_{MA\bar{A}} = \theta + 2\theta_1 + \theta_2 + \theta_3.$$

(III) Next, we add sets of parameters corresponding to heightened or diminished effects related to pairs of directed arcs:

(a) $\rho_{11}, \rho_{22}, \rho_{33}$ for *mutuality* effects [see Figure 14.2(iii)],
(b) $\rho_{12}, \rho_{13}, \rho_{23}$ for *exchange* effects [see Figure 14.2(iv)],
(c) $\theta_{12}, \theta_{13}, \theta_{23}$ for *multiplexity* effects [see Figure 14.2(v)],

This yields, for example,

$$\xi_{MA\bar{A}} = \theta + 2\theta_1 + \theta_2 + \theta_3 + \rho_{11} + \rho_{12} + \rho_{13} + \rho_{23} + \theta_{12} + \theta_{13},$$
$$\xi_{MAM} = \theta + 2\theta_1 + \theta_2 + 2\theta_3 + \rho_{11} + \rho_{33} + \rho_{12} + 2\rho_{13} + \rho_{23}$$
$$+ \theta_{12} + 2\theta_{13} + \theta_{23}.$$

There are additional sets of parameters corresponding to the remaining 4 levels in Figure 14.2. At level IV, one of these parameters involves only multiplexity and thus is denoted by a triple subscripted θ, i.e., θ_{123}. The remaining parameters involve mixtures of mutuality, exchange, and multiplexity, and are denoted by subscripted $(\rho\theta)$s. Overbars on subscripts are used to distinguish asymmetric directed arcs going in opposite directions, e.g., $(\rho\theta)_{12\bar{3}}$.

The parameters in this class of models are GLIM-like in structure (e.g., see Nelder and Wedderburn, 1972), in that a parameter is included in the model if and only if the corresponding effect is present. The entries of the resulting 'design matrix' for the parameter structure for any given model are 0s, 1s, and

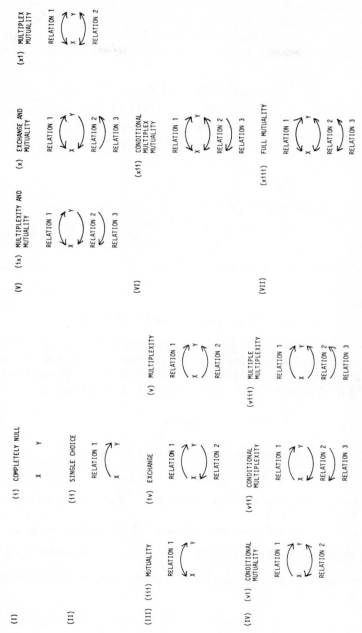

Figure 14.2 Patterns of flow dependency in dyadic patterns

2s. This particular problem could be handled in GLIM directly only through the explicit construction of this design matrix, which is a formidable task.

The parameters have a hierarchical structure, i.e., if we set some parameters equal to zero, all related higher-order terms are also zero. For example,

$$
\begin{aligned}
\theta_{12} = 0 \Rightarrow \theta_{123} &= (\rho\theta)_{112} = (\rho\theta)_{221} = (\rho\theta)_{3\bar{1}2} \\
&= (\rho\theta)_{1123} = (\rho\theta)_{112\bar{3}} = (\rho\theta)_{2213} \\
&= (\rho\theta)_{2213} = (\rho\theta)_{1122} = (\rho\theta)_{11223} \\
&= (\rho\theta)_{11332} = (\rho\theta)_{22331} \\
&= (\rho\theta)_{112233} = 0,
\end{aligned}
$$

and

$$
\begin{aligned}
\rho_{11} = 0 \Rightarrow (\rho\theta)_{112} &= (\rho\theta)_{113} = (\rho\theta)_{1123} = (\rho\theta)_{112\bar{3}} \\
&= (\rho\theta)_{1122} = (\rho\theta)_{1133} = (\rho\theta)_{11223} \\
&= (\rho\theta)_{11332} = (\rho\theta)_{112233} = 0.
\end{aligned}
$$

In the next section we discuss how to fit these models to the social network data.

14.4 FITTING THE MODELS TO DATA

Fitting the log-linear models of the preceding section to data in Table 14.2 follows, in principle, directly from the general results for log-linear models in Haberman (1974) or Appendix II of Fienberg (1980). The minimal sufficient statistics (*MSS*s) take the form of linear combinations of the $\{z_{abc}\}$,

$$
\sum_{\text{all cells}} \alpha_{abc} z_{abc}, \tag{14.3}
$$

where for a *MSS* corresponding to a 'generic' parameter, β,

$$
\alpha_{abc} = \text{multiple of } \beta \text{ in } \xi_{abc}. \tag{14.4}
$$

The multiples of all parameters are either 0, 1, or 2, and thus all the αs are either 0, 1, or 2.

If we let the expected value for the (a, b, c) cell be $m_{abc} = N p_{abc}$, where $N = \binom{g}{2}$, then the likelihood equations are found by setting the *MSS*s equal to their estimated expected values; for a generic parameter the likelihood equation is

$$
\sum_{\text{all cells}} \alpha_{abc} \hat{m}_{abc} = \sum_{\text{all cells}} \alpha_{abc} z_{abc}. \tag{14.5}
$$

We can solve a set of likelihood equations, each of the form (14.5), by using a version of the generalized iterative scaling algorithm due to Darroch and Ratcliff (1972), with starting values as follows:

$$\hat{m}^{(0)}_{abc} = \begin{cases} 1 & \text{if } a, b, \text{ and } c \text{ are each equal to } M \text{ or } N, \\ \frac{1}{2} & \text{if one or more of } a, b, \text{ and } c \text{ equals } A. \end{cases} \quad (14.6)$$

There are two drawbacks to this approach. First, one needs to work with data arrays of the irregular shape of Table 14.2. Second, the convergence of generalized iterative scaling can be excruciatingly slow.

All, however, is not lost. Two results, one simple and one relatively complex, lead us to a very straightforward alternative approach for computing the $\{\hat{m}_{abc}\}$.

Result 1: For the class of affine translations of hierarchical loglinear models described in Section 14.3, each set of MSSs is equivalent to a set of marginal totals for the 2^6 table (i.e., the w-table) with doubled and duplicated counts.

For example, the simple model with only a choice parameter, θ_1, and a mutuality parameter, ρ_{11}, for the first relation has MSS's $\{z_{M++}, z_{A++}, z_{N++}\}$, and

$$\left. \begin{array}{l} z_{M++} = \frac{1}{2} w_{11++++}, \\ z_{A++} = w_{10++++} = w_{01++++}, \\ z_{N++} = \frac{1}{2} w_{00++++}. \end{array} \right\} \quad (14.7)$$

Result 2: For each affine translation of a log-linear model for the z-table, there is a corresponding log-linear model for the w-table, with equivalent estimated expected values, once we take account of the duplication and doubling.

For example, for the model with choice and mtuality parameters, i.e.

$$\{\theta, \theta_1, \theta_2, \theta_3, \rho_{11}, \rho_{22}, \rho_{33}\}, \quad (14.8)$$

the corresponding log-linear model for the w-table that yields equivalent maximum-likelihood estimators (MLEs) is, in GLIM-like notation,

$$\begin{aligned} \log m_{ii'jj'kk'} = {} & \lambda + \lambda_1 \delta_i + \lambda_{1'} \delta_{i'} \\ & + \lambda_2 \delta_j + \lambda_{2'} \delta_{j'} \\ & + \lambda_3 \delta_k + \lambda_{3'} \delta_{k'} \\ & + \lambda_{11} \delta_i \delta_{i'} + \lambda_{22} \delta_j \delta_{j'} \\ & + \lambda_{33} \delta_k \delta_{k'}. \end{aligned} \quad (14.9)$$

Here $m_{ii'jj'kk'}$ is the expected value for the (i, i', j, j', k, k') cell, and each δ-term equals 1 if the subscript takes the value 1, and is zero otherwise.

To understand *Result 2* we need to note the following correspondences between the **w**-table and the **z**-table:

	w-table	**z**-table
Cell:	(i, i', j, j', k, k')	(a, b, c)
Symmetric flows:	$i = i', j = j', k = k'$	$a, b, c = M$ or N

Because of the doubling of the counts in Table 14.1, we have:

$$\log m_{ii'jj'kk'} = \begin{cases} \log (2\,m_{abc}) & \text{for symmetric flows,} \\ \log (m_{abc}) & \text{for asymmetric flows.} \end{cases} \tag{14.10}$$

Substituting expression (14.2) into (14.10) and noting that $m_{abc} = \binom{g}{2} p_{abc}$, we get

$$\log m_{ii'jj'kk'} = \left[2\binom{g}{2} \right] + \xi_{abc}. \tag{14.11}$$

Thus the models for $\log m_{ii'jj'kk'}$ and ξ_{abc} differ by only a constant.

A direct consequence of these two results is that we can compute *MLE*s for the expected values under the models of Section 14.3 using standard iterative methods for contingency tables. (This is in fact what Galaskiewicz and Marsden (1978) did in their original analyses of Table 14.1!) For example, for the model with parameters given by (14.8), the *MSS*s are equivalently given by the two-way marginal totals of the **w**-table:

$$\{w_{ii'++++}\}, \{w_{++jj'++}\}, \{w_{++++kk'}\}.$$

These marginals can be fitted to the 2^6 table using the standard iterative proportional fitting procedure (or some other program such as GLIM). Because of symmetries in marginal totals, e.g.,

$$w_{10++++} = w_{01++++}, \qquad w_{++10++} = w_{++01++}, \qquad w_{++++10} = w_{++++01},$$

the resulting parameter estimates are such that

$$\hat{\lambda}_1 = \hat{\lambda}_{1'}, \qquad \hat{\lambda}_2 = \hat{\lambda}_{2'}, \qquad \hat{\lambda}_3 = \hat{\lambda}_{3'}.$$

The estimated parameters for the models for ξ_{abc} can be computed directly from these parameters:

$$\hat{\theta} = \hat{\lambda} - \log \left[2\binom{g}{2} \right]$$

$$\hat{\theta}_i = \hat{\lambda}_i, \qquad i = 1, 2, 3$$

$$\hat{\rho}_{ii} = \hat{\lambda}_{ii}, \qquad i = 1, 2, 3.$$

We note that the number of degrees of freedom ($d.f.$) for any model *must* be calculated using the model for the **z**-table, not the one for the **w**-table, and the value of any standard goodness-of-fit statistic computed directly on the fitted **w**-table must be divided by 2.

14.5 INITIAL ANALYSES OF THE TOWERTOWN DATA

In Table 14.3 we list a set of seven loglinear models that we have fitted to the Galaskiewicz–Marsden data of Table 14.1 (some of these models correspond to ones fit by Galaskiewicz and Marsden). The first six models are of increasing complexity, and only the most complex of these models, (6), provides a fit which is not significant at the 0.05 or even 0.01 level. Model (7) is a compromise between models (5) and (6), that drops one of the conditional mutuality and two of the multiplex mutuality effects, but still provides an acceptable fit to the data. Its parameter estimates are listed in Table 14.4.

The most substantial estimated effects (in terms of magnitude) are those associated with choice ($\hat{\theta}_i$s), mutuality ($\hat{\rho}_{ii}$s), conditional mutuality $(\hat{\rho\theta})_{331} = -2.15$ and multiplex mutuality $(\hat{\rho\theta})_{1133} = 2.88$. Interpreting these effects is complicated. For all hierarchical models, with nonorthogonal designs, the parameters that are easist to interpret are those associated with the highest-order effects. Here the multiplex mutuality parameter estimate implies a heightened likelihood of simultaneous reciprocation of both information and support, relative to what we would expect in a model without the multiplex mutuality parameter.

One of the major difficulties with the models of Section 14.3 is that dyads are considered to be homogeneous and thus do not allow for the inherent differences among the organizations. Without some allowance for this

Table 14.3 Various log-linear models fitted to data in Table 14.1

Model		$d.f.$	G^{2*}
(1)	$\theta, \theta_1, \theta_2, \theta_3$	32	2528.5
(2)	$\theta, \theta_1, \theta_2, \theta_3, \rho_{11}, \rho_{22}, \rho_{33}$	29	895.0
(3)	$\theta, \theta_1, \theta_2, \theta_3, \rho_{11}, \rho_{22}, \rho_{33}, \rho_{12}, \rho_{13}, \rho_{23}$	26	224.1
(4)	$\theta, \theta_1, \theta_2, \theta_3, \rho_{11}, \rho_{22}, \rho_{33}, \rho_{12}, \rho_{13}, \rho_{23}, \theta_{12}, \theta_{13}, \theta_{23}$	23	122.15
(5)	$(\rho\theta)_{112}, (\rho\theta)_{113}, (\rho\theta)_{221}, (\rho\theta)_{223}, (\rho\theta)_{331}, (\rho\theta)_{332},$ plus all implied lower-order terms	17	40.32
(6)	$(\rho\theta)_{1122}, (\rho\theta)_{1133}, (\rho\theta)_{2233},$ plus all implied lower-order terms	14	20.73
(7)	parameters from model (4) plus $(\rho\theta)_{113}, (\rho\theta)_{331}, (\rho\theta)_{112}, (\rho\theta)_{223}, (\rho\theta)_{332},$ and $(\rho\theta)_{1133}$	17	22.24

$^{*}G^2$ is the value of the log-likelihood ratio chi-squared goodness-of-fit statistic.

Table 14.4   Parameter estimates for model (7) fitted to the data from Table 14.1

Parameter	Estimate	
$\hat{\theta}$	-0.55	Normalization constant
$\hat{\theta}_1$	-3.02	
$\hat{\theta}_2$	-3.35	Choice
$\hat{\theta}_3$	-3.28	
$\hat{\rho}_{11}$	3.82	
$\hat{\rho}_{22}$	1.52	Mutuality
$\hat{\rho}_{33}$	3.28	
$\hat{\rho}_{12}$	1.01	
$\hat{\rho}_{13}$	1.73	Exchange
$\hat{\rho}_{23}$	0.60	
$\hat{\theta}_{12}$	0.78	
$\hat{\theta}_{13}$	1.34	Multiplex
$\hat{\theta}_{23}$	1.57	
$(\hat{\rho\theta})_{112}$	-0.52	
$(\hat{\rho\theta})_{113}$	-1.30	
$(\hat{\rho\theta})_{223}$	-0.70	Conditional mutuality
$(\hat{\rho\theta})_{331}$	-2.15	
$(\hat{\rho\theta})_{332}$	-0.83	
$(\hat{\rho\theta})_{1133}$	2.88	Multiplex mutuality

heterogeneity, further interpretation of fitted models makes little sense. In Table 14.5 we list pseudonyms for each of the 73 organizations, and provide a partition of them into four sub-groups:

(1) business $g_1 = 16$;
(2) political $g_2 = 24$;
(3) nonprofit voluntary associations $g_3 = 21$;
(4) nonprofit service associations $g_4 = 12$.

We postulate that the sociological factors affecting interaction should be relatively homogeneous within these groups. Thus, we can categorize the original $\binom{g}{2} = \binom{73}{2} = 2628$ dyads into the cells of an upper-triangular 4×4 array:

No. of Dyads:

	G_1	G_2	G_3	G_4	
	120	384	336	192	G_1
		276	504	288	G_2
			210	252	G_3
				66	G_4

For each cell in this array there is a 2^6 table.

Table 14.5 Partition of 73 organizations into four groups

G_1 Business	G_2 Political	G_3 Nonprofit voluntary associations	G_4 Nonprofit service organizations
2. Farm Equipment Co.	25. City Council	1. Farm Bureau	46. Health Services Center
3. Clothing Mfg. Co.	26. City Manager	9. Chamber of Commerce	52. United Fund
4. Farm Supply Co.	27. County Board	10. Banker's Association	60. St. Hilary's Catholic
5. Mechanical Co.	28. Fire Department	18. Bar Association	Church
6. Electrical Equip. Co.	29. Human Relations Dept.	19. Board of Realtors	61. 1st Baptist Church
7. Metal Products Co.	30. Mayor's Office	20. Small Business Assoc.	62. 1st Church of the
8. Music Equip. Co.	31. Police Dept.	21. Music Employee	Light
11. 1st Towertown Bank	32. Sanitation Dept.	Union #1	63. 1st Congregational
12. Towertown Savings	33. Streets and Sanitation	22. Music Employee	Church
& Loan	34. Park District	Union #2	64. 1st Methodist Church
13. Bank of Towertown	35. Zoning Board	23. Teacher's Union	65. Unity Lutheran Church
14. 2nd Towertown Bank	41. Hospital Board	24. Central Labor Union	66. University Methodist
15. Brinkman Law Firm	42. Public Hospital	36. Democratic Committee	Church
16. Cater Law Firm	44. Board of Mental Health	37. Republican Committee	69. Family Services
17. Knapp Law Firm	45. County Board of Health	38. League of Women Voters	71. YMCA
39. Towertown News	47. Highway Authority	43. Medical Society	72. Towertown Mental
40. WTWR Radio	48. School Board	48. 1st Kiwanis Club	Health Center
($g_1 = 16$)	53. High School	49. 2nd Kiwanis Club	($g_4 = 12$)
	54. Community College	50. Rotary Club	
	56. State University	51. Lions Club	
	57. Dept. of Public Aid	55. Parent–Teacher Assoc.	
	67. Housing Authority	58. 1st Assoc. of Churches	
	68. Employment Services	59. 2nd Assoc. of Churches	
	70. Youth Services	($g_3 = 21$)	
	73.		
	($g_2 = 24$)		

Within each of the four groups we can analyse flows using a 2^6 table and the models from Section 14.3. These 2^6 tables have the same doublings and duplications as the aggregated 2^6 table. The flows between groups (in pairs) now have an orientation and there are corresponding 2^6 tables describing these flows which contain no doubling and no duplication. We can analyse each of these tables with standard log-linear models that parallel those models for within-group flows. The total number of cells in the full table is $(4 \times 36) + (6 \times 64) = 528$.

In Table 14.6, we report the result of fitting separate multiplex mutuality models [model (6) of Table 14.3] to each of the ten 2^6 arrays. While this model fits extremely well (G^2 is less than the d.f.), this is in large part the result of fitting 352 parameters. An alternative modelling approach links the within- and between-group models. For example, we might take a common 'interaction structure' for all ten 2^6 tables, but allow only the choice parameters (the θ_is) to depend on groups. The result is model (2) in Table 14.6, whose fit is not horrid but is still significant at the 0.005 level. A compromise between models (1) and (2) of Table 14.6 would have a common model for within-group flows and a separate variant on model (2) for between-group flows. We report the fit of two such models in Table 14.6. Model (3b) fits extremely well, and provides a convenient starting point for further analyses of the data.

Table 14.6   Models fitted to the ten 2^6 tables formed by the partition of the 73 organizations into the 4 groups given in Table 14.8 (528 cells)

Model	G^2	d.f.
(1) *Separate* models for each 2^6 table, each based on all multiplex mutuality and implied lower-order terms	136.0	176
(2) A *common* interaction structure for all 2^6 tables, based on all multiplex mutuality and implied lower-order terms, *but* one-factor choice parameters (θ_is) depending on the groups	629.0	482
(3a) A common multiplex mutuality model for within-group flows *plus* a between group model similar to model 2	409.0	352
(3b) Model (3a) plus a set of 'information' multiplex parameters (θ_{11}) for between-groups that depend on the groups	355.7	343

14.6 A POSSIBLE GRAPHICAL DISPLAY FOR MULTIVARIATE DIRECTED GRAPHS

The second set of analyses of the preceding section leads quite naturally to analyses involving a further disaggregation of organizations. Indeed we could carry the disaggregation to the limit, with each organization forming its own group of size one. We could postulate models with different choice parameters for each organization and a common higher-order parametric structure. Actually, we would end up with individual sending and receiving parameters for each organization and each relation. The resulting model is in the same spirit as the bivariate models suggested by Holland and Leinhardt (1981).

The attractive feature of this fully disaggregated approach is that we can examine the estimated higher-order structure in a tabular form similar to that of Table 14.4, and look separately at the estimated individual parameters. The latter can be displayed in a set of three overlayed 'correspondence-like' plots of the 73 organizations. The sending and receiving parameter estimates for an organization could be used as the abscissa and ordinate for a corresponding point, and the three points for different relations could be linked to form a triangle. This plot should show not only the clustering of organizations but also the similarities of their behaviour with regard to the three different relations being considered. We have stopped short of producing the plot for the Towertown data for computational reasons. The iterative methods used here, and in Fienberg and Wasserman (1981) for the univariate version of the disaggregated model, when applied to the Towertown data simply take up too much computing storage. We hope, however, that alternative computational methods currently under development might make possible some graphical displays for multivariate directed graphs in the not-too-distant future.

REFERENCES

Bishop, Y. M. M., Fienberg, S. E., and Holland, P. W. (1975) *Discrete Multivariate Analysis*, Cambridge, Mass.: MIT Press.

Darroch, J. N. and Ratcliff, D. (1972) Generalized iterative scaling of loglinear models. *Ann. Math. Statist.*, **43**, 1470–80.

Fienberg, S. E. (1980) *The Analysis of Cross-Classified Data* (2nd edn). Cambridge, Mass.: MIT Press.

Fienberg, S. E. and Wasserman, S. (1980) Methods for the analysis of data from multivariate directed graphs. *Proc. of the Conference on Recent Developments in Statistical Methods and Applications*, pp. 137–61. Taipei, Taiwan, Institute of Mathematics, Academia Sinica.

Fienberg, S. E. and Wasserman, S. (1981) Categorical data analysis of single sociometric relations. In Leinhardt, S. (ed.) (1981) *Sociological Methodology 1981*, pp. 156–92. San Francisco: Jossey-Bass.

Galaskiewicz, J. (1979) *Exchange Networks and Community Politics*. Beverly Hills: Sage.

Galaskiewicz, J. and Marsden, P. V. (1978) Interorganizational resource networks: Formal patterns of overlap. *Social Science Research*, **7**, 89–107.

Haberman, S. (1974) *The Analysis of Frequency Data*. Chicago: University of Chicago Press.

Haberman, S. (1979) *Analysis of Qualitative Data. Volume 2: New Developments*. New York: Academic Press.

Holland, P. W. and Leinhardt, S. (1975) Local structure in social networks. In Heise, D. R. (ed.) (1975) *Sociological Methodology 1976*, pp. 1–45. San Francisco: Jossey-Bass.

Holland, P. W. and Leinhardt, S. (1981) An exponential family of probability distributions for directed graphs. *J. Amer. Statist. Assn.* **76**, 33–50.

Nelder, J. A. and Wedderburn, R. W. (1972) Generalized linear models. *J. Roy. Statist. Soc. A*, **135**, 370–84.

CHAPTER 15

Some Graphical Procedures for the Preliminary Processing of Longitudinal Data

H. Goldstein, *University of London, U.K.*

Longitudinal or repeated-measurement studies of the physical growth of children are typically designed so that each child is measured at a limited number of 'target' ages or occasions—often every year on his or her birthday. For a sample of children this procedure is designed to yield a set of measurements at each of these occasions. For each measurement, a common approach to summarizing the values thus obtained is to fit a low-order polynomial, typically referred to as a growth curve. An extensive literature on such growth-curve fitting procedures now exists (see Goldstein, 1979), but it usually assumes that each sample member has a measurement at exactly each target occasion. In practice, data are often missing for some occasions (a problem which is relatively straightforward to deal with), and more seriously, many children attend for measurement at times which are close to, but differ somewhat from, the target age.

This chapter will describe one method of 'adjusting' such measurements so that the adjusted values can be treated as if they originated from the target ages. The adequacy of the method will be studied using graphical techniques which will illustrate how those measurements which are inadequately adjusted can be detected, and also how certain kinds of outliers can be detected.

15.1 THE ADJUSTMENT PROCEDURE

Figure 15.1 shows data for a hypothetical child measured at three ages (x_1, x_2, x_3) with corresponding growth measurements (y_1, y_2, y_3). The target age for x_2, i.e. x'_2, is also shown, and the open circle represents the adjusted or target age measurement at x'_2. This is found simply by fitting a suitable curve through the observations and interpolating the value y'_2 at x'_2. Second-degree polynomials are convenient to use, being easily calculated and flexible. Other functional forms are possible but seem to possess no distinct advantages and will not be considered further.

Several questions are immediately apparent about the above adjustment

307

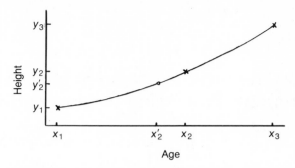

Figure 15.1   An example of adjustment of measured height (y_2) at age x_2 to target age x'_2 and height y'_2. Observed measurements denoted by ×, adjusted measurement by ○

procedure. First, it is clear that when the distance $x_2 - x'_2$ is small, the more 'acceptable' is the adjusted value since any biases are relatively small. Secondly, it is also clear that the adjustment procedure is in general more acceptable the smaller the distance $x_3 - x_1$, since the polynomial adjustment curve should then be a better representation of the true growth curve. Thirdly, if we wish to adjust x_1 to x'_1 where there are no observations at occasions below this, what curve should we use? Finally, are there any advantages to be gained from including further points and higher-degree polynomials? The first two of these points form the basis of the graphical analyses in the remainder of this paper. In response to the last two questions we argue as follows.

Adjacent adjusted measurements will, by definition, lie on polynomials of degree p with p points in common. If p is reasonably large this would effectively induce long-term regularities into the data and allow distant occasions to influence adjusted values. Since it seems desirable for the adjusted values to retain as much as possible of the true measurement variation, p should be as small as possible. A quadratic curve centred on the measurement to be adjusted provides a symmetric procedure, which a linear adjustment would not, and so seems to be the appropriate one to use in general. For an end-point adjustment, however, a straight line seems more appropriate than a quadratic since the latter uses relatively distant information. Consequently, however, the end-point adjustments may not be so satisfactory.

15.2 DATA ANALYSIS

The data to be analysed are measurements of height, weight and triceps skinfold made on a sample of 62 children at five target ages (5.0, 6.0, 7.0, 8.0,

9.0 years) (Tanner *et al.*, 1976). For each measurement of each child, adjusted values were calculated as described in the previous section. There were no missing data, so that for the first or last target ages (denoted by x_5 and x_9) linear adjustment was used, and for x_6, x_7, x_8 quadratic adjustment was used. The data are presented in full in Table 15.1, for the single growth measure, height; age, height, target age and adjusted height are given for each of the 62 children, with five sets of measurements on each.

Figure 15.2 shows a scatterplot at age 6.0 years of the difference between the observed and adjusted values of height against the difference between the actual and target ages. This reflects the expected linear relationship for these relatively small adjustments, with an increasing variance of $y_6' - y_6$ as $x_6 - x_6'$ increases. (The variance is zero at $x_6 = x_6'$.) At first sight one or both of the points ringed seem like outliers, reflecting the inadequacy of too large an adjustment. Because of the increasing variance, however, we need to standardize the variance before being able to study outliers. If this can be done satisfactorily, then it may be possible to use the outliers in order to investigate the first two points about the adequacy of the adjustment procedure.

15.3 STANDARDIZATION FOR VARIANCE

In order to allow for the changing variance we need to specify a functional relationship with $x_i - x_i'$. In the region of the target occasion, we assume that growth is linear. We have

$$y_i = \alpha + \beta x_i + \varepsilon_i.$$

Then

$$\text{var}\,(y_i - y_i' \mid x_i - x_i') = 2\sigma^2(1 - \rho_{ii}),$$

where y_i' is the value of the measurement at the target age x_i', σ^2, the variance of ε_i, is constant, and ρ_{ii} is the correlation between y_i, y_i'. Now $\rho_{ii} = 1$ if $x_i = x_i'$ and decreases as $x_i - x_i'$ increases.

One reasonable choice for relating ρ_{ii} to $x_i - x_i'$ is

$$\rho_{ii} = \exp(-A \mid x_i - x_i' \mid^K)$$

which gives to a first approximation

$$\text{var}(y_i - y_i' \mid x_i - x_i') \propto \mid x_i - x_i' \mid^K.$$

We now can study the residuals from the weighted regression of $y_i - y_i'$ on $x_i - x_i'$, standardizing the residuals by their estimated standard errors. These are given by

$$\text{S.E. (residual at } x_i - x_i') = \{\sigma^2[1 - w_i(x_i - x_i')^2/S_x^2]/w_i\}^{1/2},$$

Table 15.1 Ages, heights, target ages and adjusted heights for 62 children (basic data from Tanner *et al.*, 1976)

Serial number	Age	Height value	Target age	Adjusted value	Serial number	Age	Height value	Target age	Adjusted value
1	5.055	110.0	5.0	109.64	2	5.022	113.1	5.0	112.95
1	6.164	117.3	6.0	116.22	2	6.091	120.4	6.0	119.80
1	7.071	123.3	7.0	122.89	2	7.008	126.2	7.0	126.14
1	8.030	127.7	8.0	127.56	2	7.992	133.7	8.0	133.75
1	9.082	132.6	9.0	132.22	2	9.134	140.2	9.0	139.44
3	5.030	113.6	5.0	113.40	4	5.041	109.6	5.0	109.37
3	6.085	120.7	6.0	120.12	4	6.071	115.3	6.0	114.88
3	7.008	127.1	7.0	127.05	4	7.052	121.4	7.0	121.06
3	7.986	133.0	8.0	133.09	4	7.997	127.8	8.0	127.82
3	9.087	140.0	9.0	139.45	4	9.030	134.4	9.0	134.21
5	5.161	104.3	5.0	103.13	6	5.000	108.6	5.0	108.60
5	6.084	111.0	6.0	110.41	6	6.038	116.2	6.0	115.94
5	6.964	116.9	7.0	117.13	6	7.008	122.4	7.0	122.35
5	7.961	122.7	8.0	122.96	6	7.972	127.7	8.0	127.86
5	9.013	130.5	9.0	130.40	6	9.024	133.7	9.0	133.56
7	5.006	101.5	5.0	101.47	8	5.022	95.5	5.0	95.37
7	6.025	107.4	6.0	107.24	8	6.016	101.2	6.0	101.12
7	6.981	114.0	7.0	114.12	8	6.975	105.6	7.0	105.72
7	7.959	119.5	8.0	119.74	8	7.953	110.6	8.0	110.84
7	9.006	125.9	9.0	125.86	8	9.211	117.0	9.0	115.93
9	5.011	102.3	5.0	102.27	10	5.025	112.8	5.0	112.60
9	6.394	106.5	6.0	104.86	10	6.178	121.8	6.0	120.49
9	7.383	112.2	7.0	109.60	10	7.107	128.2	7.0	127.46
9	7.967	117.1	8.0	117.33	10	8.008	134.5	8.0	134.45
9	8.981	122.2	9.0	122.30	10	9.197	142.1	9.0	140.84
11	5.005	104.6	5.0	104.56	12	5.008	112.5	5.0	112.44
11	6.003	112.7	6.0	112.68	12	6.038	119.8	6.0	119.54
11	6.962	118.0	7.0	118.19	12	7.096	126.5	7.0	125.87
11	8.011	122.5	8.0	122.45	12	8.036	132.8	8.0	132.57
11	8.948	126.9	9.0	127.14	12	9.011	138.8	9.0	138.73
13	5.022	106.4	5.0	106.26	14	5.039	98.1	5.0	97.87
13	6.013	112.5	6.0	112.43	14	6.011	103.8	6.0	103.75
13	7.049	116.5	7.0	116.25	14	7.011	106.7	7.0	106.64
13	8.033	122.6	8.0	122.42	14	8.094	114.7	8.0	114.10
13	9.046	127.4	9.0	127.18	14	9.050	119.8	9.0	119.53
15	5.055	115.2	5.0	114.87	16	5.027	114.1	5.0	113.94
15	6.009	121.0	6.0	120.94	16	6.000	120.0	6.0	120.00
15	7.014	128.1	7.0	128.02	16	7.038	126.2	7.0	125.96
15	8.044	133.2	8.0	132.95	16	8.041	132.8	8.0	132.53
15	9.006	139.5	9.0	139.46	16	8.991	138.9	9.0	138.96

Table 15.1 Continued

Serial number	Age	Height value	Target age	Adjusted value	Serial number	Age	Height value	Target age	Adjusted value
17	5.024	110.1	5.0	109.94	18	5.107	114.6	5.0	113.95
17	5.991	116.6	6.0	116.56	18	6.045	120.3	6.0	120.03
17	6.983	121.3	7.0	121.38	18	7.005	125.9	7.0	125.87
17	8.038	126.7	8.0	126.50	18	8.055	131.1	8.0	130.79
17	9.038	132.1	9.0	131.89	18	8.986	137.1	9.0	137.19
19	5.008	109.8	5.0	109.75	20	5.013	109.1	5.0	109.03
19	5.981	115.8	6.0	115.91	20	5.967	114.4	6.0	114.58
19	6.997	121.2	7.0	121.22	20	6.980	119.9	7.0	120.02
19	8.038	128.4	8.0	128.14	20	7.980	126.5	8.0	126.62
19	8.951	134.5	9.0	134.83	20	8.980	131.7	9.0	131.80
21	5.011	106.4	5.0	106.34	22	5.096	103.5	5.0	102.95
21	5.969	111.6	6.0	111.77	22	6.047	108.9	6.0	108.59
21	6.986	117.5	7.0	117.58	22	7.003	116.2	7.0	116.18
21	8.082	123.3	8.0	122.88	22	8.003	122.2	8.0	122.18
21	9.117	128.4	9.0	127.82	22	8.957	127.0	9.0	127.22
23	5.077	110.0	5.0	109.57	24	5.077	108.9	5.0	108.37
23	6.170	116.1	6.0	115.00	24	6.170	116.4	6.0	115.25
23	6.956	121.9	7.0	122.18	24	6.956	121.6	7.0	121.86
23	8.112	127.5	8.0	126.95	24	8.112	127.5	8.0	126.92
23	8.970	131.8	9.0	131.95	24	8.970	132.0	9.0	132.16
25	5.045	117.5	5.0	117.21	26	5.055	110.5	5.0	110.19
25	6.003	123.6	6.0	123.58	26	5.951	115.5	6.0	115.78
25	7.049	131.3	7.0	130.98	26	6.951	121.2	7.0	121.45
25	8.192	137.8	8.0	136.50	26	7.940	125.9	8.0	126.21
25	8.907	143.4	9.0	144.13	26	8.942	131.4	9.0	131.72
27	5.049	111.1	5.0	110.83	28	5.055	110.4	5.0	110.10
27	6.194	117.5	6.0	116.33	28	5.970	115.4	6.0	115.58
27	7.011	122.8	7.0	122.73	28	7.126	122.8	7.0	122.08
27	8.109	128.8	8.0	128.21	28	8.101	127.6	8.0	127.04
27	9.107	134.1	9.0	133.53	28	8.962	132.9	9.0	133.13
29	5.047	105.1	5.0	104.85	30	5.063	103.2	5.0	102.79
29	5.967	109.9	6.0	110.07	30	5.964	109.1	6.0	109.30
29	6.943	114.8	7.0	115.09	30	7.074	114.3	7.0	113.96
29	8.088	120.9	8.0	120.48	30	7.899	118.0	8.0	118.51
29	8.935	124.6	9.0	124.88	30	9.137	125.1	9.0	124.31
31	5.052	105.1	5.0	104.87	32	5.066	107.5	5.0	107.01
31	5.961	109.1	6.0	109.30	32	6.082	115.0	6.0	114.39
31	6.937	115.0	7.0	115.35	32	7.027	122.1	7.0	121.91
31	8.046	120.5	8.0	120.26	32	8.082	129.0	8.0	128.48
31	8.931	125.3	9.0	125.67	32	9.063	135.1	9.0	134.71

Table 15.1   Continued

Serial number	Age	Height value	Target age	Adjusted value	Serial number	Age	Height value	Target age	Adjusted value
33	5.052	109.5	5.0	109.20	34	5.093	112.3	5.0	111.72
33	6.140	115.8	6.0	114.87	34	6.071	118.4	6.0	117.97
33	6.948	121.8	7.0	122.15	34	7.063	124.2	7.0	123.84
33	7.907	127.6	8.0	128.11	34	8.071	129.7	8.0	129.35
33	9.077	133.3	9.0	132.92	34	9.145	134.2	9.0	133.59
35	5.030	109.0	5.0	108.80	36	5.038	108.8	5.0	108.55
35	6.046	115.9	6.0	115.59	36	6.035	115.3	6.0	115.10
35	7.222	123.8	7.0	122.44	36	7.033	120.0	7.0	119.83
35	8.024	128.2	8.0	128.06	36	8.027	125.4	8.0	125.25
35	9.211	135.2	9.0	133.96	36	9.044	131.5	9.0	131.24
37	5.011	113.5	5.0	113.43	38	5.003	115.5	5.0	115.48
37	6.027	120.1	6.0	119.93	38	6.005	122.9	6.0	122.87
37	6.994	125.8	7.0	125.83	38	6.997	129.0	7.0	129.02
37	8.011	131.4	8.0	131.34	38	8.014	136.0	8.0	135.91
37	9.063	136.8	9.0	136.48	38	8.995	142.2	9.0	142.23
39	5.090	106.9	5.0	106.42	40	5.099	105.8	5.0	105.42
39	6.005	111.8	6.0	111.77	40	6.003	109.3	6.0	109.29
39	6.984	116.9	7.0	116.99	40	6.984	114.2	7.0	114.27
39	7.981	123.2	8.0	123.30	40	8.011	117.8	8.0	117.76
39	9.047	127.7	9.0	127.50	40	9.036	122.6	9.0	122.43
41	5.211	101.9	5.0	100.06	42	5.038	109.3	5.0	109.07
41	6.003	108.8	6.0	108.78	42	5.964	114.9	6.0	115.11
41	7.003	116.0	7.0	115.98	42	6.994	120.7	7.0	120.73
41	8.039	122.1	8.0	121.87	42	8.013	125.9	8.0	125.83
41	8.995	127.8	9.0	127.83	42	8.970	130.7	9.0	130.85
43	5.030	101.2	5.0	100.99	44	5.013	113.2	5.0	113.14
43	6.016	108.0	6.0	107.90	44	6.005	118.0	6.0	117.98
43	6.997	113.4	7.0	113.42	44	7.002	123.0	7.0	122.99
43	8.016	118.8	8.0	118.71	44	8.022	127.4	8.0	127.28
43	9.104	125.1	9.0	124.50	44	8.975	133.4	9.0	133.56
45	5.032	105.1	5.0	104.92	46	5.014	112.8	5.0	112.71
45	5.978	110.3	6.0	110.41	46	5.970	118.9	6.0	119.09
45	7.002	114.7	7.0	114.69	46	6.959	125.3	7.0	125.53
45	8.035	121.7	8.0	121.51	46	7.998	130.3	8.0	130.31
45	9.076	125.6	9.0	125.32	46	8.970	135.9	9.0	136.07
47	5.115	107.1	5.0	106.41	48	5.265	102.9	5.0	101.17
47	5.929	112.0	6.0	112.42	48	6.367	110.1	6.0	108.10
47	6.984	118.2	7.0	118.29	48	7.096	112.9	7.0	112.47
47	8.030	123.3	8.0	123.15	48	8.145	118.9	8.0	118.15
47	9.074	128.5	9.0	128.13	48	9.126	123.3	9.0	122.73

Table 15.1 Continued

Serial number	Age	Height value	Target age	Adjusted value	Serial number	Age	Height value	Target age	Adjusted value
49	5.011	112.2	5.0	112.12	50	5.110	110.7	5.0	110.11
49	6.030	120.0	6.0	119.77	50	6.019	115.6	6.0	115.50
49	7.074	127.8	7.0	127.30	50	7.082	121.5	7.0	121.06
49	8.003	133.5	8.0	133.48	50	7.992	126.3	8.0	126.34
49	9.071	140.0	9.0	139.57	50	9.063	132.2	9.0	131.85
51	5.014	110.5	5.0	110.41	52	5.038	110.8	5.0	110.50
51	6.052	117.0	6.0	116.69	52	6.055	118.8	6.0	118.40
51	7.145	123.0	7.0	122.17	52	7.044	125.3	7.0	125.02
51	8.063	128.5	8.0	128.15	52	8.066	131.5	8.0	131.08
51	9.066	133.6	9.0	133.26	52	9.063	138.1	9.0	137.68
53	5.008	111.4	5.0	111.34	54	5.024	99.0	5.0	98.89
53	6.099	120.0	6.0	119.29	54	6.057	103.8	6.0	103.54
53	7.077	126.3	7.0	125.80	54	7.060	108.1	7.0	107.85
53	8.074	132.8	8.0	132.31	54	8.052	112.1	8.0	111.87
53	9.110	139.8	9.0	139.06	54	9.065	117.1	9.0	116.78
55	5.020	99.4	5.0	99.29	56	5.005	112.7	5.0	112.66
55	6.014	104.8	6.0	104.73	56	6.044	120.0	6.0	119.70
55	7.105	109.9	7.0	109.36	56	7.033	126.4	7.0	126.18
55	8.042	115.1	8.0	114.90	56	8.074	133.7	8.0	133.22
55	9.179	119.5	9.0	118.81	56	9.033	139.4	9.0	139.20
57	5.024	110.7	5.0	110.56	58	5.017	106.9	5.0	106.79
57	6.041	116.7	6.0	116.46	58	6.088	113.9	6.0	113.38
57	7.027	122.4	7.0	122.23	58	6.984	118.7	7.0	118.79
57	8.027	128.9	8.0	128.74	58	8.000	124.6	8.0	124.60
57	9.033	133.9	9.0	133.74	58	8.981	129.4	9.0	129.49
59	5.014	116.3	5.0	116.21	60	5.039	106.2	5.0	105.96
59	6.030	122.7	6.0	122.50	60	6.052	112.5	6.0	112.20
59	7.006	129.3	7.0	129.26	60	7.008	117.7	7.0	117.66
59	8.003	135.4	8.0	135.38	60	8.003	123.4	8.0	123.38
59	8.978	141.7	9.0	141.84	60	8.984	128.2	9.0	128.28
61	5.003	104.8	5.0	104.78	62	5.005	114.2	5.0	114.17
61	6.019	111.9	6.0	111.78	62	5.991	120.4	6.0	120.46
61	6.975	117.3	7.0	117.45	62	7.044	127.1	7.0	126.82
61	7.997	123.7	8.0	123.72	62	8.060	133.5	8.0	133.14
61	8.995	128.8	9.0	128.83	62	9.057	139.1	9.0	138.78

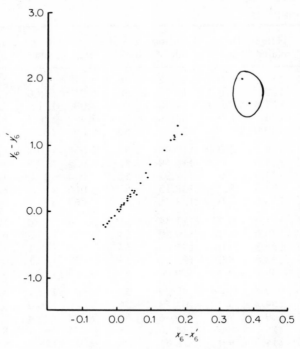

Figure 15.2 Height of 62 children at age 6. Scatter-plot of difference between observed and adjusted measurement $(y_6 - y_6')$ against difference between actual and target age $(x_6 - x_6')$

where

σ^2 = residual mean square,
w_i = regression weight = $|x_i - x_i'|^K$,
$S_x^2 = \Sigma w_i(x_i - x_i')^2$.

Note that the regression line is forced to go through the origin.

Figure 15.3 shows the standardized residuals plotted against the fitted values from a linear regression fitted to the data of Figure 15.2 with $K = 1$. It is clear that the variance of these increases with increasing $|x_i - x_i'|$ with a single large negative residual at $(2.3, -5.3)$

Figure 15.4 is similar to Figure 15.3 but taking $K = 2$ and this seems to make a satisfactory allowance for the variance, no pattern in residuals being apparent and the outlier in Figure 15.3 no longer an extreme value. Similar residual plots have been studied for other ages and variables and the value $K = 2$ seems to be generally satisfactory and is used in the remainder of this chapter. Note that there are no obvious outliers in Figure 15.4.

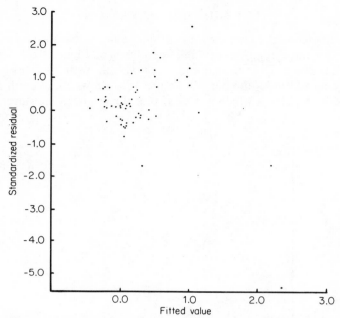

Figure 15.3 Standardized residuals for weighted linear regression with $K = 1$ against fitted values for data in Figure 15.2. Equation of fitted line is $y = 6.037x$

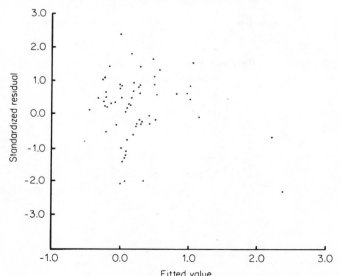

Figure 15.4 Standardized residuals from weighted linear regression with $K = 2$ plotted against fitted values for data in Figure 15.2. Equation of fitted line is $y = 6.074x$

15.4 OUTLIER DETECTION

In the remainder of the chapter we consider some of the outliers in the data and offer an interpretation of their significance. Figure 15.5 shows the residual plot for height measurements at age 9, with the most extreme residual being for child number 25. Figure 15.6 shows the growth measurement for this child from which it is clear that the adjusted measurement is in

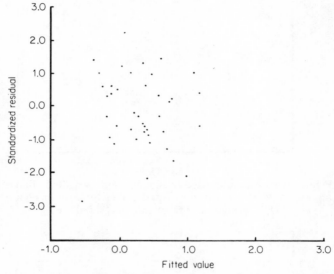

Figure 15.5 Residual plot $(K = 2)$ at age 9 for height measurements

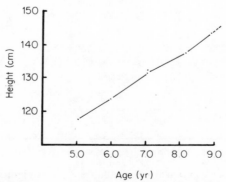

Figure 15.6 Plot of height measurements for child 25

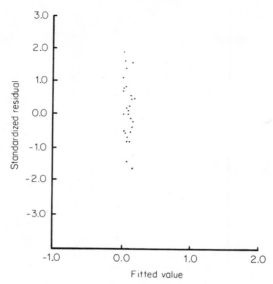

Figure 15.7   Residual plot ($K = 2$) at age 5 for
height measurements. Subset of residuals only

fact an extrapolation outside the range of observed values and is also the
'earliest' measurement at this age. Nevertheless, the measurement itself is not
very extreme and in practice we probably would not wish to exclude it from
the data.

Figure 15.7 shows a plot of a subset of the standardized residuals at age 5
for height, with child number 9 as an outlier. In fact this child's growth rate
was only 2.6 cm/yr, between 5 and 6 years, which is below the first percentile
of the appropriate velocity standards (Tanner *et al.*, 1966), so that the
adjustment for this child becomes too small in comparison to the other children. In this case, therefore, the procedure detects a measurement outlier
rather than an inappropriate adjustment.

Figure 15.8, likewise, is detecting an outlier (child 25) resulting from
extreme measurements of weight. This child has a growth velocity from 6–7
years below the first percentile and from 7–8 years above the 99th percentile,
leading to an adjustment which is too large and suggesting that the 7-year
measurement may be too low.

Finally, Figure 15.9 shows a subset of standardized residuals from skinfold
measurement at age 7 with child 25 again having a large positive outlier.
Figure 15.10 shows the actual skinfold measurements for child 25, illustrating
as before that a small growth velocity followed by a large one is not well
approximated by a quadratic curve. In this case, since the pattern is the same
as with weight, we may be inclined to accept the measurements as accurate,

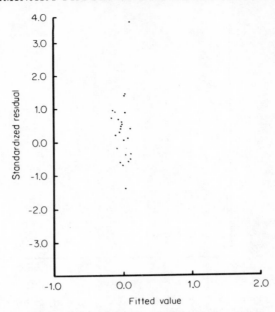

Figure 15.8   Residual plot ($K = 2$) at age 7 for weight measurements. Subset of residuals only

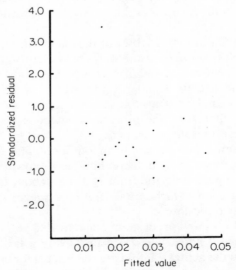

Figure 15.9   Residual plot ($K = 2$) at age 7 for triceps skinfold measurements. Subset of residuals only

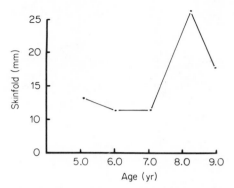

Figure 15.10 Plot of skinfold measurements for child 25

although the possibility of, for example, an incorrectly recorded age would need to be investigated. If the measurements are accepted, then we might prefer to use a linear adjustment using ages 6 and 7 (which here would cover the target age) rather than a quadratic.

15.5 CONCLUSIONS

We have shown how residual plots of adjusted measurements can detect outliers resulting from a number of causes. The examples have been used to illustrate typical findings. As a rule, outliers for large values of $x_i - x_i'$ indicate an inappropriate adjustment, either through too large a distance or with measurements too far apart for the adjusting curve to be used satisfactorily. Those outliers occurring with small values of $x_i - x_i'$ tend to reflect data errors, but may also indicate that a different order polynomial should be used for adjustment.

The procedure described can be fully automated to detect outliers and produce relevant data plots so that editing decisions can be made. It could usefully be adopted routinely for the preliminary processing of longitudinal growth data.

REFERENCES

Goldstein, H. (1979) *The Design and Analysis of Longitudinal Studies.* London: Academic Press.

Tanner, J. M., Whitehouse, R. H., Marubini, E., and Resele, L. F. (1976) The adolescent growth spurt for boys and girls of the Harpenden growth study. *Ann. Hum. Biol.,* **3**, 109–26.

Tanner, J. M., Whitehouse, R. H., and Takaishi, M. (1966) Standards from birth to maturity for height, weight, height velocity and weight velocity. British Children 1965, II. *Arch. Dis. Child,* **41**, 613–35.

CHAPTER 16

Interpreting Archaeological Data

I. Graham, *University of London, U.K.**

This chapter describes the application of the technique of spectral analysis to data derived from the two-dimensional distribution of graves in the Iron Age cemetery at Hallstatt, Austria.

This cemetery is one of the most important in our understanding of the Iron Age, and indeed gives its name to one of the divisions of the Iron Age. The site was excavated by Ramsauer between 1846 and 1863, but only recently has been subjected to detailed study using statistical methods (Hodson, 1977).

The basic data provided by the excavator consist of a cemetery plan and descriptions and illustrations of the many objects in the graves. This work was never published by Ramsauer but several hand-copied versions of the excavation report exist, and Plate 16.1 shows the cemetery plan now in the possession of the Society of Antiquaries of London.

These data will be used to illustrate the application of spectral analysis to archaeological problems, which is part of a larger study of the application of statistics to archaeology being carried out at the Institute of Archaeology in London.

16.1 SPATIAL ANALYSIS

The very basic problems in the analysis of two-dimensional distributions of archaeological objects may be summarized as follows.

(1) Is the distribution of a class of object significantly different from a distribution that could arise from a random process, and if so, how can this non-randomness be described?

(2) Given the spatial distributions of two classes of object is it possible to quantify the relationship between these distributions?

*Revised with permission from Graham, I. (1980) Spectral analysis and distance methods in the study of archaeological distributions. *Journal of Archaeological Science*, 7, 105–29. Copyright by Academic Press Inc. (London) Ltd.

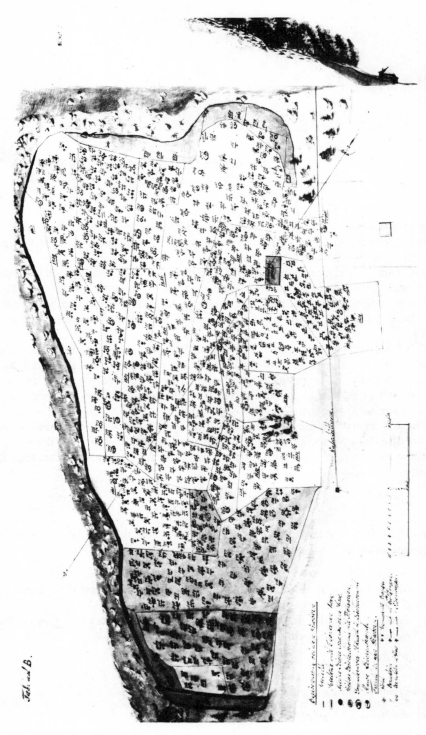

Plate 16.1 Ramsauer's site plan of the Hallstatt Cemetery. Published by kind permission of the Society of Antiquaries of London

Examples of these problems arise in the investigation of material from large cemeteries. It may be suspected that the distribution of a type of object is concentrated in one part of the cemetery, and archaeological conclusions may be drawn from this. But it is necessary to test if the apparently significant distribution could have arisen by chance. In seriation studies (Graham, 1980) graves are related by the combinations of objects that they contain, and mathematical methods are used to try to derive chronological sequences. However, some types of object may never appear together in the same grave, not for reasons of chronology but because they are perhaps linked with the sex of the occupant of the grave. Thus a measure of the similarity of types of object might be based, not on co-occurrence in graves but on occurrence in nearby graves, i.e. on the similarity of the distributions of the different types of object.

16.1.1 The definition of 'random'

Before the significance of the departure of the properties of a distribution from those expected to arise from a random process can be tested the meaning of 'random' must be defined. The most common definition of spatial randomness (see, e.g. Rogers, 1974, p. 3) has two components:

(1)   A point has an equal probability of occurring at any position on the two-dimensional surface.
(2)   The position of a point is independent of the position of any other point.

The testing of a hypothesis based on this definition of spatial randomness has formed a prominent part of the archaeological literature concerned with the study of object distributions (e.g. Whallon, 1973, 1974; Hodder and Orton, 1976). However, this form of randomness is often *a priori* extremely unlikely on archaeological sites, and testing for departure from an unlikely hypothesis provides very little useful information.

In the present case of objects in a cemetery, the standard definition of spatial randomness is obviously unsatisfactory. The position of each grave is known, and objects can only occur within graves. Thus, for some studies, it may be more suitable to adopt as the definition of randomness that each grave has an equal probability of containing an object of a particular type. However, this may be misleading if the cemetery is known to contain some graves with more variety of objects than others, in that again the random hypothesis is obviously different from reality. It is more realistic in this case to test for randomness with the null hypothesis that the distribution is due to the random association of objects with graves, the probability of a particular type of object occurring in a grave being proportional to the number of different objects known to occur in that grave.

A good distribution analysis method will indicate not only that a distribution is non-random, but will also give some idea of the nature of the non-randomness. This should include information as to whether objects tend to clump together or to avoid each other, and the scale, shape and number of objects in any clusters.

The definition of lack of association between spatial distributions is rather more complex, but a satisfactory definition for the present purpose is that the probability of occurrence of one type in a grave is independent of the occurrence of the other type in that grave, *or in nearby graves*. Thus the apparent magnitude of the association will depend on what *nearby* is taken to mean, depending in turn on the scale of association that is to be investigated. On the largest scale, where *nearby* may be considered to mean *within the cemetery*, distributions are always likely to be significantly associated as all the objects must be contained in graves within the borders of the cemetery. At the other extreme, at very small scales, *nearby* implies *within the same grave*, and a significant association is one in which types co-occur in graves more frequently than would be expected by chance.

Thus it is to be expected that a good measure of spatial association will have a value that varies with the scale of the association being measured, and that the magnitude of the association can be tested for significance at any scale. The significance of association does not depend on either distribution being non-random. It should be measurable even between two distributions which individually appear to be random, but which have more nearby occurrences than would be expected by chance.

The above definitions of spatial randomness and association make it very difficult to devise simple *analytical* tests for the significance of any apparent non-randomness or association. Thus, in the mathematical techniques described below significance estimation will be approached by Monte Carlo methods. That is, the properties of a large group of distributions generated artificially and known to be random or non-associated will be compared with the archaeologically generated distribution.

Monte Carlo methods require the generation and testing of large numbers of random distributions, but the fairly low numbers of objects occurring on archaeological sites and the use of high-speed digital computers make this quite practicable.

16.1.2 Spectral analysis

Spectral analysis (Bartlett, 1963, 1964) is a very powerful method for the detection of non-randomness and its description. It operates by representing the distribution of points by a series of functions, each of which has a clearly defined scale and spatial structure. Thus by examining the relative magnitudes of the functions it is possible to investigate the spatial structure at any desired scale. This technique has been used especially in astronomy, in attempts to detect clustering or anti-clustering in galaxies and radio sources (Yu and Peebles, 1969; Peebles, 1973; Webster, 1976).

A function to represent the scatter of graves in the cemetery is set up by erecting a two-dimensional delta function at the coordinates of each grave. The delta function has Fourier components of the form:

$$J_{s(pq)} = \exp[i(x_s' w_{x(p)} + y_s w_{y(q)})]$$

where x_s' and y_s' are the coordinates of the sth point, normalized to lie in the range 0 to 2π, and $w_{x(p)}$ and $w_{y(q)}$ are the spatial frequencies in the $+x$ and $+y$ directions.

Thus the spectrum of the ensemble of delta functions has the form:

$$J_{pq} = \sqrt{\frac{2}{n}} \sum_{s=1}^{n} \exp\left[i\left(\frac{2\pi px_s}{L} + \frac{2\pi qy_s}{L}\right)\right],$$

where L is the maximum dimension of the cemetery. The angular frequencies take the set of values $2\pi p/L$, where p is a positive or negative integer, which results in wavelengths of L/p.

The power spectrum may then be calculated by multiplying J_{pq} by its complex conjugate to obtain $I_{pq} = J_{pq} J^*{}_{pq}$, or if the complex number J_{pq} is represented as $J_{pq} = A_{pq} + iB_{pq}$, then $I_{pq} = A_{pq}^2 + B_{pq}^2$.

In this study the value of L has been taken as 180 m, which is the approximate extent of the cemetery in the x-direction. The power spectrum has been calculated for $0 \leqslant p < 60$ and $-60 < q < 60$, which goes down to wavelengths of 3 m. To display the power spectra I_{pq} has been summed in blocks of 6×6 in p and q, which is a conventional procedure to provide a reasonable variance in the spectral estimate. A one-dimensional spectrum is produced by binning with radially symmetric bins in p and q, i.e. $p^2 + q^2 =$ constant, or by a profile along the p- or q-axis.

For random distributions the expected value of the spectral power can be shown to be independent of the wavelength. Webster (1976, and in private communication) has shown that it is distributed as χ_2^2. If, however, the points are not distributed at random but are clustered, the spectral contributions from the points in a cluster tend to be in phase for wavelengths larger than the scale-size of the cluster. This gives a spectral power approximately N times greater than in the random case, where N is the number of points in the cluster. At wavelengths shorter than the cluster size the spectral power falls off to the value appropriate to the random distribution of points within the clusters. Thus the method can estimate both the number of points in the clusters and also the cluster size by observing the fall-off in spectral power with decreasing wavelength.

The large number of components in the two-dimensional spectrum make its interpretation rather difficult. However, if the small-scale, high-frequency, components are removed from the transformed data and the transformation reversed, a smoothed version of the original data is obtained. The effect of this is shown in one dimension in Figure 16.1, where the point distribution of Figure 16.1(a) gives rise to the power spectrum of Figure 16.1(b). Removing the high-frequency components from the Fourier spectrum gives Figure 16.1(c) and inverting the transform results in the smoothed distribution of Figure 16.1(d).

The spectra of two different two-dimensional distributions may be compared by calculating the cross-spectrum

$$K_{pq} = J_{1pq}J^*_{2pq};$$

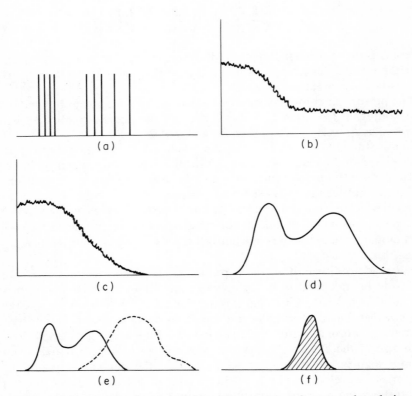

Figure 16.1 Distribution smoothing and comparison by spectral analysis. The clustered distribution of points (a) produces the spectrum (b). High-frequency, small scale-size components are removed to give the spectrum (c), which would, when transformed back, give the smoothed distribution (d). A pair of smoothed distributions (e) may then be compared, by computing their product (f). The area of (f) will depend on the amount of correlation between the two smoothed distributions

if

$$J_{1pq} = A + iB \qquad \text{and} \qquad J_{2pq} = C + iD,$$

then

$$K_{pq} = AC + BD + i(BC - DA).$$

K_{pq} is the Fourier transformation of the cross-correlation of the two distributions. Each component of K_{pq} contains information on the cross-correlation at a particular scale size.

A general coefficient of the similarity of the distributions may be obtained by weighting the spectra to remove the high-frequency components of the cross-correlation, and evaluating the cross-correlation (see Figure 16.1). This is equivalent to evaluating the area of the product of the two spatial distributions, after smoothing with a convolution function whose shape depends on the weighting used in the Fourier plane. For the present analysis a Gaussian weighting has been used, producing the effect of convolving the distributions with a Gaussian function. The width of the Gaussian may be varied, to control the severity of the smoothing.

16.1.3 Preliminary results

The spectral analysis methods described above have been investigated using data from the Hallstatt cemetery. Three different methods have been used to select distributions of graves for analysis:

(a) Random selection

For the Monte Carlo studies graves have been selected at random from the cemetery, with a probability of selection of a grave proportional to the number of different types of object known to occur in that grave. The selection was made without replacement, i.e. no grave appears twice in the same sample. The process may be repeated as many times as necessary to generate as many random distributions as are required for the analysis, and for this study 100 sets of 36 random graves were generated.

(b) Distributions with strong spatial structure

These are collections of graves excavated by Ramsauer in a single year, and are highly clustered. They serve only to illustrate the effects of clustering that is already visually obvious. Two examples are shown in Figure 16.2; the graves excavated in 1848 and 1850.

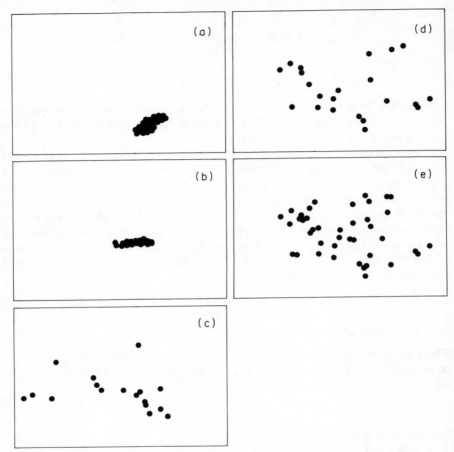

Figure 16.2   (a) Graves excavated in 1848; (b) graves excavated in 1850; (c) graves containing type 9600; (d) graves containing type 12100; (e) graves containing type 15100

(c) Archaeological distributions

These are graves selected by the presence of a particular type of object, where the structure of the distribution must be investigated. Ten types have been used, from a classification by Hodson (1977), and the types and the numbers that occur in the cemetery are shown in Table 16.1. Figure 16.2 shows three examples of these distributions for types 9600, 12100 and 15100. Types 12100 and 15100 are relatively early types and have similar distributions, whilst 9600 is a later type and has a quite different distribution. When comparisons are made among the distributions of the ten types, a similarity or distance matrix is obtained, depending on the method used. This matrix has

Table 16.1 In the 'Date?' column, *A* refers to early objects, and *B* to later types. *A/B* is a type whose attribution is not clear

	Type	No. of graves	Description	Date?
1	2130	10	Eared-bow fibula	*B*
2	3110	37	Amber ring	*B*
3	5120	31	Flattish D-section bracelet	*A*
4	5310	21	Heavy, globe-decorated bracelet	*A/B*
5	5320	36	Heavy, wing-decorated bracelet	*B*
6	8210	15	Clip-ended belt buckle	*A*
7	8240	21	Narrow T-ended belt buckle	*A*
8	9600	17	Row-decorated metal belts	*B*
9	12100	22	Wire coil	*A*
10	15100	41	Globe-headed hairpin	*A*
	1848	44	Graves excavated in 1848	
	1850	31	Graves excavated in 1850	

100 elements and would be very difficult to interpret, and so the method of non-metric multidimensional scaling (Shepard, 1962; Kruskal, 1964a,b) has been used to obtain a two-dimensional representation of the information in the matrix.

16.2 RESULTS

The results of the power-spectrum analysis of 100 sets of 36 random graves appear in Figure 16.3, as a one-dimensional profile through the two-

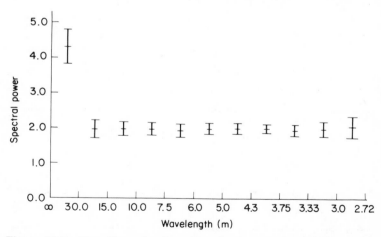

Figure 16.3 One-dimensional profile of the power spectrum for 100 sets of 36 random graves. The wavelength, or scale size, decreases to the right. The error bars are ± one standard deviation, the central point shows the mean value

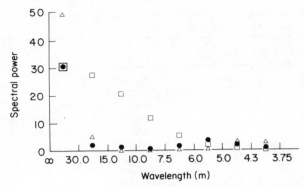

Figure 16.4   Power spectra of distributions of graves
excavated in a single year: (a) 1848; (b) 1850 *x*-axis;
(c) 1850 *y*-axis. Key: (a) ●; (b) △; (c) □

dimensional power spectrum. The magnitude of the lowest spatial frequencies
of the power spectrum is higher than would be expected from the simple
random hypothesis, due to the clustering of the graves *at the scale of the
cemetery*. Higher spatial frequencies show the randomness of the graves
within the cemetery, but with slight evidence for regularity in grave positions
with a scale of about 3 m, to be seen in the gradual increase at higher frequencies. This may be due to true regularity in the spacing of the graves, or is

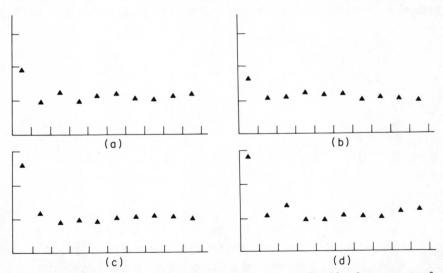

Figure 16.5   Power spectra of distributions of graves defined by the presence of
particular object types. Horizontal scales are as in Figure 16.3: (a) Type 2130; (b)
Type 3110; (c) Type 5310; (d) Type 15100

perhaps simply due to the way in which the plan of the cemetery was drawn with fairly large symbols for the graves.

The power spectra of the groups of graves excavated in 1848 and 1850 show very dramatically the effects of clustering (Figure 16.4). In the one-dimensional profile through its spectrum the 1850 group shows very high power at longer wavelengths, decreasing rapidly to the expected value for random graves for wavelengths shorter than 15 m. In the two-dimensional spectrum the fall-off in power is much more rapid in the $+x$-direction than in the $+y$-direction. This arises from the shape of the 1850 grave distribution, which measures about 5 m in the $+y$-direction but about 24 m in the $+x$-direction.

Figure 16.5 shows the one-dimensional power spectra for the distributions of types 2130, 3110, 5310 and 15100. The corresponding two-dimensional spectra show general agreement with the conclusions of both the local density and nearest-neighbour analysis; the magnitudes of the lower spatial frequency components are highest for the distributions that are most concentrated, and lowest for the distributions that are most dispersed.

Figure 16.6 shows the result of the spectral comparison of the 100 pairs of random distributions. The error bars on the spectrum show the mean value plus and minus one standard deviation. If the distributions were completely independent a mean value of zero would be expected, but as the distributions are samples from the same set of about 1000 graves, there is a small positive correlation at all spatial frequencies. This is, of course, largest on the largest scale where the graves are all clustered in the cemetery.

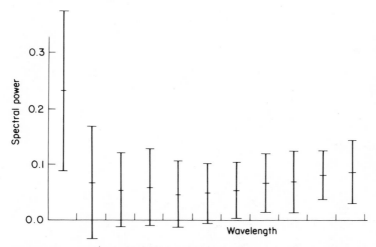

Figure 16.6   One-dimensional profile of the spectral comparison of 100 pairs of 36 random graves. The horizontal scale is the same as in Figure 16.3

Table 16.2 Spectral comparison similarity matrix, for distributions defined by the presence of ten types

	1	2	3	4	5	6	7	8	9	10
1	1.0									
2	0.60	1.0								
3	0.38	0.45	1.0							
4	0.40	0.50	0.52	1.0						
5	0.24	0.52	0.41	0.56	1.0					
6	0.25	0.34	0.45	0.33	0.37	1.0				
7	0.33	0.52	0.52	0.46	0.40	0.36	1.0			
8	0.60	0.65	0.40	0.38	0.35	0.22	0.45	1.0		
9	0.29	0.48	0.51	0.35	0.40	0.51	0.48	0.41	1.0	
10	0.27	0.61	0.53	0.48	0.48	0.52	0.58	0.50	0.84	1.0

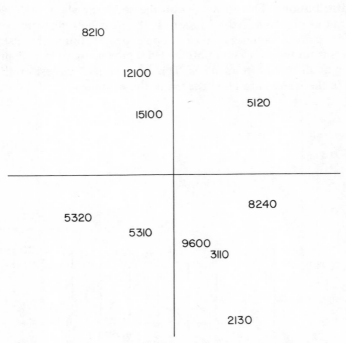

Figure 16.7 Two-dimensional non-metric scaling of the spectral-analysis similarity matrix. Spectra weighted by a two-dimensional Gaussian, half-power width 10 m (Program KYST2, Bell Telephone Laboratories, stress = 0.015)

Each comparison between two distributions now produces a matrix of values, which gives the association of the distributions at different scales. To summarize these data it is necessary to derive a single value for the association coefficient from the matrix.

The comparisons have been made by smoothing the spectra with a Gaussian function with a half-width of 10m, which cuts off the high-frequency components. The smoothed transforms have then been used to calculate the area under the product of the smoothed distributions at a particular scale.

Table 16.2 shows the similarity matrix for the distributions of the ten types of objects, and Figure 16.7 the two-dimensional summary of this produced by multidimensional scaling. The early and late types in the cemetery are clearly distinguished.

REFERENCES

Bartlett, M. S. (1963) The spectral analysis of point processes. *J. Roy. Statist. Soc. B*, **25**, 264–96.

Bartlett, M. S. (1964) The spectral analysis of two-dimensional point processes. *Biometrika*, **51**, 299–311.

Graham, I. (1980) Spectral analysis and distance methods in the study of archaeological distributions. *Journal of Archaeological Science*, **7**, 105–29.

Hodder, I. and Orton, C. (1976) *Spatial Analysis in Archaeology*. Cambridge: Cambridge University Press.

Hodson, F. R. (1977) Quantifying Hallstatt: Some initial results. *American Antiquity*, **42**, 394–412.

Kruskal, J. B. (1964a) Multidimensional scaling by optimizing goodness of fit to a nonmetric hypothesis. *Psychometrika*, **29**, 1–27.

Kruskal, J. B. (1964b) Nonmetric multidimensional scaling: A numerical method. *Psychometrika*, **29**, 115–29.

Peebles, P. J. E. (1973) Statistical analysis of catalogs of extra-galactic objects. I. Theory. *Astrophysical Journal*, **185**, 413–40.

Rogers, A. (1974) *Statistical Analysis of Spatial Dispersion*. London: Pion.

Shepard, R. N. (1962) The analysis of proximities: Multidimensional scaling with an unknown distance function. *Psychometrika*, **27**, 219–46.

Webster, A. (1976) The clustering of radio sources—I. The theory of power-spectrum analysis. *Monthly Notices; Royal Astronomical Society*, **175**, 61–70.

Whallon, R. (1973) Spatial analysis of occupation floors I: Application of dimensional analysis of variance. *American Antiquity*, **38**, 266–78.

Whallon, R. (1974) Spatial analysis of occupation floors II: The application of nearest neighbor analysis. *American Antiquity*, **39**, 16–34.

Yu, J. T. and Peebles, P. J. E. (1969) Superclusters of galaxies? *Astrophysical Journal*, **158**, 103–13.

CHAPTER 17

Bayesian Approaches to Multivariate Structure

A. F. M. Smith and D. J. Spiegelhalter, *University of Nottingham, U.K.*

Comparisons of alternative multivariate models and choices from among them on the basis of significance test procedures form an established part of day-to-day statistical practice. And yet there is still much to explore at a fundamental level about the nature of significance tests and the role of null hypotheses; see Cox (1977). More generally, the whole issue of model choice continues to attract a good deal of theoretical attention. In particular, the work of Akaike (1973) has stimulated numerous papers relating to the so-called Akaike Information Criterion (AIC) and, more recently, a somewhat different criterion was introduced by Schwarz (1978).

In the case of nested models, $M_0 \subset M_1$, with total numbers of unknown parameters d_0 and d_1, respectively, both forms of criterion compare M_0 and M_1 on the basis of

$$\lambda - m(d_1 - d_0), \qquad (17.1)$$

where λ is minus twice the logarithm of the maximized likelihood ratio and m is some constant. For the AIC, or its variants, m is taken to be a fixed integer quantity (for example, $m = 2$, 3 or 4); for the Schwarz criterion, m is taken to be the logarithm of sample size. The two criteria differ in the manner in which they adjust the usual likelihood ratio statistic, taking into account the difference in dimensionality of M_0 and M_1. Stone (1979) pointed out a connection between the Schwarz criterion and the Bayesian significance-testing approach pioneered by Jeffreys (1961; first published 1939); and Smith and Spiegelhalter (1980) provided a unified development of a number of model choice criteria by examining the prior specifications under which (17.1) is equal to $-2 \log B_{01}$, where B_{01}, the *Bayes factor*, is defined by

$$B_{01} = \frac{p(\text{data} \mid M_0)}{p(\text{data} \mid M_1)} : \qquad (17.2)$$

the ratio of posterior to prior odds on M_0.

In this chapter, we shall derive the forms of (17.2) for a number of standard

335

hypotheses, or simplifying model assumptions, regarding the mean vectors (Section 17.2) or covariance matrices (Section 17.3) of multivariate normal samples. The quantities obtained could be used in several ways: by taking minus twice the logarithm, we arrive at a Schwarz-type criterion for multivariate normal model choice; by taking the logarithm, we arrive at a measure of the *weight of evidence* provided by the data for M_0 against M_1 (Jeffreys, 1961 Appendix B, suggests the following 'order-of-magnitude' interpretation of B_{01}, based on the logarithmic scale:

$$B_{01} > 1, \quad \text{evidence supports } M_0,$$
$$1 > B_{01} > 10^{-1/2}, \text{ very slight evidence against } M_0,$$
$$10^{-1/2} > B_{01} > 10^{-1}, \text{ moderate evidence against } M_0,$$
$$10^{-1} > B_{01} > 10^{-2}, \text{ strong to very strong evidence against } M_0,$$
$$10^{-2} > B_{01}, \quad \text{decisive evidence against } M_0);$$

finally, in combination with prior probabilities for M_0, M_1, (17.2) can be used to obtain posterior probabilities for the alternative models. Such probabilities could be used as the basis of 'weighted-average' forms of inference, avoiding the 'either–or' selection of a particular model. (An example of this in the context of discriminant functions is given in Section 17.4.)

As is well known (see, for example, Lindley, 1957), the Jeffreys form, (17.2), can, on the basis of the same data set, have implications which are diametrically opposite to those of a standard significance test. In particular, the Bayes factor may give high support to M_0 when in fact M_1 is true and the same data set would lead to rejection of M_0 by the significance test. A more detailed study of this phenomenon (Smith and Spiegelhalter, 1980) shows that, in a sense, this can only happen if models M_0 and M_1 are 'very close'. When this is the case, for almost all practical purposes one might as well use the simpler model, M_0, rather than the correct, but more complex, model, M_1. In the above-mentioned paper, we describe the behaviour of B_{01} in such cases as being that of an 'automatic Occam's razor'—cutting back to the simpler model whenever there is nothing to be lost by so doing. Moreover, we have remarked that this behaviour is particularly desirable when—as is often the case—the null hypothesis defining M_0 is really a proxy for a small neighbourhood of the null value.

Throughout, we shall be working within the framework of multivariate normal assumptions. One method of relaxing such assumptions is to work with a multivariate generalization of the univariate 'contaminated normal' distribution, but this approach will not be discussed further in this chapter. An alternative approach is to seek data transformations which make the assumptions of multivariate normality 'plausible' in some sense. This approach will be illustrated in Section 17.5.

17.1 VAGUE PRIOR INFORMATION AND IMAGINARY OBSERVATIONS

In order to compute the form of (17.2), we require

$$p(\text{data} \mid M_i) = \int p(\text{data} \mid \boldsymbol{\phi}_i, M_i) p(\boldsymbol{\phi}_i \mid M_i) d\boldsymbol{\phi}_i \qquad (17.3)$$

for $i = 0,1$, where $\boldsymbol{\phi}_i$ denotes the unknown parameters appearing in the likelihood under the assumption of M_i; the first term in the integral defines this likelihood, and the second term specifies a prior density for $\boldsymbol{\phi}_i$.

For example, in the case of a sample $\mathbf{X}_1, \ldots, \mathbf{X}_n$ from a normal distribution $N_p(\boldsymbol{\theta}, \boldsymbol{\Sigma})$, which we define to be model M_1, with M_0 defined by the hypothesis $\boldsymbol{\theta} = \mathbf{0}$, we have $\boldsymbol{\phi}_1 = (\boldsymbol{\theta}, \boldsymbol{\Sigma})$, $\boldsymbol{\phi}_0 = \boldsymbol{\Sigma}$, and (17.3) requires us to specify $p(\boldsymbol{\theta}, \boldsymbol{\Sigma} \mid M_1), p(\boldsymbol{\Sigma} \mid M_0)$. The forms of the likelihoods are, of course, straightforwardly specified for given $\mathbf{X}_i = \mathbf{x}_i, i = 1, \ldots, n$.

We shall assume throughout that we are dealing with situations where prior information about unknown parameters is weak and is to be represented using standard, improper, limiting forms of prior density. For the above example, invariance arguments (see, for example, Jeffreys, 1961) suggest the following improper forms:

$$p(\boldsymbol{\Sigma} \mid M_0) = c(\boldsymbol{\Sigma}) \mid \boldsymbol{\Sigma} \mid^{-(p+1)/2}$$

$$p(\boldsymbol{\theta}, \boldsymbol{\Sigma} \mid M_1) = p(\boldsymbol{\theta} \mid \boldsymbol{\Sigma}, M_1) p(\boldsymbol{\Sigma} \mid M_1) = c(\boldsymbol{\theta})(2\pi)^{-p/2} \mid \boldsymbol{\Sigma} \mid^{-1/2} c(\boldsymbol{\Sigma}) \mid \boldsymbol{\Sigma} \mid^{-(p+1)/2}$$

$$(17.4)$$

where $c(\boldsymbol{\theta})$, $c(\boldsymbol{\Sigma})$ are undefined constants.

Substitutions into (17.3) lead to (17.2) having the form

$$B_{01} = [c(\boldsymbol{\theta})]^{-1} g_p(\mathbf{x}_1, \ldots, \mathbf{x}_n) \qquad (17.5)$$

for some function g_p of the data. But this quantity is *indeterminate*, since the constant $c(\boldsymbol{\theta})$ is undefined, and so, as it stands, is useless as a measure of evidence for or against M_0. The same is true of any Bayes factor for comparing models of differing dimensionalities using improper forms of prior specifications. We arrive at the general indeterminate form

Bayes factor = unspecified constant × function of the data.

How, then, do we obtain an operationally meaningful measure of weight of evidence against M_0 and for M_1, given a vague prior specification within each model?

Our solution is based on the idea of *imaginary observations*, a variation on a theme of Good (1947), who has expressed the belief (Good, 1976, Section IX) that such an idea 'will revolutionize multivariate Bayesian statistics'.

We proceed as follows:

(1) suppose the data were such that $g_p(\mathbf{x}_1, \ldots, \mathbf{x}_n)$ suggested the maximal possible support for M_0;
(2) suppose also that the sample size were the smallest possible that permitted a comparison of M_0 and M_1.

Then, on the basis of (1) we should want $B_{01} > 1$ (the data has supported M_0), but, on the basis of (2) (the data set is of minimal possible size for model discrimination), we should require $B_{01} = 1 + \varepsilon$, where $\varepsilon > 0$ is rather small. More colloquially, if a data set is of minimal size (for the purpose of model comparison) we shouldn't get 'too excited', even if it provides maximal support for M_0.

If in (17.5) we take $B_{01} \approx 1$ for $g_p(\mathbf{x}_1, \ldots, \mathbf{x}_{n^*}) = g$, say, the value giving maximal support to M_0 based on a minimal sample size, n^*, we can deduce that a reasonable choice of $c(\boldsymbol{\theta})$ (giving a consistent approximation, to within an appropriate order of magnitude, for the weight of evidence implied by (17.2)) is given by $c(\boldsymbol{\theta}) = g$. The argument generalizes to any M_0, M_1 within a multivariate normal framework and details are given in the next two sections for a number of standard tests involving means and covariances.

Let us summarize again the general idea. Bayes factors for nested models $M_0 \subset M_1$ based on improper priors involve an unspecified constant, or a ratio of such constants. To obtain an operationally acceptable value for the unspecified constant term, we note that a minimal size data set providing maximal support for M_0 should lead us to a value $B_{01} = 1 + \varepsilon \approx 1$. Having identified the form of the function of the data arising in B_{01}, its value for the imaginary data set can be substituted and the value of the constant term obtained.

17.2 HYPOTHESES INVOLVING MEANS

17.2.1 One-sample: hypothesis of zero mean

If we write $\mathbf{x} = (\mathbf{x}_1, \ldots, \mathbf{x}_n)$ for the example considered in Section 17.1, we have,

$$p(\mathbf{x} \mid \boldsymbol{\Sigma}, M_0) = (2\pi)^{-np/2} \mid \boldsymbol{\Sigma} \mid^{-n/2} \exp\left\{ -\frac{1}{2}\left[\sum_{i=1}^{n} \mathbf{x}_i^{\mathrm{T}} \boldsymbol{\Sigma}^{-1} \mathbf{x}_i \right] \right\}$$

(the superscript ^{T} denotes a vector or matrix transpose)

$$p(\mathbf{x} \mid \boldsymbol{\theta}, \boldsymbol{\Sigma}, M_1) = (2\pi)^{-np/2} \mid \boldsymbol{\Sigma} \mid^{-n/2} \exp\left\{ -\frac{1}{2} \sum_{i=1}^{n} [(\mathbf{x}_i - \boldsymbol{\theta})^{\mathrm{T}} \boldsymbol{\Sigma}^{-1} (\mathbf{x}_i - \boldsymbol{\theta})] \right\}$$

$$(17.6)$$

together with the prior specification defined by (17.4). We note first that the quadratic forms appearing in the exponents in (17.6) can be rewritten, respectively, as

$$\operatorname{tr}(\boldsymbol{\Sigma}^{-1}\mathbf{S}),$$

$$(\boldsymbol{\theta} - \bar{\mathbf{x}})^{\mathrm{T}}\,(n^{-1}\boldsymbol{\Sigma})^{-1}(\boldsymbol{\theta} - \bar{\mathbf{x}}) + \operatorname{tr}(\boldsymbol{\Sigma}^{-1}\bar{\mathbf{S}}) \qquad (17.7)$$

where

$$\bar{\mathbf{x}} = n^{-1}\sum_{i=1}^{n}\mathbf{x}_i, \qquad \mathbf{S} = \sum_{i=1}^{n}\mathbf{x}_i\mathbf{x}_i^{\mathrm{T}}, \qquad \bar{\mathbf{S}} = \sum_{i=1}^{n}(\mathbf{x}_i - \bar{\mathbf{x}})(\mathbf{x}_i - \bar{\mathbf{x}})^{\mathrm{T}}.$$

Using (17.7), integration with respect to $\boldsymbol{\theta}$ is straightforward in the case of M_1 and we obtain

$$p(\mathbf{x}\mid\boldsymbol{\Sigma}, M_1) = \int p(\mathbf{x}\mid\boldsymbol{\theta}, \boldsymbol{\Sigma}, M_1)p(\boldsymbol{\theta}\mid\boldsymbol{\Sigma}, M_1)\,d\boldsymbol{\theta},$$

$$= n^{p/2}(2\pi)^{-np/2}\mid\boldsymbol{\Sigma}\mid^{-n/2}\exp\{-\tfrac{1}{2}\operatorname{tr}(\boldsymbol{\Sigma}^{-1}\bar{\mathbf{S}})\}.$$

The form of (17.2) is then given by

$$B_{01} = \frac{\int p(\mathbf{x}\mid\boldsymbol{\Sigma}, M_0)p(\boldsymbol{\Sigma}\mid M_0)\,d\boldsymbol{\Sigma}}{\int p(\mathbf{x}\mid\boldsymbol{\Sigma}, M_1)p(\boldsymbol{\Sigma}\mid M_1)\,d\boldsymbol{\Sigma}} \qquad (17.8)$$

and the integrals arising in (17.8) are easily evaluated using the fact that, if $\mathbf{U}$ is a $p \times p$ positive matrix, then

$$\int\mid\mathbf{U}\mid^{-r/2}\exp\{-\tfrac{1}{2}\operatorname{tr}(\mathbf{U}^{-1}\mathbf{G})\}\,d\mathbf{U} = \mid\mathbf{G}\mid^{-(r-p-1)/2}K(r, p),$$

where

$$K(r, p) = 2^{p(r-p-1)}\pi^{p(p-1)/4}\prod_{j=1}^{p}\Gamma\!\left(\frac{r-p-j}{2}\right); \qquad (17.9)$$

see, for example, Press (1972, p. 110).

For the intergrals appearing in (17.8), $\mathbf{U} = \boldsymbol{\Sigma}, r = n + p + 1, \mathbf{G} = \mathbf{S}$ (in the numerator), $\mathbf{G} = \bar{\mathbf{S}}$ (in the denominator), and we obtain, using (17.9),

$$B_{01} = \frac{n^{p/2}}{c(\boldsymbol{\theta})}\left\lVert\frac{\mathbf{S}}{\bar{\mathbf{S}}}\right\rVert^{-n/2} = \frac{n^{p/2}}{c(\boldsymbol{\theta})}\left(1 + \frac{T^2}{n-1}\right)^{-n/2}, \qquad (17.10)$$

where T^2 is Hotelling's statistic

$$T^2 = n(n-1)\bar{\mathbf{x}}^{\mathrm{T}}\mathbf{S}^{-1}\bar{\mathbf{x}}. \qquad (17.11)$$

Now let us use the imaginary data set approach to find a suitable value for $c(\boldsymbol{\theta})$.

First, we note that a minimal data set for discriminating between M_1 $[\mathbf{X}_i \sim \mathbf{N}_p(\boldsymbol{\theta}, \boldsymbol{\Sigma})]$ and M_0 $[\mathbf{X}_i \sim \mathbf{N}_p(0, \boldsymbol{\Sigma})]$ consists of n $(= p + 1)$ p-dimensional observations. Secondly, we see that such a sample gives maximal support to M_0 when $T^2 = 0$. If we set $B_{01} \approx 1$ in such a case, we have

$$c(\boldsymbol{\theta}) = (p + 1)^{p/2}.$$

Our proposed form for the Bayes factor is therefore

$$B_{01} = \left(\frac{n}{p+1}\right)^{p/2}\left(1 + \frac{T^2}{n-1}\right)^{-n/2}. \tag{17.12}$$

From (17.12), it is straightforward to tabulate, for various choices of p and n, the values of T^2 corresponding to 'weights of evidence' as measured by B_{01}.

17.2.2 Two samples: hypothesis of equality of mean vectors

Suppose that under M_1 we have

$$\mathbf{X}_i \sim \mathbf{N}_p(\boldsymbol{\theta}_1, \boldsymbol{\Sigma}), \qquad i = 1, \ldots, n,$$

and

$$\mathbf{Y}_i \sim \mathbf{N}_p(\boldsymbol{\theta}_2, \boldsymbol{\Sigma}), \qquad i = 1, \ldots, m,$$

and that M_0 corresponds to the hypothesis $\boldsymbol{\theta}_1 = \boldsymbol{\theta}_2 \, (= \boldsymbol{\theta}$, say, unknown). Let us further suppose that the improper prior densities for $\boldsymbol{\theta}_1, \boldsymbol{\theta}_2, \boldsymbol{\Sigma}$ are specified as follows:

$$\left.\begin{aligned} p(\boldsymbol{\theta} \,|\, \boldsymbol{\Sigma}, M_0) &= c(\boldsymbol{\theta})(2\pi)^{-p/2} |\, \boldsymbol{\Sigma} \,|^{-1/2} \\ p(\boldsymbol{\Sigma} \,|\, M_0) &= c(\boldsymbol{\Sigma}) |\, \boldsymbol{\Sigma} \,|^{-(p+1)/2} \end{aligned}\right\} \tag{17.13}$$

and

$$\left.\begin{aligned} p(\boldsymbol{\theta}_1, \boldsymbol{\theta}_2 \,|\, \boldsymbol{\Sigma}, M_1) &= \prod_{j=1}^{2} \{ c_j(\boldsymbol{\theta})(2\pi)^{-p/2} |\boldsymbol{\Sigma}|^{-1/2} \\[2mm] p(\boldsymbol{\Sigma} \,|\, M_1) &= c(\boldsymbol{\Sigma}) |\boldsymbol{\Sigma}|^{-(p+1)/2}, \end{aligned}\right\} \tag{17.14}$$

where $c(\boldsymbol{\theta})$, $c_1(\boldsymbol{\theta})$, $c_2(\boldsymbol{\theta})$, $c(\boldsymbol{\Sigma})$ are unspecified constants.

The integrations required to form (17.2) proceed similarly to those of the previous section and are easily carried out using (17.9). If we define

$$\mathbf{z} = (\mathbf{z}_1, \ldots, \mathbf{z}_{n+m}) = (\mathbf{x}_1, \ldots, \mathbf{x}_n, \mathbf{y}_1, \ldots, \mathbf{y}_m),$$

and write

$$\mathbf{S}_1 = \sum_{i=1}^{n} (\mathbf{x}_i - \bar{\mathbf{x}})(\mathbf{x}_i - \bar{\mathbf{x}})^{\mathrm{T}}, \quad \mathbf{S}_2 = \sum_{i=1}^{m} (\mathbf{y}_i - \bar{\mathbf{y}})(\mathbf{y}_i - \bar{\mathbf{y}})^{\mathrm{T}}, \quad \mathbf{S} = \sum_{i=1}^{m+n} (\mathbf{z}_i - \bar{\mathbf{z}})(\mathbf{z}_i - \bar{\mathbf{z}})^{\mathrm{T}}, \tag{17.15}$$

it is straightforward to verify that the Bayes factor is given by

$$B_{01} = \frac{c(\boldsymbol{\theta})}{c_1(\boldsymbol{\theta}) c_2(\boldsymbol{\theta})} \left(\frac{nm}{n+m}\right)^{-p/2} \left[\frac{|\, \mathbf{S}_1 + \mathbf{S}_2 \,|}{|\, \mathbf{S} \,|}\right]^{(n+m)/2}. \tag{17.16}$$

In this case, a minimal data set corresponds to $n = p$, $m = p + 1$, and maximal support for M_0 is obtained when $\mathbf{S}_1 + \mathbf{S}_2 = \mathbf{S}$ (corresponding to $\bar{\mathbf{x}} = \bar{\mathbf{y}} = \bar{\mathbf{z}}$). Taking $B_{01} \approx 1$ for such a data set implies that

$$\frac{c(\mathbf{\theta})}{c_1(\mathbf{\theta})c_2(\mathbf{\theta})} = \left(\frac{2p + 1}{p(p + 1)}\right)^{p/2}.$$

Rearranging the final term of (17.16), we obtain the Bayes factor

$$B_{01} = \left(\frac{2p + 1}{p(p + 1)}\right)^{p/2}\left(\frac{nm}{n + m}\right)^{p/2}\left(1 + \frac{mn}{m + n}(\bar{\mathbf{x}} - \bar{\mathbf{y}})^{\mathrm{T}}(\mathbf{S}_1 + \mathbf{S}_2)^{-1}(\bar{\mathbf{x}} - \bar{\mathbf{y}})\right)^{-(n+m)/2}.$$

$$(17.17)$$

expressed as a function of the standard Mahalanobis distance statistic.

In the case $p = 1$, this reduces to

$$B_{01} = \left(\frac{3}{2}\frac{nm}{n + m}\right)^{1/2}\left(1 + \frac{t^2}{n + m - 2}\right)^{-(n+m)/nm}, \qquad (17.18)$$

where t is the usual two-sample t-test statistic.

17.2.3 Several samples: hypothesis of equality of means

Proceeding as in the previous section, but with k groups, involving $n_1, \ldots, n_k$ observations, and with obvious generalizations of (17.14) and (17.15), we obtain

$$B_{01} = \frac{c(\mathbf{\theta})}{c_1(\mathbf{\theta}) \cdots c_k(\mathbf{\theta})}\left[\frac{n_1 \cdots n_k}{n_1 + \cdots + n_k}\right]^{p/2}\left[\frac{|\mathbf{S}_1 + \cdots + \mathbf{S}_k|}{|\mathbf{S}|}\right]^{(n_1 + \cdots + n_k)/2}.$$

With $B_{01} \approx 1$ for an imaginary data set involving $n_1 = p + 1$, $n_2 = \cdots = n_k = p$, $\mathbf{S}_1 + \cdots + \mathbf{S}_k = \mathbf{S}$ (implied by the equality of all sample means), we can easily identify the constant term and thus obtain

$$B_{01} = \left[\frac{kp + 1}{p^{k-1}(p + 1)}\right]^{p/2}\left[\frac{n_1 \ldots n_k}{n_1 + \cdots + n_k}\right]^{p/2}\left[\frac{|\mathbf{S}_1 + \cdots + \mathbf{S}_k|}{|\mathbf{S}|}\right]^{(n_1 + \cdots + n_k)/2}. \quad (17.19)$$

17.3 HYPOTHESES INVOLVING COVARIANCES

17.3.1 Two samples: hypothesis of equal covariances

Suppose that under M_1 we have $\mathbf{X}_i \sim \mathrm{N}_p(\mathbf{\theta}_1, \mathbf{\Sigma}_1)$, $i = 1, \ldots, n$ and $\mathbf{Y}_i \sim \mathrm{N}_p(\mathbf{\theta}_2, \mathbf{\Sigma}_2)$, $i = 1, \ldots, m$, and that M_0 corresponds to the hypothesis $\mathbf{\Sigma}_1 = \mathbf{\Sigma}_2$ ($= \mathbf{\Sigma}$, say, unknown). Let us further suppose that the improper prior densities for

$\theta_1, \theta_2, \Sigma_1, \Sigma_2$ are specified as follows:

$$\left.\begin{array}{l} p(\theta_1, \theta_2 \mid \Sigma, M_0) = \prod_{j=1}^{2} [c_j(\theta)(2\pi)^{-p/2} \mid \Sigma \mid^{-1/2}], \\[12pt] p(\Sigma \mid M_0) = c(\Sigma) \mid \Sigma \mid^{-(p+1)/2}, \end{array}\right\} \qquad (17.20)$$

and

$$\left.\begin{array}{l} p(\theta_1, \theta_2 \mid \Sigma_1, \Sigma_2, M_1) = \prod_{j=1}^{2} [c_j(\theta)(2\pi)^{-p/2} \mid \Sigma_j \mid^{-1/2}], \\[12pt] p(\Sigma_1, \Sigma_2 \mid M_1) = \prod_{j=1}^{2} c_j(\Sigma) \mid \Sigma_j \mid^{-(p+1)/2}, \end{array}\right\} \qquad (17.21)$$

where $c_1(\theta)$, $c_2(\theta)$, $c(\Sigma)$, $c_1(\Sigma)$, $c_2(\Sigma)$ are unspecified constants.

Again, the integrations required for (17.2), proceed straightforwardly using (17.9), and with S_1, S_2 defined by (17.15), we obtain

$$B_{01} = \frac{c(\Sigma)}{c_1(\Sigma)c_2(\Sigma)} \frac{K(n+m+p+1, p)}{K(n+p+1, p)K(m+p+1, p)} \frac{\mid S_1 \mid^{n/2} \mid S_2 \mid^{m/2}}{\mid S_1 + S_2 \mid^{(n+m)/2}}. \quad (17.22)$$

In this case, a minimal data set requires $n = m = p + 1$ and maximal support for M_0 occurs when $S_1 = S_2$. If $B_{01} \approx 1$ for such a data set, we have

$$\frac{c(\Sigma)}{c_1(\Sigma)c_2(\Sigma)} = 2^{p(p+1)} \frac{[K(2p+2, p)]^2}{K(3p+3, p)}. \qquad (17.23)$$

Using the definition of $K(r, p)$ given in (17.9), together with well-known properties of the gamma function, the Bayes factor (17.22) obtained by substituting in the form (17.23) is easily calculated in any particular application.

In the case $p = 2$, considerable simplification is possible and we obtain

$$B_{01} = \frac{8}{3} \frac{\Gamma(n+m+1)}{\Gamma(n-1)\Gamma(m-1)} \frac{\mid S_1 \mid^{n/2} \mid S_2 \mid^{m/2}}{\mid S_1 + S_2 \mid^{(n+m)/2}}. \qquad (17.24)$$

Some examples of the use of (17.24) are given in Section 17.6.

17.3.2 Several samples: hypothesis of equal covariances

For k groups, involving $n_1, \ldots, n_k$ observations, the analysis of the previous section is easily generalized. If $n = n_1 + \cdots + n_k$, we have

$$B_{01} = \frac{c(\Sigma)}{c_1(\Sigma) \cdots c_k(\Sigma)} \frac{K(n+p+1, p)}{\prod_{i=1}^{k} K(n_i+p+1, p)} \prod_{i=1}^{k} \left[\frac{\mid S_i \mid}{\mid S_1 + \cdots + S_n \mid} \right]^{n_i/2}. \qquad (17.25)$$

A minimal data set giving maximal support to M_0 requires $n_i = p + 1$,

$i = 1, \ldots, k$, and $\mathbf{S}_1 = \cdots = \mathbf{S}_k$, so that

$$\frac{c(\boldsymbol{\Sigma})}{c_1(\boldsymbol{\Sigma}) \cdots c_k(\boldsymbol{\Sigma})} = k^{kp(p+1)/2} \frac{[K(2p + 2, p)]^k}{K[(k + 1)(p + 1), p]}. \qquad (17.26)$$

Substituting (17.26) into (17.25) and using (17.9) to rewrite the $K(r, p)$ terms, the first two factors of (17.25) become

$$k^{kp(p+1)/2} \frac{\left[\prod_{j=1}^{p} \Gamma\left(\frac{p + 2}{2} - j\right) \right]^k}{\prod_{j=1}^{p} \Gamma\left(\frac{k(p + 1) + 1)}{2} - j\right)} \frac{\prod_{j=1}^{p} \Gamma\left(\frac{n + 1}{2} - j\right)}{\prod_{i=1}^{k} \prod_{j=1}^{p} \Gamma\left(\frac{n_i + 1}{2} - j\right)}$$

and the Bayes factor is easily calculated.

17.4 A MIXTURE FORM OF CLASSIFICATION RULE

One application of the preceding approach is to the classification of an observation $\mathbf{z}$ into one of two populations, P_1 and P_2, using information obtained from a training sample from each population, which we denote by $T_1 = \{\mathbf{x}_i\}$, $i = 1, \ldots, n$ and $T_2 = \{\mathbf{y}_i\}$, $i = 1, \ldots, m$, respectively. If we assume that $\mathbf{X}_i \sim \mathbf{N}(\boldsymbol{\theta}_1, \boldsymbol{\Sigma}_1)$, $\mathbf{Y}_i \sim \mathbf{N}(\boldsymbol{\theta}_2, \boldsymbol{\Sigma}_2)$ and that the prior probability that $\mathbf{z} \in P_1$ is π_1, then a common procedure is to employ a pre-test of the hypothesis $M_0 : \boldsymbol{\Sigma}_1 = \boldsymbol{\Sigma}_2$ against $M_1 : \boldsymbol{\Sigma}_1 \neq \boldsymbol{\Sigma}_2$ and then, depending on the result, to adopt a linear or quadratic discriminant function. To be precise, the exact predictive t-distribution for $\mathbf{z}$ should be calculated (Aitchison, Habbema and Kay, 1977) and $\mathbf{z}$ allocated to P_1 if

$$\pi_1 p(\mathbf{z} \mid T_1, T_2, P_1) > (1 - \pi_1) p(\mathbf{z} \mid T_1, T_2, P_2),$$

given equal misclassification losses. In the following discussion, we show that the either/or choice between assuming equal or unequal covariance matrices may be avoided by means of the Bayes factor procedure.

We adopt the notation $\mathbf{Z} \sim t_p(\boldsymbol{\theta}, \mathbf{R}, \nu)$ if

$$p(\mathbf{z}) = \frac{\Gamma\left(\frac{\nu + p}{2}\right)}{(\pi\nu)^{p/2} \Gamma\left(\frac{\nu}{2}\right) |\mathbf{R}|^{1/2}} \left[1 + \frac{(\mathbf{z} - \boldsymbol{\theta})^{\mathrm{T}} \mathbf{R}^{-1}(\mathbf{z} - \boldsymbol{\theta})}{\nu} \right]^{-(\nu+p)/2};$$

then, assuming the prior structure and notation of Section 17.3, the predictive density under M_0, assuming $\mathbf{z} \in P_1$, is given by

$$\mathbf{Z} \mid T_1, T_2, M_0, P_1 \sim t_p\left(\overline{\mathbf{x}}, \frac{(\mathbf{S}_1 + \mathbf{S}_2)}{(n + m - 1)}\left(\frac{n + 1}{n}\right), n + m - 1 \right)$$

and, under M_1, assuming $\mathbf{z} \in P_1$, is given by

$$\mathbf{Z} \mid T_1, T_2, M_1, P_1 \sim t_p\left(\bar{\mathbf{x}}, \frac{\mathbf{S}_1}{(n-1)} \frac{(n+1)}{n}, n-1\right)$$

with corresponding expressions if $\mathbf{z} \in P_2$. Under M_0, the intersection of the predictive densities is the solution of a quadratic form.

The Bayes factor on M_0 relative to M_1 may be calculated from the training samples using the formulae of Section 17.3.1. If we are willing to place a prior probability $p(M_0)$ on the simpler model, say $p(M_0) = p(M_1) = \frac{1}{2}$, then the posterior weight on M_0 is given by

$$p(M_0 \mid T_1, T_2) = B_{01}/(1 + B_{01}).$$

The full predictive density of $\mathbf{z}$, is then given by

$p(\mathbf{z} \mid T_1, T_2, P_i) =$

$\qquad p(\mathbf{z} \mid T_1, T_2, P_i, M_0)p(M_0 \mid T_1, T_2) + p(\mathbf{z} \mid T_1, T_2, P_i, M_1)p(M_1 \mid T_1, T_2),$

which is seen to be a mixture of two multivariate t-distributions with common mean but different covariance matrices.

The resulting 'discriminating surface' will lie between those corresponding to M_0 and M_1. It is clear that this procedure readily extends to more than two populations, in which case the exact predictive ordinates of $\mathbf{z}$ under each population are compared. These may be compared with the maximum ordinate achievable in each population, in order to assess whether $\mathbf{z}$ is an outlier of *all* the groups.

17.5 TRANSFORMATION TO NORMALITY

As we remarked in the introduction, before using any of these procedures based on multivariate normal assumptions we should consider the possibility of transforming the data in order to make this assumption more plausible.

One simple approach is as follows. Let us suppose that $\mathbf{x}_i$ is a p-dimensional observation with jth component $x_{ij}, j = 1, \ldots, p$. We shall consider the possibility of a separate power transformation on each component of $\mathbf{x}_i$ defined by

$$x_{ij}^{(\lambda_j)} = \begin{cases} (x_{ij}^{\lambda_j} - 1)/\lambda_j & \text{for } \lambda_j \neq 0, \\ \log x_{ij} & \text{for } \lambda_j = 0. \end{cases}$$

The vector of transformed components will be written $\mathbf{x}_i^{(\lambda)}$, where $\lambda = (\lambda_1, \ldots, \lambda_p)$.

If we now assume that $\mathbf{X}_i^{(\lambda)} \sim N_p(\boldsymbol{\theta}, \boldsymbol{\Sigma})$, $i = 1, \ldots, n$, we have, writing

$$\mathbf{x} = (\mathbf{x}_1, \ldots, \mathbf{x}_n),$$

$$p(\mathbf{x} \mid \boldsymbol{\theta}, \boldsymbol{\Sigma}, \lambda) = (2\pi)^{-n/2} \mid \boldsymbol{\Sigma} \mid^{-n/2} \exp\left\{ -\frac{1}{2} \sum_{i=1}^{n} \left[(\mathbf{x}_i^{(\lambda)} - \boldsymbol{\theta})^{\mathrm{T}} \boldsymbol{\Sigma}^{-1}(\mathbf{x}_i^{(\lambda)} - \boldsymbol{\theta}) \right] \right\} J_{\lambda},$$

where

$$J_\lambda = \sum_{j=1}^{p} \sum_{i=1}^{n} x_{ij}^{\lambda_j - 1},$$

the Jacobian of the transformation.

If we now consider a joint prior specification of the form

$$p(\boldsymbol{\theta}, \boldsymbol{\Sigma}, \lambda) = p(\boldsymbol{\theta} \mid \boldsymbol{\Sigma}) \, p(\boldsymbol{\Sigma}) p(\lambda),$$

where the first two terms are defined as in the second line of (17.4), then it is easily seen that

$$p(\lambda \mid \mathbf{x}) \propto p(\mathbf{x} \mid \lambda) p(\lambda) \propto \mid S_\lambda \mid^{-n/2} J_\lambda p(\lambda), \tag{17.27}$$

where

$$p(\mathbf{x} \mid \lambda) = \iint p(\mathbf{x} \mid \boldsymbol{\theta}, \boldsymbol{\Sigma}, \lambda) p(\boldsymbol{\theta}, \boldsymbol{\Sigma}, \lambda) \, d\boldsymbol{\theta} \, d\boldsymbol{\Sigma}$$

and

$$\mathbf{S}_\lambda = \sum_{i=1}^{n} (\mathbf{x}_i^{(\lambda)} - \bar{\mathbf{x}}^{(\lambda)})(\mathbf{x}_i^{(\lambda)} - \bar{\mathbf{x}}^{(\lambda)})^{\mathrm{T}}.$$

In the case $p = 2$, (17.27) can easily be displayed as a bivariate contour plot in order to discover if there are interesting values (λ_1, λ_2) which suggest a transformation to a joint distribution more closely bivariate normal.

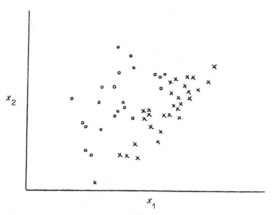

Figure 17.1   Haemophilia data; ○ carriers, ×
non-carriers

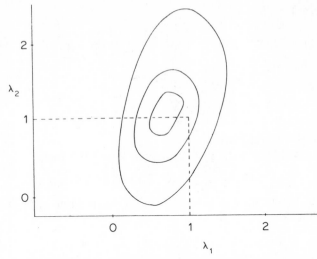

Figure 17.2   Non-carriers; posterior contours for (λ_1, λ_2)

In Figure 17.1, we display scatter plots of bivariate data taken from Hermans and Habbema (1975) and showing observations from 22 obligatory carriers of haemophilia A and 30 non-carriers. In Figure 17.2 we show a contour plot for (λ_1, λ_2) for the non-carrier group and in Figure 17.3 we give the corresponding plot for the carrier group. The contours given are at 90%, 60% and 10% of the maximum, respectively. In both cases, the values $\lambda_1 = 1$, $\lambda_2 = 1$ are well supported, indicating that no further transformation of the variables is required. In this example, $p(\lambda)$ was taken to be uniform.

The approach outlined here is similar to one given by Box and Cox (1964),

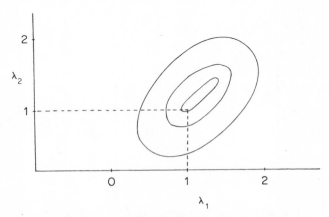

Figure 17.3   Carriers; posterior contours for (λ_1, λ_2)

but differs in the form of prior specification used: a recent development using a prior form similar to ours is given by Pericchi (1981).

17.6 NUMERICAL ILLUSTRATIONS

In this section, we shall give two examples to illustrate the method outlined in Section 17.3.1 concerning the hypothesis of equality for two covariance matrices.

If we consider the haemophilia data of Section 17.5, the sample covariance matrices for the two groups are given by

$$\mathbf{S}_1 = \begin{bmatrix} 63.48 & 50.57 \\ 50.57 & 50.58 \end{bmatrix}, \quad \mathbf{S}_2 = \begin{bmatrix} 46.55 & 24.54 \\ 24.54 & 37.82 \end{bmatrix}.$$
$$(n = 30) \qquad\qquad (m = 22)$$

Using the asymptotic form of likelihood ratio test statistic, we obtain a value of 10.08, which, assuming an approximate χ_3^2 distribution, gives a p-value around 0.02. In this case, the message is much the same as that provided by the Bayes factor, (17.24), which gives $B_{01} = 0.15$, or a posterior probability of 0.13 on M_0 (equal covariances) if we assume equal prior probabilities on M_0 and M_1.

An example for which contrasting inferences are obtained from the Bayes factor and the significance test is the following, taken from Maxwell (1977). Two groups, classified as *good* readers and *poor* readers, were given a number of cognitive tests, of which two were entitled 'Information' and 'Comprehension'. The sample covariance matrices were

$$\mathbf{S}_1 = \begin{bmatrix} 279.4 & 183.9 \\ 183.9 & 518.8 \end{bmatrix}, \quad \mathbf{S}_2 = \begin{bmatrix} 596.4 & 401.7 \\ 401.7 & 679.5 \end{bmatrix},$$
$$(n = 75) \qquad\qquad (m = 75)$$

and the likelihood ratio test statistic is equal to 10.54, again giving a p-value less than 0.02. However, in this case, $B_{01} = 1.22$ and this results in a posterior probability of 0.55 on M_0. This provides a good illustration of the Lindley paradox mentioned in the introduction.

In particular, when the mixed form of classification rule of Section 17.4 is developed in this case, the resulting discriminant function lies approximately mid-way between the function implied under M_0 (approximately a *linear* discriminant) and that implied under M_1 (approximately a *quadratic* discriminant).

REFERENCES

Aitchison, J., Habbema, J. D. F., and Kay, J. W. (1977) A critical comparison of two methods of statistical discrimination. *Applied Statistics*, **26**, 15–25.

Akaike, H. (1973) Information theory and an extension of the maximum likelihood principle. *2nd International Symposium on Information Theory*, pp. 267–81. Budapest: Akademiai Kaido.

Box, G. E. P. and Cox, D. R. (1964) An Analysis of Transformations. *J. Roy. Statist. Soc., B*, **26**, 211–52.

Cox, D. R. (1977) The role of significance tests. *Scand. J. Statist.*, **4**, 49–71.

Good, I. J. (1947) *Probability and the Weighing of Evidence*. London: Charles Griffin.

Good, I. J. (1976) The Bayesian influence. In Harper, W. L. and Hawker, C. A. (eds.) (1976) *Foundations of Probability Theory, Statistical Inference and Statistical Theories of Science*, Vol. II. Dordrecht, Reidel.

Hermans, J. and Habbema, J. D. F. (1975) Comparisons of five methods to estimate posterior probabilities. *EDV in Medizin und Biologie*, 1/2, 14–9.

Jeffreys, H. (1961; first published 1939) *Theory of Probability*. 3rd edn. Oxford: University Press.

Lindley, D. V. (1957) A statistical paradox. *Biometrika* **44**, 187–92.

Maxwell, A. E. (1977) *Multivariate Analysis in Behavioural Research*. London: Chapman and Hall.

Pericchi, L. R. (1981) A Bayesian approach to transformation to normality. *Biometrika*, **68**, 35–43.

Press, S. J. (1972) *Applied Multivariate Analysis*. New York: Holt, Rinehart and Winston.

Schwarz, G. (1978) Estimating the dimension of a model. *Ann. Statist.* **6**, 461–4.

Smith, A. F. M. and Spiegelhalter, D. J. (1980) Bayes factors and choice criteria for the linear model. *J. Roy Statist. Soc. B*, **42**, 213–20.

Stone, M. (1979) On model selection criteria of Akaike and Schwarz., *J. Roy. Statist. Soc. B.*, **41**, 276–8.

Bibliography

Anderberg, M. R. (1973) *Cluster Analysis for Applications*. New York: Academic Press.

Andrews, D. F., Bickel, P. J., Hampel, F. R. Huber, P. J., Rogers, W. H., and Tukey, J. W. (1972) *Robust Estimates of Location: Survey and Advances*. Princeton: University Press.

Bachi, R. (1968) *Graphical Rational Patterns: A New Approach to Graphical Presentation of Statistics*. Jerusalem: Israel Universities Press.

Barnett, V. and Lewis, T. (1978) *Outliers in Statistical Data*. Chichester: Wiley.

Batchelor, B. G. (1974) *Practical Approach to Pattern Classification*. London: Plenum.

Benzécri, J.-P. (1973) *L'analyse des Correspondances*. (*Volume 2 of L'analyse des Données*). Paris: Dunod.

Bertin, J. (1980) *Graphics and the Graphical Analysis of Data*. (Translated by W. J. Berg, technical editor H. Wainer) Berlin and Elmsford, New York: Walter de Gruyter.

Bijnen, E. J. (1973) *Cluster Analysis: Survey and Evaluation of Techniques*. (Translated from the Dutch by C. E. Brand-Maher). Tilburg University Press.

Bishop, Y. M. M., Fienberg, S. E. and Holland, P. W. (1975) *Discrete Multivariate Analysis: Theory and Practice*. Cambridge, Mass: MIT Press.

Blackith, R. E. and Reyment, R. A. (1971) *Multivariate Morphometrics*. London: Academic Press.

Bowman, W. J. (1968) *Graphic Communication*. New York: Wiley.

Box, G. E. P., Hunter, W. G., and Hunter, T. S. (1978) *Statistics for Experimenters. An Introduction to Design, Data Analysis and Model Building*. New York: Wiley.

Chambers, J. M. (1977) *Computational Methods for Data Analysis*. New York: Wiley.

Chatfield, C. and Collins, A. J. (1980) *Introduction to Multivariate Analysis*. London: Chapman and Hall.

Cooley, W. W. and Lohnes, P. R. (1971) *Multivariate Data Analysis*. New York: Wiley.

Daniel, C. and Wood, F. S. (1971) *Fitting Equations to Data: A Computer Analysis of Multifactor Data for Scientists and Engineers*. New York: Wiley.

Davis, J. C. and McCullagh, M. J. (eds.) (1975) *Display and Analysis of Spatial Data*. New York: Wiley.

Dempster, A. P. (1969) *Elements of Multivariate Analysis*. Reading, Mass.: Addison-Wesley.

Dickinson, G. C. (1973) *Spatial Mapping and the Presentation of Statistics*. 2nd edn. London: Arnold; New York: Crane, Russak.

Duda, R. O. and Hart, P. E. (1973) *Pattern Classification and Scene Analysis*. New York: Wiley.

Duran, B. S. and Odell, P. L. (1974) *Cluster Analysis: A Survey*. (no. 100 of lecture notes in Economics and Mathematics Systems) Berlin: Springer.

Ehrenberg, A. S. C. (1975) *Data Reduction. Analysing and Interpreting Statistical Data*. London: Wiley.

Enslein, K., Ralston, A., and Wilf, H. S. (eds.) (1974) *Statistical Methods for Digital Computers (Mathematical Methods for Digital Computers, Vol. 3.)* New York: Wiley.

Everitt, B. S. (1974) *Cluster Analysis.* London: Heinemann (for the Social Science Research Council).

Everitt, B. S. (1978) *Graphical Techniques for Multivariate Data.* London: Heinemann.

Fukunaga, K. (1972) *Introduction to Statistical Pattern Recognition.* New York: Academic Press.

Gnanadesikan, R. (1977) *Methods for Statistical Data Analysis of Multivariate Observations.* New York: Wiley.

Gorsuch, R. L. (1974) *Factor Analysis.* Philadelphia: W. B. Saunders.

Greenacre, M. J. (1978) *Some Objective Methods of Graphical Display of a Data Matrix.* Translation of Ph.D. thesis (Université de Paris, VI), published as a special report by University of South Africa, Pretoria.

Harman, H. H. (1976) *Modern Factor Analysis.* 3rd edition, Chicago: University of Chicago Press.

Hartigan, J. A. (1975) *Clustering Algorithms.* New York: Wiley.

Hartwig, F. and Dearing, B. D. (1979) *Exploratory Data Analysis.* London: Sage Publications.

Hodson, F. R., Kendall, D. G., and Taŭtu, P. (eds.) (1971) *Mathematics in the Archaeological and Historical Sciences. Proceedings of the Anglo-Rumanian Conference, Mamaia 1970, organised by The Royal Society of London, and The Academy of the Socialist Republic of Rumania.* Edinburgh: Edinburgh University Press.

Horst, P. (1965) *Factor Analysis of Data Matrices.* New York: Holt.

Jardine, N. and Sibson, R. (1971) *Mathematical Taxonomy.* New York: Wiley.

Jöreskog, K. G. (1963) *Statistical Estimation in Factor Analysis: A New Technique and its Foundation.* Stockholm: Almqvist and Wiksell.

Kruskal, J. B. and Wish, M. (1978) *Multidimensional Scaling.* London: Sage Publications.

Kruskal, W. H. and Tanur, J. M. (eds.) (1978) *International Encyclopedia of Statistics.* New York: Free Press.

Lawley, D. N. and Maxwell, A. E. (1971) *Factor Analysis as a Statistical Method.* 2nd edn. London: Butterworth.

Lazarsfeld, P. F. and Henry, N. W. (1968) *Latent Structure Analysis.* Boston: Houghton Mifflin.

McNeil, D. R. (1977) *Interactive Data Analysis.* New York: Wiley.

Mardia, K. V., Kent, J. T., and Bibby, J. M. (1979) *Multivariate Analysis.* London: Academic Press.

Marriott, F. H. C. (1974) *The Interpretation of Multiple Observations.* London: Academic Press.

Mosteller, F. and Tukey, J. W. (1977) *Data Analysis and Regression. A Second Course in Statistics.* Reading, Mass.: Addison-Wesley.

Newman, W. M. and Sproull, R. F. (1973) *Principles of Interactive Computer Graphics.* New York: McGraw-Hill.

Nishisato, S. (1980) *Analysis of Categorical Data: Detailed Scaling and Its Applications.* Toronto: University of Toronto Press.

O'Muircheartaigh, C. A. and Payne, C. (eds.) (1977) *The Analysis of Survey Data; Vol. 1: Exploring Data Structures.* London: Wiley.

Overall, J. E. and Klett, C. J. (1972) *Applied Multivariate Analysis.* New York: McGraw-Hill.

Schmidt, C. F. and Schmidt, S. E. (1979) *Handbook of Graphic Presentation*. New York: Wiley.

Shepard, R. N., Romney, A. K., and Nerlove, S. B. (eds.) (1972) *Multidimensional Scaling: I Theory, II Applications*. New York: Seminar Press.

Sneath, P. H. A. and Sokal, R. R. (1973) *Numerical Taxonomy: The Priniciples and Practice of Numerical Classification*. San Francisco: Freeman.

Späth, H. (1980) *Cluster Analysis Algorithms for Data Reduction and Classification of Objects*. Chichester: Ellis Horwood.

Torgerson, W. S. (1958) *Theory and Methods of Scaling*. New York: Wiley.

Tryon, R. C. and Bailey, D. D. (1970) *Cluster Analysis*. New York: McGraw-Hill.

Tukey, J. W. (1977) *Exploratory Data Analysis*. Reading Mass.: Addison-Wesley.

Wang, P. C. C. (ed.) (1976) *Graphical Representation of Multivariate Data*. New York: Academic Press.

Composite Reference List

This list of published articles includes all those that have been referred to in the various chapters of the book. The chapters to which a reference relates are indicated in parentheses after the reference. In addition, some extra references have been included, representing work which is relevant to the theme of the book and which expounds basic research results or reviews a particular field.

Aitchison, J., Habbema, J. D. F., and Kay, J. W. (1977) A critical comparison of two methods of statistical discrimination. *Applied Statistics,* **26**, 15–25. (**17**)

Akaike, H. (1973) Information theory and an extension of the maximum likelihood principle. *2nd International Symposium on Information Theory*, pp. 267–81. Budapest: Akademiai Kaido. (**17**)

Anderson, E. (1935) The irises of the Gaspe Peninsula. *Bull. Amer. Iris Soc.,* **59**, 2–5. (**10**)

Anderson, E. (1936) The species problem in Iris. *Ann. Mo. bot. Gdn.* **23**, 511–25. (**10**)

Anderson, E. (1957) A semigraphical method for the analysis of complex problems. *Proc. of the Nat. Academy of Sciences,* **13**, 923–7 (reprinted as Anderson, 1960). (**6, 12**)

Anderson, E. (1960) A semigraphical method for the analysis of complex problems. *Technometrics,* **2**, 387–91. (**6, 12**)

Andrews, D. F. (1972) Plots of high-dimensional data. *Biometrics,* **28**, 125–36. (**12**)

Andrews, D. F. (1978) Exploratory data analysis. In Kruskal, W. H. and Tanur, J. M. (eds.) (1978) *International Encyclopedia of Statistics*, pp. 97–107. New York: Free Press.

Andrews, D. F., Gnanadesikan, R., and Warner, J. L. (1973) Methods for assessing multivariate normality. In Krishnaiah, P. R. (ed.) (1973), *Multivariate Analysis III*. New York: Academic Press. (**10**)

Ashton, E. H., Healy, M. J. R., and Lipton, S. (1957) The descriptive use of discriminant functions in physical anthropology. *Proc. Roy. Soc. B,* **146**, 552–72. (**11**)

Banfield, C. F. and Gower, J. C. (1980) A note on the graphical representation of multivariate binary data. *Applied Statistics,* **29**, 238–45. (**6**)

Barnard, G. A. (1963) Contribution to the discussion of Bartlett (1963). (**4**)

Barnett V. (1976) The ordering of multivariate data (with discussion). *J. Roy. Statist. Soc. A.,* **139**, 318–54. (**1**)

Bartlett, M. S. (1937) Properties of sufficiency and statistical tests. *Proc. Roy. Soc. A,* **168**, 268–82. (**4**)

Bartlett, M. S. (1963) The spectral analysis of point processes. *J. Roy. Statist. Soc. B,* **25**, 264–96. (**4, 16**)

Bartlett, M. S. (1964) Spectral analysis of two-dimensional point processes. *Biometrika,* **51**, 299–311. (**4, 16**)

Bartlett, M. S. (1978) *Stochastic Processes* (3rd edn). Cambridge: Cambridge University Press. **(4)**

Bebbington, A. C. (1978) A method of bivariate trimming for robust estimation of the correlation coefficient. *Applied Statistics*, **27** 221–6. **(1)**

Bennett, J. F. and Hays, W. L. (1960) Multidimensional unfolding determining the dimensionality of ranked preference data. *Psychometrika*, **25**, 27–43.

Benzécri, J.-P. (1973) *L'analyse des correspondances.* (Volume 2 of *L'analyse des Données*). Paris: Dunod. **(7)**

Bertin, J. (1973) *Semiologie Graphique* (2nd edn, in French). Paris and The Hague: Mouton. **(12)**

Bertin, J. (1977) *La Graphique et le Traitement Graphique de L'Information.* Paris: Flammarion. **(12)**

Besag, J. (1977) Contribution to the discussion of Ripley (1977). **(4)**

Besag, J. and Diggle, P. J. (1977) Simple Monte Carlo tests for spatial pattern. *Applied Statistics*, **26**, 327–33. **(3, 4)**

Besag, J. and Gleaves, J. T. (1973) On the detection of spatial pattern in plant communities. *Bull. Int. Statist. Inst.*, **45**, (1), 153–8. **(4)**

Boneva, L. I. Kendall, D. G., and Stefanov, I. (1971) Spline transformations: three new diagnostic aids for the statistical data-analyst (with discussion). *J. Roy. Statist. Soc. B*, **33**, 1–71. **(4)**

Bowyer, A. (1978) A computer model of sliding friction. *Proc. 4th Leeds–Lyon symposium on surface roughness. I. Mech. E. pubs.* **(3)**

Bowyer, A. (1980) Experiments and Computer Modelling in Stick-slip. *PhD Thesis*, University of London. **(3)**

Bowyer, A. (1981) Computing Dirichlet tesselations. *The Computer Journal,* **24**, 162–6. **(2)**

Box, G. E. P. and Cox, D. R. (1964) An analysis of transformations. *J. Roy. Statist. Soc. B*, **26**, 211–52. **(9, 17)**

Bradu, D. and Gabriel, K. R. (1978) The biplot as a disgnostic tool for models of two-way tables. *Technometrics*, **20**, 47–68. **(6, 8)**

Bradu, D. and Grine, F. E. (1979) Multivariate Analysis of Diademodontine Crania from South Africa and Zambia. *South African Journal of Science,* **75**, 441–8. **(8)**

Breiman, L., Meisel, W. and Purcell, E. (1977) Variable kernel estimates of multivariate densities. *Technometrics*, **19**, 135–44. **(3)**

Brier, G. W. and Meltesen, G. T. (1976) Eigenvector analysis for prediciton of time series. *Journal of Applied Meteorology*, **15**, 1307–12. **(8)**

Brindley, G. S. and Lewin, W. S. (1968) The sensations produced by electrical stimulation of the visual cortex. *Journal of Physiology*, **196**, 479–93. **(13)**

Broadbent, S. R. (1980) Simulating the ley hunter. *J. Roy. Statist. Soc. A*, **143**, 109–40. **(5)**

Byth, K. and Ripley, B. D. (1980) On sampling spatial patterns by distance methods. *Biometrics*, **36**, 279–84. **(4)**

Carnal, H. (1970) Die konvexe Hülle von *n* rotations-symmetrisch verteilten Punkten. *Z. Wahrscheinlichskeitstheorie und Verw. Gebiete*, **15**, 168–76.

Carroll, J. D. and Arabie, P. (1980) Multidimensional Scaling. *Ann. Rev. Psychol.*, **31**, 607–49.

Carroll, J. D. and Chang, J. J. (1970) Analysis of individual differences in multidimensional scaling via an *n*-way generalization of 'Eckart–Young' decomposition. *Psychometrika*, **35**, 283–319.

Carroll, J. D. and Kruskal, J. B. (1978) Multidimensional scaling of two-way and three-way arrays. In Kruskal, W. H. and Tanur, J. M. (eds.) (1978) *International Encyclopedia of Statistics.* New York: Free Press.

Chambers, J. M. (1975) Structured computational graphics for data analysis. *Bull. Int. Statist. Inst.*, **46**, 467–86.

Chernoff, H. (1973) Using faces to represent points in *k*-dimensional space graphically. *J. Amer. Statist. Assn.*, **68**, 361–8. **(6)**

Chhikara, R. S. and Register, D. T. (1979) A numerical classification method for partitioning of a large multidimensional mixed data set. *Technometrics*, **21**, 531–8.

Chino, N, (1978) A graphical technique for representing the asymmetric relationships between *N* objects. *Behaviormetrika*, **5**, 23–40. **(6)**

Cleveland, W. S. (1979) Robust locally weighted regression and smoothing scatterplots. *J. Amer. Statist. Assn.*, **74**, 829–36. **(12)**

Cleveland, W. S. and Kleiner, B. (1975) A graphical technique for enhancing scatterplots with moving statistics. *Technometrics*, **17**, 447–54. **(12)**

Constantine, A. G. and Gower, J. C. (1978) Graphical representation of asymmetric matrices. *Applied Statistics*, **27**, 297–304. **(6)**

Cooley, J. W. and Tukey, J. W. (1965) An algorithm for the machine calculation of complex Fourier series. *Math. Comput.* **19**, 297–301. **(3)**

Cormack, R. M. (1971) A review of classification. *J. Roy. Statist. Soc. A.*, **134**, 321–67.

Corsten, L. C. A. and Gabriel, K. R. (1976) Graphical exploration in comparing variance matrices. *Biometrics*, **32**, 851–63. **(8)**

Cox, D. R. (1955) Some statistical methods related with series of events (with discussion). *J. Roy. Statist. Soc. B*, **17**, 129–64. **(4)**

Cox, D. R. (1977) The role of significant tests. *Scand. J. Statist.*, **4**, 49–71. **(17)**

Cox, D. R. (1978) Some remarks on the role in statistics of graphical methods. *Applied Statistics*, **27**, 4–9.

Cox, T. F. (1979) A method for mapping the dense and sparse regions of a forest stand. *Applied Statistics*, **28**, 14–19. **(4)**

Coxeter, H. S. M. (1961) *Introduction to Geometry* (pp. 289–90, stereographic projection). New York: Wiley. **(10)**

Coxeter, H. S. M. (1963). *Regular Polytopes* (2nd edn). New York: Macmillan. **(10)**

Daniels, H. E. (1952) The covering circle of a sample from a circular normal distribution. *Biometrika*, **39**, 137–43. **(1)**

Darroch, J. N. and Ratcliff, D. (1972) Generalized iterative scaling of loglinear models. *Ann. Math. Statist.*, **43**, 1470–80. **(14)**

Day, N. E. (1969) Estimating the components of a mixture of normal distributions. *Biometrika*, **56**, 463–74. **(11)**

Delaney, M. J. and Healy, M. J. R. (1964) Variation in the long-tailed field-mouse (*Apodemus Syyaticus* (*l*)) in northwest Scotland II. Simultaneous examination of all characters. *Proc. Roy. Soc. B*, **161**, 200–7. **(11)**

Delfiner, P. and Delhomme, J. P. (1975) Optimum interpolation by kriging. In Davis, J. C. and McCullagh, M. J. (eds.) (1975) *Display and Analysis of Spatial Data*, pp. 96–114. London: Wiley. **(2)**

Devlin, S. J., Gnanadesikan, R., and Kettenring, J. R. (1975) Robust estimation and outlier detection with correlation coefficients. *Biometrika*, **62**, 531–46. **(1)**

Diaconis, P. and Friedman, J. H. (1980) *M* and *N* plots. *Stanford Linear Accelerator Centre Report PUB-2495.* **(10)**

Diggle, P. J. (1975) Robust density estimation using distance methods. *Biometrika*, **62**, 39–48. **(4)**

Diggle, P. J. (1977a) A note on robust density estimation for spatial point patterns. *Biometrika*, **64**, 91–5. **(4)**

Diggle, P. J. (1977b) The detection of random heterogeneity in plant populations. *Biometrics*, **33**, 390–4. **(4)**

Diggle, P. J. (1978) On parameter estimation for spatial point processes. *J. Roy. Statist. Soc. B*, **40**, 178–81. **(4)**

Diggle, P. J. (1979a) Statistical methods for spatial point patterns in ecology. In Cormack, R. M. and Ord, J. K. (eds.) (1979) *Spatial and Temporal Analysis in Ecology*, pp. 95–150. Fairland: International Co-operative Publishing House. **(4)**

Diggle, P. J. (1979b) On parameter estimation and goodness-of-fit testing for spatial point patterns. *Biometrics*, **35**, 87–101. **(4)**

Diggle, P. J., Besag, J. and Gleaves, J. T. (1976) Statistical analysis of spatial point patterns by means of distance methods. *Biometrics*, **32**, 659–67. **(4)**

Dunn, D. M. and Landwehr, J. M. (1980) Analysing clustering effects across time. *J. Amer. Statist. Assn.*, **75**, 8–15.

Dyer, D. D. (1973) On moments estimation of the parameters of a truncated bivariate normal distribution. *Applied Statistics*, **22**, 287–91. **(1)**

Eckart, C. and Young, G. (1936) The approximation of one matrix by another of lower rank. *Psychometrika*, **1**, 211–318. **(6)**

Eddy, W. F. (1980) The distribution of the convex hull of a Gaussian sample. *J. Appl. Prob.*, **17**, 686–95. **(1)**

Eddy, W. F., and Hartigan, J. A. (1977) Uniform convergence of the empirical distribution function over convex sets. *Ann. Statist.*, **5**, 370–4. **(1)**

Efron, B. (1965) The convex hull of a random set of points. *Biometrika*, **52**, 331–43. **(1)**

Efron, B. (1979) Bootstrap methods—another look at the jackknife. *Ann. Statist.*, **7**, 1–26. **(3)**

Emery, J. L. and Carpenter, R. G. (1974) Pulmonary mast cells in infants and their relation to unexpected death in infancy. In Robinson, R. R. (ed.) (1974) *Proceedings of the Francis E. Camps International Symposium on Sudden and Unexpected Deaths in Infancy*, pp. 7–19. Canadian Foundation for the Study of Infant Deaths, Toronto: **(3)**

Epanechnikov, V. A. (1969) Nonparametric estimation of a multivariate probability density. *Theor. Prob. Appl.*, **14**, 153–8. **(3, 4)**

Everitt, B. S. and Nicholls, P. (1975) Visual techniques for representing multivariate data. *Statistician*, **24** (1), 37–49.

Everitt, B. S. and Rushton, D. N. (1978) A method for plotting the optimum positions of an array of cortical electrical phosphenes. *Biometrics*, **34**, 399–410. **(13)**

Fienberg, S. E. (1979) Graphical methods in statistics. *The American Statistician*, **33**, 165–78. **(12)**

Fienberg, S. E. (1980) *The Analysis of Cross-Classified Data* (2nd edn). Cambridge, Mass.: MIT Press. **(14)**

Fienberg, S. E. and Wasserman, S. (1980) Methods for the analysis of data from multivariate directed graphs. *Proceedings of the Conference on Recent Developments in Statistical Methods and Applications*, pp. 137–61. Taipei, Taiwan: Institute of Mathematics, Academia Sinica. **(14)**

Fienberg, S. E. and Wasserman, S. (1981) Categorical data analysis of single sociometric relations. In Leinhardt, S. (ed.) (1981) *Sociological Methodology 1981*, pp. 156–92. San Francisco: Jossey-Bass. **(14)**

Fisher, R. A. (1936) The use of multiple measurements in taxonomic problems. *Ann. Eugen.*, **7**, 179–88. Reprinted in Fisher, R. A. (1950). *Contributions to Mathematical Statistics*, New York: Wiley. **(1, 10)**

Friedman, H. P. (1979) The use of graphics software in concert with multivariate statistical tools for interactive data analysis. In Gentleman, J. F. (ed.) (1979) *Proc. of the Computer Science and Statistics 12th Annual Symposium on the Interface*, pp. 160–90. Waterloo Canada: Department of Statistics, University of Waterloo.

Friedman, H. P., Farrell, E. S. Goldwyn, R. M., Miller, M., and Sigel, J. H. (1972) A graphic way of describing changing multivariate patterns. *Proc. of the Computer Science and Statistics Sixth Annual Symposium on the Interface*, Oct. 16–17, 1972, pp. 56–9. Berkeley: University of California. **(12)**

Friedman, J. H., Bentley, J. L., and Finkel, R. A. (1975) An algorithm for finding best matches in logarithmic time. *Stanford University Technical Report STAN-CS-75-482*. **(11)**

Friedman, J. H., Bentley, J. L., and Finkel, R. A. (1977) An algorithm for finding best matches in logarithmic time. *ACM Trans. on Math. Software*, **3**, 209–26. **(11)**

Friedman, J. H. and Tukey, J. W. (1974) A projection pursuit algorithm for exploratory data analysis. *IEEE Trans. Comp.* **C-23**, 881–90. **(11)**

Friedman, J. H., Tukey, J. W., and Tukey, P. A. (1980) Approaches to analysis of data that concentrate near intermediate-dimensional manifolds. In Diday, E. *et al.* (eds.) (1980) *Data Analysis and Informatics*. Amsterdam and New York: North-Holland. **(11, 12)**

Fryer, M. J. (1977) A review of some non-parametric methods of density estimation. *J. Inst. Maths. Appl.*, **20**, 335–54. **(3)**

Gabriel, K. R. (1971) The biplot—graphic display of matrices with application to principal component analysis. *Biometrika*, **58**, 453–67. **(6, 8)**

Gabriel, K.R. (1972) Analysis of meteorological data by means of canonical decomposition and biplots. *Journal of Applied Meteorology*, **11**, 1071–7. **(8)**

Gabriel, K. R. (1980) Biplot. In Johnson, N. L. and Kotz, S. (eds.) (1980) *Encyclopedia of Statistical Sciences*, Vol. 1. New York: Wiley. **(8)**

Gabriel, K. R. and Zamir, S. (1979) Lower rank approximation of matrices by least squares with any choice of weights. *Technometrics*, **21**, 489–98. **(8)**

Galaskiewicz, J. (1979) *Exchange Networks and Community Politics*. Beverly Hills: Sage. **(14)**

Galaskiewicz, J. and Marsden, P. V. (1978) Interorganizational resource networks: Formal patterns of overlap. *Social Science Research*, **7**, 89–107. **(14)**

Gentleman, W. M. and Sande, G. (1966) Fast Fourier transforms—for fun and profit. *AFIPS Proceedings of the Fall Joint Computer Conference*, **19**, 563–78. **(3)**

Gerrard, D. J. (1969) Competition quotient: a new measure of the competition affecting individual forest trees. *Res. Bull. No. 20*, Agricultural Experiment Station, Michigan State University. **(4)**

Ghent, A. W. (1963) Studies of regeneration of forest stands devastated by spruce budworm. *For. Sci.*, **9**, 295–310. **(4)**

Gnanadesikan, R. (1973) Graphical methods for informal inference in multivariate data analysis. *Bull. Int. Statist. Inst.*, **45**, 195–206.

Gnanadesikan, R., Kettenring, J. R. (1972) Robust estimates, residuals, and outlier detection with multiresponse data. *Biometrics*, **28**, 81–124. **(6, 10, 11)**

Gnanadesikan, R., Kettenring, J. R., and Landwehr, J. M. (1977) Interpreting and assessing the results of cluster analyses. *Bull. Int. Statist. Inst.* **47**, 451–63. **(12)**

Gnanadesikan, R., Kettenring, J. R., and Landwehr, J. M. (1981) Projection plots for displaying clusters. To appear in Kallianpur, G., Krishnaiah, P. R. and Ghosh, J. K. (eds.) (1981). *Statistics and Probability: Essays in Honor of C. R. Rao*. Amsterdam: North-Holland. **(12)**

Gold, E. M. (1973) Metric unfolding: data requirement for unique solution and clarification of Schonemann's algorithm. *Psychometrika*, **38**, 555–69. **(6)**

Goldman, J. (1976) Detection in the presence of spherically symmetric random vectors. *IEEE Trans. Inf. Th.*, **IT-22**, 52–9. **(10)**

Good, I. J. (1976) The Bayesian influence. In Harper, W. L. and Hawker. C. A. (eds.) (1976) *Foundations of Probability Theory, Statistical Inference and Statistical Theories of Science*, Vol. II. Dordrecht: Reidel. **(17)**

Good, I. J. and Gaskins, R. A. (1980) Density estimation and bump-hunting by the penalized likelihood method exemplified by scattering and meteorite data. *J. Amer. Stat. Assn.*, **75**, 42–56. **(3)**

Gower, J. C. (1966) Some distance properties of latent root and vector methods used in multivariate analysis. *Biometrika*, **53**, 325–38. **(6)**

Gower, J. C. (1967) Multivariate analysis and multidimensional geometry. *The Statistician*, **17**, 13–25. **(6)**

Gower, J. C. (1967) A comparison of some methods of cluster analysis. *Biometrics*, **23**, 623–37.

Gower, J. C. (1971a) A general coefficient of similarity and some of its properties. *Biometrics*, **27**, 857–72. **(6)**

Gower, J. C. (1971b) Statistical methods of comparing different multivariate analyses of the same data. In Hodson, F. R., Kendall, D. G., and Taŭtu, P. (1971) (eds.) *Mathematics in the Archaeological and Historical Sciences*, pp. 138–49. Edinburgh: Edinburgh University Press. **(6)**

Gower, J. C. (1974) The mediancentre (Algorithm AS78). *Applied Statistics*, **23**, 466–70. **(1)**

Gower, J. C. (1975) Generalised Procrustes analysis. *Psychometrika*, **40**, 33–51. **(6, 13)**

Gower, J. C. (1977) The analysis of asymmetry and orthogonality. In Barra, J. *et al.* (eds.) (1977) *Recent Developments in Statistics*, pp. 109–23. Amsterdam, North-Holland. **(6)**

Gower, J. C. (1980) Problems in interpreting asymmetrical chemical relationships. In Bisby, F. (ed.) (1980) *Chemosystematics: Principles and Practice*. New York: Academic Press. **(6)**

Gower, J. C. and Ross, G. J. S. (1969) Minimum spanning trees and single linkage cluster analysis. *Applied Statistics*, **18**, 54–64. **(6)**

Graham, I. (1980) Spectral analysis and distance methods in the study of archaeological distributions. *Journal of Archaeological Science*, **7**, 105–29. **(16)**

Gratton, R. J. (1981) Density estimation and likelihood inference for implicit statistical models. *Ph.D. Thesis,* University, Newcastle upon Tyne. **(4)**

Green, P. J. (1976) Contribution to the discussion of Barnett (1976). **(1)**

Green, P. J. and Sibson, R. (1978) Computing Dirichlet tessellations in the plane. *The Computer Journal*, **21**, 168–73. **(1, 2)**

Green, P. J. and Silverman, B. W. (1979) Constructing the convex hull of a set of points in the plane. *The Computer Journal*, **22**, 262–6. **(1)**

Greenacre, M. J. (1978) Some objective methods of graphical display of a data matrix. Translation of doctoral thesis (Université de Paris, VI), published as *special report* by University of South Africa, Pretoria. **(6, 7)**

Guttman, L. (1941) The quantification of a class of attributes: A theory and method of scale construction. In Horst, P. *et al.* (1941). *The Prediction of Personal Adjustment*, Bulletin No. 48, pp. 319–48. New York: The Social Science Research Council. **(7)**

Guttman, L. (1946) An approach for quantifying paired comparisons and rank order. *Ann. Math. Statist.*, **17**, 144–63. **(7)**

Habbema, J. D. F., Hermans, J., and Van der Broek, K. (1974) A stepwise discriminant analysis program using density estimation. *COMPSTAT 1974, Proceedings in Computational Statistics*, pp. 101–10. Wien: Physica Verlag, **(3)**

Haber, M. (1975) The singular value decomposition of random matrices. *Ph.D. thesis at Hebrew University*, Jerusalem. **(8)**

Haberman, S. (1974) *The Analysis of Frequency Data*. Chicago: University of Chicago Press. **(14)**

Haberman, S. (1979) *Analysis of Qualitative Data. Volume 2: New Developments*. New York: Academic Press. **(14)**

Harshman, R. (1978) Models for analysis of asymmetric relationships among *N* objects or stimuli. Paper presented at the first joint meeting of the Psychometric Society and the Society for Mathematical Psychology. (6)

Hartigan, J. A. (1975) Printer graphics for clustering. *J. Statist. Comput. Simul.*, **4**, 187–213. (10)

Healy, M. J. R. (1968) Multivariate normal plotting. *Applied Statistics*, **1**, 157–61.

Heiser, W. and de Leeuw, J. (1979) How to use SMACOF-I. A program for metric multidimensional scaling. *Internal Report*, Department of Data theory. University of Leiden. (6)

Hermans, J. and Habbema, J. D. F. (1975) Comparisons of five methods to estimate posterior probabilities. *EDV in Medizin und Biologie*, **1/2**, 14–9. (17)

Hill, M. O. (1973) Reciprocal averaging: an eigenvector method of ordination. *J. Ecology*, **61**, 237–49. (7)

Hill, M. O. (1974) Correspondence analysis: a neglected multivariate method. *Applied Statistics*, **23**, 340–54. (7)

Hirschfeld, H. O. (1935) A connection between correlation and contingency. *Proc. Camb. Phil. Soc.*, **31**, 520–4. (7)

Hodder, I. and Orton, C. (1976) *Spatial Analysis in Archaeology*. Cambridge: Cambridge University Press. (16)

Hodson, F. R. (1977) Quantifying Hallstatt: Some initial results. *American Antiquity*, **42**, 394–412. (16)

Holland, P. W. and Leinhardt, S. (1975) Local structure in social networks. In Heise, D. R. (ed.) (1975) *Sociological Methodology 1976*, pp. 1–45. San Francisco: Jossey-Bass. (14)

Holland, P. W. and Leinhardt, S. (1981) An exponential family of probability distributions for directed graphs. *J. Amer. Statist. Assn.*, **76**, 33–50. (14)

Hope, A. C. A. (1968) A simplified Monte Carlo significance test procedure. *J. Roy. Statist. Soc. B*, **30**, 582–98. (4)

Hotelling, H. (1933) Analysis of a complex of statistical variables into principal components. *J. Educ. Psychol.*, **24**, 417–41, 498–520. (7)

Householder, A. S. and Young, G. (1938) Matrix approximation and latent roots. *Am. Math. Monthly*, **45**, 165–71. (8)

Hunter, J. E. (1981) Chapter on factor analysis in Monge, P. R. and Capella, J. N. (eds.) (1981) *Multivariate Techniques in Human Communications Research*. Academic Press (to appear). New York. (11)

Hutchings, M. J. (1978) Standing crop and pattern in pure stands of *Mercurialis perennis and Rubus fruticosus* in mixed deciduous woodland. *Oikos*, **31**, 351–7. (4)

Jeffreys, H. (1939/61) *Theory of Probability*. Oxford: University Press. (1st and 3rd edns). (17)

Jenner, W. E. (1963) *Rudiments of Algebraic Geometry*. (Chapter VI: Plücker Co-ordinates and Grassmann varieties.) Oxford: Oxford University Press. (10)

Kendall, D. G. (1975) The recovery of structure from fragmentary information. *Phil. Trans. Roy. Soc. (A)*, **279**, 547–82.

Kendall, D. G. (1977) The diffusion of shape. *Adv. Appl. Prob.*, **9**, 428–30. (5)

Kendall, D. G. (1981a) Shape-manifolds, Procrustacean metrics and complex projective spaces (in preparation) (5)

Kendall, D. G. (1981b) Foundations of a theory of random shape (in preparation) (5)

Kendall, D. G. and Kendall, W. S. (1980) Alignments in two-dimensional random sets of points. *Adv. Appl. Prob.*, **12**, 380–424. (3, 5)

Kendall, M. G. (1966) Discrimination and classification, in Krishnaiah, P. R. (ed.) (1966) *Multivariate Analysis*. Vol. I. New York: Academic Press. (1)

Kendall, W. S. (1981) Random Gaussian traiangles and *k*-point collinearities (in preparation) (5)

Kester, N. (1979) Diagnosing and fitting concurrent and related models for two-way and higher-way layouts. *Ph.D. Thesis*, University of Rochester, New York. (**8**)

Kleiner, B. and Hartigan, J. A. (1981) Representing points in many dimensions by trees and castles *J. Amer. Statist. Assn.* **76**, 260–9. (**6, 12**)

Kruskal, J. B. (1964a) Multidimensional scaling by optimizing goodness of fit to a nonmetric hypothesis. *Psychometrika*, **29**, 1–27. (**16**)

Kruskal, J. B. (1964b) Nonmetric multidimensional scaling: A numerical method. *Psychometrika*, **29**, 115–29. (**16**)

Kruskal, J. B. (1969) Toward a practical method which helps uncover the structure of a set of multivariate observations by finding the linear transformation which optimizes a new 'index of condensation'. In Milton, R. C. and Nelder, J. A. (eds.) (1969) *Statistical Computation*. New York: Academic Press. (**10, 11, 12**)

Kruskal, J. B. (1972) Linear transformation of multivariate data to reveal clustering. In Kruskal, J. B. (ed.) (1972) *Multidimensional Scaling: Theory and Applications in the Behavioural Sciences, Vol. 1, Theory*. New York and London: Seminar Press. (**10, 11, 12**)

Kudo, A. (1956) On the testing of outlying observations, *Sankhya A*, **17**, 67–76. (**1**)

Lawson, C. L. (1977) Software for C^1 surface interpolation. In Rice, J. (ed.) (1977) *Mathematical Software III,*, pp. 161–94. New York: Academic Press. (**2**)

Lebart, L. and Fénelon, J.-P. (1971) *Statistique et informatique appliquées*. Paris: Dunod.

Lebart, L., Morineau, A., and Tabard, N. (1977) *Techniques de la description statistique*. Paris, Dunod.

Lindley, D. V. (1957) A statistical paradox. *Biometrika*, **44**, 187–92. (**17**)

Loftsgaarden, D. O. and Quesenberry, C. P. (1965) A nonparametric estimate of a multivariate density function. *Ann. Math. Statist.*, **36**, 1049–51. (**3, 4, 11**)

Lohrding, R. K. Johnson, M. M., and Whiteman, D. E. (1978) Computer graphics for extracting information from data. In Gallant, A. R. and Gerig, T. M. (eds.) (1978) *Proceedings of the Computer Science and Statistics Eleventh Annual Symposium on the Interface*, pp. 114–24. Raleigh, N.C.: North Carolina State University.

MacWilliams, F. J. and Sloane, N. J. A. (1977) *The Theory of Error-correcting Codes*. (Chapter 2 for simple codes). Amsterdam: North Holland. (**10**)

McNeil, D. R. and Tukey, J. W. (1975) Higher-order diagnosis of two-way tables. *Biometrics*, **31**, 487–510. (**8**)

M.A.F.F. (1972) *Agricultural statistics 1970–1971*. London: HMSO. (**6**)

Mallows, C. L. (1973) Some comments on C_p. *Technometrics*, **15**, 661–75. (**9**)

Mandel, J. (1961) Non-additivity in two-way analysis of variance. *J. Amer. Statist. Assn.*, **56**, 878–88. (**8**)

Mandel, J. (1969) The partitioning of interaction in analysis of variance. *Journal Nat. Bur. Stand. (U.S.)*, **73B**, 309–28. (**8**)

Mardia, K. V. (1975) Statistics of directional data. *J. Roy. Statist. Soc. B*, **37**, 349–93. (**3**)

Mardia, K. V., Edwards, R., and Puri, M. L. (1977) Analysis of central place theory. *Bull. Int. Statist. Inst.*, **41**, (4), 93–110. (**5**)

Marlow, S. and Powell, M. J. D. (1976) A Fortran subroutine for plotting the part of a conic that is inside a given triangle. *UKAEA Harwell Paper AERE-R 8336*. London, HMSO. (**3**)

Marriott, F. H. C. (1979) Monte Carlo tests: how many simulations? *Applied Statistics*, **28**, 75–7. (**4**)

Matheron, G. (1973) The intrinsic random functions and their applications. *Adv. Appl. Prob.*, **5**, 439–68. (**2**)

Mielke, P. W., Berry, K. J., and Johnson, E. S. (1976) Multi-response permutation procedures for a priori classifications. *Communications in Statistics, Theory-Methods,* **A5** (14), 1409–24. **(8)**

Monkhouse, F. J. and Wilkinson, H. R. (1963) *Maps and Diagrams.* London: Methuen; New York: Harper & Row. **(12)**

Monro, D. M. (1976) Algorithm AS 97. Real discrete fast Fourier transform. *Applied Statistics,* **25**, 166–72. **(3)**

Nath, G. B. (1971) Estimation in truncated bivariate normal distributions. *Applied Statistics,* **20**, 313–19. **(1)**

Nathanson, J. A. (1971) Applications of multivariate analysis in astronomy. *Applied Statistics,* **20**, 239–49. **(6)**

Nelder, J. A. and Members of the Rothamsted Statistics Department (1977) *GENSTAT A General Statistical Programme.* Harpenden: Statistics Department, Rothamsted Experimental Station. **(13)**

Nelder, J. A. and Wedderburn, R. W. (1972). Generalized linear models. *J. Roy. Statist. Soc. A*, **135**, 370–84. **(14)**

Nishisato, S. (1978) Optimal scaling of paired comparison and rank order data: an alternative to Guttman's formulation. *Psychometrika,* **43**, 263–71. **(7)**

Numata, M. (1961) Forest vegetation in the vicinity of Choshi. Coastal flora and vegetation at Choshi, Chiba Prefecture IV (in Japanese). *Bull Chosi Marine Lab. Chiba Univ.,* **3**, 28–48. **(4)**

Pericchi, L. R. (1981) A Bayesian approach to transformations to normality. *Biometrika,* **68**, 35–43. **(17)**

Parzen, E. (1963) On estimation of a probability density function and mode. *Ann. Math. Statist.*, **34**, 1065–76. **(4)**

Parzen, E. (1979) Non-parametric statistical data modeling. *J. Amer. Stat. Assn.*, **74**, 105–21. **(3)**

Pearson, K. (1901) On lines and planes of closest fit to a system of points. *Phil. Mag.* ser. 6, **2**, 559–72. **(7)**

Peebles, P. J. E. (1973) Statistical analysis of catalogs of extra-galactic objects. I. Theory. *Astrophysical Journal,* **185**, 413–40. **(16)**

Phillips, R. L. (1978) An interactive graphical data analysis system. In Gallant, A. R. and Gerig, T. M. (eds.) (1978) *Proceedings of the Computer Science and Statistics Eleventh Annual Symposium on the Interface,* pp. 125–33. Raleigh, N.C.: North Carolina State University.

Preparata, F. P. and Hong, S. J. (1977) Convex hulls of finite sets of points in two and three dimensions. *Comm. A.C.M.*, **20**, 87–93. **(1)**

Press, S. J. (1972) *Applied Multivariate Analysis.* New York: Holt, Rinehart and Winston. **(17)**

Quesenberry, C. P. and Gessaman, M. P. (1968) Nonparametric discrimination using tolerance regions. *Ann. Math. Statist.*, **39**, 664–73. **(1)**

Raynaud, H. (1970) Sur l'enveloppe convexe des nuages de points aléatoires dans R^n I. *J. Appl. Prob.,* **7**, 35–48. **(1)**

Reeve, E. C. R. (1940) Relative growth of anteaters. *Proc. Zool. Soc. Lond.*, **A110**, 47–80. **(8)**

Renyi, A. and Sulanke, R. (1963/4) Uber die konvexe Hülle von *n* zufällig gewählten Punkten I and II. *Z. Wahrscheinlichkeitstheorie und Verw. Gebiete*, **2**, 75–84 and **3**, 138–47. **(1)**

Ripley, B. D. (1977) Modelling spatial patterns (with discussion) *J. Roy. Statist. Soc. B*, **39**, 172–212. **(4)**

Rogers, A. (1974) *Statistical Analysis of Spatial Dispersion.* London: Pion. **(16)**

Rosenblatt, M. (1956) Remarks on some non-parametric estimates of a density function. *Ann. Math. Statist.*, **27**, 832–7. **(3)**

Rosenblatt, M. (1971) Curve estimates. *Ann. Math. Statist.*, **42**, 1815–42. **(3)**

Ross, G. J. S. (1972) Discussion of Sibson, R. (1972) Order invariant methods for data analysis. *J. Roy. Statist. Soc.*, *B*, **34**, 343–4. **(6)**

Rushton, D. N. and Brindley, G. S. (1977) Short- and long-term stability of cortical electrical phosphenes. In Rose, F. C. (ed.) (1977) *Physiological Aspects of Clinical Neurology*, pp. 123–53. Oxford: Blackwell. **(13)**

Sager, T. W. (1979) An iterative method for estimating a multivariate mode and isopleth. *J. Amer. Statist. Assn.*, **74**, 329–39. **(1)**

Sammon, J. E. Jr. (1969) A nonlinear mapping for data-structure analysis. *IEEE Trans. Comp.* **C-18**, 401–7. **(11)**

Schonemann, P. H. (1970) On metric multidimensional unfolding. *Psychometrika*, **35**, 349–66. **(6)**

Schwarz, G. (1978) Estimating the dimension of a model. *Ann. Statist.* **6**, 461–4. **(17)**

Seal, H. L. (1964) *Multivariate Statistical Analysis for Biologists*. New York: Wiley. **(8)**

Seheult, A. H., Diggle, P. J., and Evans, D. A. (1976) Contribution to the discussion of Barnett (1976). **(1)**

Shepard, R. N. (1962) Analysis of proximities, multidimensional scaling with an unknown distance function, Parts 1 and 2. *Psychometrika*, **27**, (1) 125–40, (2) 219–46. **(16)**

Shepard, R. N. and Carroll, J. D. (1966) Parametric representation of nonlinear data in structures. In Krishnaiah, P. R. (ed.) (1966). *Multivariate Analysis*. New York: Academic Press, 561–92. **(12)**

Sibson, R. (1978) Studies in the robustness of multidimensional scaling: Procrustes statistics. *J. Roy. Statist. Soc.*, **40**, 234–8. **(6)**

Sibson, R. (1980) A vector identity for the Dirichlet tessellation. *Math. Proc. Camb. Phil. Soc.*, **87**, 151–5. **(2)**

Sibson, R. and Thomson, G. D. (1981) A seamed quadratic element for contouring. *The Computer Journal* (in press). **(2, 3)**

Silverman, B. W. (1978) Choosing a window width when estimating a density. *Biometrika*, **65**, 1–11. **(3)**

Silverman, B. W. (1980) Density estimation: Are theoretical results useful in practice? In Chakravarti, I. M. (ed.) (1980) *Asymptotic Theory of Statistical Tests and Estimation*, pp. 179–203. New York: Academic Press. **(3)**

Silverman, B. W. (1981a) Using kernel density estimates to investigate multimodality. *J. Roy. Statist. Soc. B*, **43**, (to appear) **(3)**

Silverman, B. W. (1981b) Kernel density estimation using the fast Fourier transform. *Internal Report*, School of Mathematics, University of Bath, U.K. **(3)**

Silverman, B. W. and Titterington, D. M. (1981) Minimum covering ellipses. To appear in *SIAM J. on Scientific and Statistical Computing.* **(1)**

Siotani, M. (1959) The extreme value of the generalized distances of the individual points in the multivariate normal sample. *Ann. Inst. Statist. Math., Tokyo*, **10**, 183–208. **(1)**

Small, C. G. Random uniform triangles and the alignment problem. *Ph.D. Thesis*, Cambridge University (in preparation). **(5)**

Small, C. G. Characterization of distributions through shapes of samples. *Ph.D. Thesis*, Cambridge University (in preparation). **(5)**

Smith, A. F. M. and Spiegelhalter, D. J. (1980) Bayes factors and choice criteria for the linear model. *J. Roy. Statist. Soc. B*, **42**, 213–20. **(17)**

Sneath, P. H. A. (1957) The application of computers to taxonomy. *J. Gen. Microbiol*, **17**, 201–26. **(6)**

Sommerville, D. M. Y. (1929, republished in 1958 edition) *An Introduction to the Geometry of N Dimensions*. (Chapter 10 for regular polytopes.) New York: Dover Publications. **(10)**

Springall, A. (1978) A review of multidimensional scaling. *B.I.A.S.*, **5** (2), 146–92.

Stephens, M. A. (1969) Techniques for directional data. Technical Report 150, Dept. of Statistics, Standford, Calif. (**3**)

Stone, M. (1979) On model selection criteria of Akaike and Schwarz., *J. Roy. Statist. Soc. B.*, **41**, 276–8. (**17**)

Strauss, D. J. (1975) A model for clustering. *Biometrika*, **62**, 467–75. (**4**)

Takane, Y., Young, F., and de Leeuw, J. (1977) Non-metric individual differences multidimensional scaling: an alternating least squares method with optimal scaling features. *Psychometrika*, **42**, 7–67. (**6**)

Tanner, J. M., Whitehouse, R. H., Marubini, E. and Resele, L. F. (1976) The adolescent Growth Spurt for boys and girls of the Harpenden Growth Study. *Ann. Hum. Biol.*, **3**, 109–26. (**15**)

Tanner, J. M., Whitehouse, R. H., and Takaishi, M. (1966) Standards from birth to maturity for height, weight, height velocity and weight velocity. British Children 1965, II. *Arch. Dis. Child*, **41**, 613–35. (**15**)

Tarter, M. (1975) Implementation and applications of bivariate Gaussian mixture decomposition. *J. Amer. Statist. Assn.*, **70**, 47–55. (**12**)

Tarter, M. and Raman, S. (1972) A Systematic approach to graphical methods in biometry. In Le Cam, L. M., Neyman, J. and Scott, E. L. (eds.) (1972) *Proc. 6th Berk. Symp. on Math. Statist. and Prob.*, Vol. IV, pp. 199–222. University of California Press. (**11**, **12**)

Thurstone, L. L. (1947, 2nd edn. 1957) *Multiple-Factor Analysis.* Chicago: University of Chicago Press. (**11**)

Titterington, D. M. (1975) Optimal design: some geometrical aspects of D-optimality *Biometrika*, **62**, 313–20. (**1**)

Titterington, D. M. (1978) Estimation of correlation coefficients by ellipsoidel trimming. *Applied Statistics*, **27**, 227–34. (**1**)

Toussaint, G. T. (1978) The convex hull as a tool in pattern recognition, in *Proc. APOSR Workshop in communication theory and applications*, Provincetown, Mass. (**1**)

Tsianco, M. C. (1980) Use of biplots and 3D-bimodels in diagnosing models for two-way tables. *Ph.D. Thesis,* University of Rochester, New York. (**8**)

Tukey, J. W. (1947) Non parametric estimation. II. Statistically equivalent blocks and tolerance regions in the continuous case. *Ann. Math. Statist.*, **18**, 529–39. (**1**, **11**)

Tukey, J. W. (1962) The future of data analysis. *Ann. Math. Statist.*, **33**, 1–67.

Tukey, J. W. (1975) Mathematics and the picturing of data, In *Proc. International Congress of Mathematicians.*, Vol. 2, pp. 523–31. Vancouver, (1974). (**1**)

Tukey, J. W. Friedman, J. H., and Fisherkeller, M. A. (1976) PRIM-9, an interactive multidimensional data display and analysis system. *Proc. 4th International Congress for Stereology*, Sept. 4–9, 1975, Gaithersburg, Maryland. (**10**, **11**, **12**)

Tukey, J. W. and Tukey, P. A. (1977) Aide-Memoire for: Methods for direct and indirect graphic display for data sets in 3 and more dimensions. Presented at University of Western Ontario, November, 1977. (**12**)

Wahba, G. (1979) How to smooth curves and surfaces with splines and cross-validation. University of Wisconsin, Department of Statistics. *Technical Report, No. 555.* (**2**)

Wahba, G. and Wold, S. (1975) A completely automatic French curve; fitting spline functions by cross-validation. *Comm. Stat.*, **4**, 1–17. (**2**)

Wainer, H. and Thissen, D. (1981) Graphical data analysis. *Ann. Rev. Psychol.*, **32**, 191–241.

Webster, A. (1976) The clustering of radio sources—I. The theory of power-spectrum analysis. *Monthly Notices; Royal Astronomical Society*, **175**, 61–70. (**16**)

Wegman, E. J. (1972) Non-parametric probability density estimation. I: *Technometrics*, **14**, 533–46; II: *J. Statist. Comp & Sim.*, **1**, 225–46. **(3)**

Wertz, W. and Schneider, B. (1979) Statistical Density Estimation: a bibliography. *Int. Stat. Rev.*, **47**, 155–75. **(3)**

Whallon, R. (1973) Spatial analysis of occupation floors I: Application of dimensional analysis of variance. *American Antiquity*, **38**, 266–78. **(16)**

Whallon, R. (1974) Spatial analysis of occupation floors II: The application of nearest neighbour analysis. *American Antiquity*, **39**, 16–34. **(16)**

Wilk, M. B. and Gnanadesikan, R. (1961) Graphical analysis of multi-response experimental data using ordered distances. *Proc. Nat. Acad. Sci. USA*, **47**, 1209–12.

Wilk, M. B. and Gnanadesikan, R. (1964) Graphical methods for internal comparisons in multiresponse experiments. *Ann. Math. Statist.*, **35**, 613–31.

Wilk, M. B. and Gnanadesikan, R. (1968) Probability plotting methods for the analysis of data. *Biometrika*, **55**, 1–17.

Williams, W. T. and Gillard, P. (1971) Pattern analysis of a grazing experiment. *Aust. J. Agric. Res.*, **22**, 245–60. **(6)**

Woodroofe, M. (1970) On choosing a Delta-sequence. *Ann. Math. Statist.*, **41**, 1665–71. **(3)**

Young, F. W. (1975) An asymmetric Euclidean model for multi-process asymmetric data. In *U.S.–Japan Seminar on Theory, Methods and Applications of Multidimensional Scaling and Related Techniques*, pp. 79–88. University of California. **(6)**

Yu, J. T. and Peebles, P. J. E. (1969) Superclusters of galaxies? *Astrophysical Journal*, **158**, 103–13. **(16)**

INDEX

Adaptive estimates, 15
Adjacency matrix, 290, 292
Adjacency peeling, 11, 12
Agglomeration of data, 195, 215,
    228–237, 253, 268–269
Agriculture, applications in, 87–90
AITCHISON, J., 343, 347, 353
AKAIKE, H., 335, 348, 353
Akaike information criterion, 335
ANDERBERG, M. R., 349
ANDERSON, E., 84, 117, 202, 213, 256,
    274, 353
Anderson glyphs, *see* Pictorial display of
    data
ANDREWS, D. F., 3, 14, 15, 18, 175–185,
    198, 213, 273, 274, 349, 353
Andrews' plot, 273
Angle plots, 198
Anteaters, 157–160
Antelopes, 122–136
ARABIE, P., 274, 354
Archaeology, applications in, 78–79,
    107–111, 161–163, 321–333
ASHTON, E. H., 227, 242, 353
Astronomy, applications in, 96–97,
    101–103, 324–325

BACHI R., 349
Back variables, *see* Pictorial display of
    data
BAILEY, D. D., 351
Balloon density, 193–194, 200, 233–237
    expanding balloon, 233–234
    kernel-balloon density, 235
    three-balloon density, 234
Balloonogram, 235–236, 262
BANFIELD, C. F., 97, 117, 353
BARNARD, G. A., 58, 72, 353

BARNETT, V., 3, 9, 14, 18, 19, 349, 353,
    361
BARRA, J., 358
BARTLETT, M. S., 55, 60, 63, 69, 72, 324,
    333, 353, 354
Barycentric coordinates, 87, 88
BATCHELOR, B. G., 349
Bayesian methods, 335–348
Bayesian significance test, 335
BEBBINGTON, A. C., 14, 18, 354
BENNETT, J. F., 354
BENTLEY, J. L., 234, 243, 357
BENZECRI, J.-P., 122, 131, 145, 349, 354
BERRY, K. J., 160, 173, 360
BERTIN, J., 254, 274, 349, 354
BESAG, J., 41, 51, 55, 60, 69, 72, 354, 356
BIBBY, J. M., 350
BICKEL, P. J., 349
BIJNEN, E. J., 349
Biochemistry, applications in, 153–155
Biology, applications in, 55–68,
    122–131, 132–136, 157–160
Biplot, 90–94, 147–173
    approximate, 149–150
    for data inspection, 150–160
    for model validation, 160–171
    row, and column markers, 147
    use of concentration ellipse, 153–154
BISHOP, Y. M. M., 289, 305, 349
Bivariate normal distribution, 8, 48–49
Bivariate sample
    convex hull, 3–8, 11–14
    extremes, 3
    interquartile set, 5, 8
    location estimate, 15–17
    median, 5, 7
    mediancentre, 5
    minimum covering circle, 8
    minimum covering ellipse, 9, 13

Bivariate sample (*cont.*)
  peeling, 3–19
  signature, 15, 16
  statistically equivalent blocks, 10
  test edges, 4, 6
  trimming, 3, 8
BLACKITH, R. E., 349
Blindness, substitution of vision, 279–287
Blood samples, analysis of, 178–180
Blunt triangles, in archaeology, 78
Blunting of data, 195, 241–242
  by Russian roulette, 241–242
BONEVA, L. I., 37, 38, 39, 51, 64, 72, 354
Botany, applications in, 202–207, 220–222, 242
BOWMAN, W. J., 349
BOWYER, A., 31, 34, 41, 51, 354
BOX, G. E. P., 182, 185, 346, 348, 349, 354
Box-and-whisker plot, bivariate, 5
BRADU, D., 92, 93, 117, 161, 162, 163, 173, 354
BREIMAN, L., 46, 52, 354
BRIER, G. W., 167, 173, 354
BRINDLEY, G. S., 279, 287, 354, 362
BROADBENT, S. R., 78, 80, 354
Van der BROEK, K., 40, 43, 52, 358
Business and commerce, applications in, 289–306
BYTH, K., 69, 72, 354

Canonical correlation, 119, 120, 121, 227
Cap sizes, 215–216
CARNAL, H., 12, 18, 354
CARPENTER, R. G., 38, 52, 356
CARROLL, J. D., 107, 117, 274, 354, 362
Castles, *see* Pictorial display of data
Cellulation, *see* Pictorial display of data
Central place theory, in geography, 78
Centring of data, 196
CHAMBERS, J. M., 349, 355
CHANG, J. J., 107, 117, 354
CHATFIELD, C., 349
CHERNOFF, H., 84, 117, 257, 275, 355
Chernoff faces, *see* Pictorial display of data
CHHIKARA, R. S., 355
Child development, physical growth, 307–319
  growth curve, 307

CHINO, N., 104, 117, 355
Chronology, 323
Classical scaling, *see* Scaling
Classification, 343–344
CLEVELAND, W. S., 203, 212, 251, 275, 355
Clottedness of data, 219, 220
  index, 220
Cloud seeding, 140, 155–157
Cluster analysis, 112, 113, 116, 227
Cluster factor analysis, 227
COGBILL, S., 79
COLLINS, A. J., 349
Commerce and business, applications in, 289–306
Complete spatial randomness, 55, 57–60, 64–66
  nearest-neighbour analysis, 57–59
  test of, 55, 57–60
Concentration ellipse, 153–154
Confirmatory analysis of data, 39–40
CONSTANTINE, A. G., 105, 117, 355
Contingency table, 119, 122, 300
  multi-dimensional, 285
  multi-way, 300
  two-way, 119, 122
Contour plot, 33, 46, 47, 191, 192, 264–267, 269–271
Convex hull, 3–8
  distribution theory, 11–14
  for bivariate sample, 3–8, 11–14
Convex hull peels, 3–8, 11–14
COOLEY, J. W., 44, 52, 355
COOLEY, W. W., 349
c-order groups, 3
CORMACK, R. M., 355, 356
Correlation
  canonical, 119, 120, 121, 227
  cross-correlation, 327
  estimation, 14–15
  for trimmed data, 14
  Kendall's τ, 14
Correspondence analysis, 93–95, 119–146
  applications, 131–144
  chi-squared metric, 125
  data 'doubling', 137
  geometric interpretation, 122–131
  inertia, 126, 127
  moment of inertia, 126
  principal axis of inertia, 126, 127
  profile, 122, 123

relationship with other techniques, 119–122
CORSTEN, L. C. A., 155, 156, 173, 355
Cot death, density estimate, 38
Covariances, hypotheses involving, 341–343
COX, D. R., 63, 72, 182, 185, 335, 346, 348, 354, 355
COX, T. F., 67, 72, 355
COXETER, H. S. M., 205, 207, 213, 355
Crime rates, 86, 88–92
Cross-correlation, 327
Curvature reduction, 197

DANIEL, C., 274, 275, 349
DANIELS, H. E., 9, 18, 355
DARROCH, J. N., 289, 299, 305, 355
Data matrix, 95, 119
examined by biplot, 150–160
DAVIS, J. C., 33, 35, 349
DAY, N. E., 228, 242, 355
DEARING, B. D., 350
DELANEY, M. J., 227, 242, 355
Delaunay triangulation, 11, 12, 24, 26, 78–79
DELFINER, P., 24, 35, 355
DELHOMME, J. P., 24, 35, 355
Demography, applications in, 247–248, 259, 289–306
DEMPSTER, A. P., 153, 173, 349
Dendogram, 111, 112, 113, 115
Dendral components, 226–227
Density estimation, 37–53, 64–66
annular densities, 237, 273
bivariate, 46–51
cascade densities, smoothing parameters, 237
choice of, 41–43
computation, 43–51
Epanechnikov's kernel, 65
Fourier transform estimate, 41, 43–45
kernel estimate, 37, 43–51, 64–66, 223, 235
kernel function, 37
nearest-neighbour estimate, 46, 194, 233, 234
non-parametric estimate, 37
normal kernel, 43–51
smoothing parameter, 37
univariate, 43–45
window width, 37, 47–49
DEVLIN, S. J., 9, 355

Diabetes data, 210–211
DIACONIS, P., 210, 213, 355
DICKENSON, G. C., 349
DIGBY, P. G. N., 83–118
DIGGLE, P. J., 4, 15, 19, 40, 51, 55–73, 55, 57, 62, 68, 69, 72, 354, 355, 356, 362
Dimensionality of data, 194
scales of 194–195
Directed arc, 290
Directed graph, multivariate, 289–306
adjacency matrix, 290, 292
dyad, 291, 292
multivariate graphical display, 304–305
multivariate log-linear models, 295–301
multivariate model fitting, 298, 305
stochastic model for multivariate, 291, 292
univariate, 290
Discriminant analysis, 8, 40, 120, 121, 221, 227, 343–344, 347
Displaying goodness-of-fit, 88–90
Dissimilarity matrix, 95, 96
Distance matrix, 95, 96, 106–111, 328
DIXON, W. J., 193
Dodecahedral(dodeca-) views of data, 205, 208, 209
Dual scaling, see Scaling
DUDA, R. O., 349
DUNN, D. M., 356
DURAN, B. S., 349
Dyad, 291, 292
Dyadic link, 291–292, 295
Dyadic structure, 291–292, 295
DYER, D. D., 8, 18, 356

ECKART, C., 91, 117, 356
Ecological applications, 57, 122–131, 132–136
EDDY, W. F., 4, 5, 13, 18, 356
Education, applications in, 347
EDWARDS, R., 78, 80, 360
EFRON, B., 12, 18, 40, 52, 356
EHRENBERG, A. S. C., 349
Elliptical peeling, 9, 13
EMERY, J. L., 38, 52, 356
ENSLEIN, K., 350
Enzyme activity, 153–155
EPANECHNIKOV, V. A., 43, 52, 64, 65, 72, 356

EVANS, D. A., 4, 15, 19, 362
EVERITT, B. S., 111, 117, 279–287, 282, 350, 356
Exploratory analysis of data, 38

Faces, *see* Pictorial display of data
Factor analysis, 228
FARRELL, E. S., 256, 275, 356
Fast Fourier transform, 44
FÉNELON, J.-P., 131, 146, 360
FIENBERG, S. E., 268, 275, 289–306, 292, 295, 298, 305, 349, 356
Finite element methods of interpolation, 23–42
FINKEL, R. A., 234, 243, 357
FISHER, R. A., 14, 18, 202, 213, 227, 356
FISHERKELLER, M. A., 272, 275, 363
Food consumption, 150–154
Fossils, 161–163
Fourier transform, method for density estimation, *see* Density estimation
FRIEDMAN, H. P., 256, 275, 356
FRIEDMAN, J. H., 210, 213, 220–226, 234, 239, 243, 272, 273, 275, 355, 357, 363
Front (view) variables, *see* Pictorial display of data
FRYER, M. J., 37, 43, 52, 357
FUKUNAGA, K., 350

GABRIEL, K. R., 90, 91, 92, 93, 117, 147–173, 150, 155, 156, 158, 159, 161, 163, 173, 354, 355, 357
GALASKIEWICZ, J., 289, 292, 293, 300, 301, 305, 357
Game reserves, 122–136
GASKINS, R. A., 40, 52, 357
GENSTAT, 284, 287
GENTLEMAN, J. F., 356
GENTLEMAN, W. M., 44, 52, 357
Geography, applications in, 56, 67, 93–95, 100, 103–106, 150–154
GERRARD, D. J., 65, 66, 72, 357
GESSAMAN, M. P., 10, 18, 361
GHENT, A. W., 56, 72, 357
GILLARD, P., 83, 118, 364
GLEAVES, J. T., 69, 72, 354, 356
GLIM, 296, 298, 300
Glyphs, *see* Pictorial display of data
GNANADESIKAN, R., 9, 18, 85, 117, 197, 198, 213, 227, 228, 243, 274, 275, 350, 353, 355, 357, 364

GOLD, E. M., 100, 117, 357
GOLDMAN, J., 199, 213, 357
GOLDSTEIN, H., 307–319
GOLDWYN, R. M., 256, 275, 356
GOOD, I. J., 40, 52, 337, 348, 357
GORSUCH, R. L., 350
GOWER, J. C., 5, 18, 83–118, 87, 89, 97, 104, 105, 110, 111, 117, 279–287, 283, 355, 358
GRAHAM, I., 321–333, 323, 358
Graphical methods,
  Andrews' plot, 273
  archival graphics, 190
  balloon density, 193–194, 200, 233–237
  cap sizes, 215–216
  curvature reduction, 197
  data-driven view selection, 215–243
  dodecahedral (dodeca-) view, 205, 208, 209
  for data in 3 or more dimentions, 187–275
  for model validation, 175–185
  for multivariate data, 83–118, 175–185, 187–275
  for multivariate directed graphs, 304–305
  for spatial data, 55–73
  gimbling, 272
  gyring, 272
  impact graphics, 190, 191, 192
  isoflats, 201
  isolines, 201, 202
  isoplanes, 201
  macrokinematic display, 272
  microkinematic display, 272
  minimal rising forest, 274
  minimal rising tree, 273
  multiwindow display, 231–232, 262
  ouija plot, 273
  prechosen sequences of views, 189–213
  radius (and angle) plots, 198
  rootogram, 199, 207
  smoothing, 245, 246–250
  squint angle, 215
  summarization, 245–246
  supplemented views, 253–274
  three-way brush of isolines, 202
  transformation of variables, 193, 196, 197, 217–218
  wabing, 272–273

GRATTON, R. J., 65, 72, 358
GREEN, P. J., 3–19, 4, 11, 18, 31, 358
GREENACRE, M. J., 93, 100, 117, 119–146, 131, 145, 350, 358
GRINE, F. E., 161, 162, 163, 173, 354
GROSS, A., 251
GUTTMAN, L., 120, 146, 358

HABBEMA, J. D. F., 40, 43, 52, 343, 346, 347, 348, 353, 358, 359
HABER, M., 150, 173, 358
HABERMAN, S., 295, 298, 305, 359
Hallstatt cemetery, 321, 322, 327
HAMPEL, F. R., 349
HARMAN, H. H., 350
HARSHMAN, R., 103, 104, 117, 358
HART, P. E., 349
HARTIGAN, J. A., 5, 18, 85, 86, 97, 103, 105, 115, 117, 118, 207, 213, 257, 275, 350, 356, 359, 360
HARTWIG, F., 350
HAYS, W. L., 354
HEALY, M. J. R., 227, 242, 353, 355, 359
HEISER, W., 107, 118, 359
HENRY, N. W., 350
HERMANS, J., 40, 43, 52, 346, 348, 358, 359
HILF, R., 154
HILL, M. O., 120, 130, 146, 359
Hill climbing methods, 219, 265
  projection pursuit algorithm, 219, 220, 223–226, 240
HINES, R. J. O., 69
HINES, W. G. S., 69
HIRSCHFELD, H. O., 120, 146, 359
HODDER, I., 323, 333, 359
HODSON, F. R., 321, 328, 333, 350, 358, 359
HOLLAND, P. W., 289, 295, 305, 306, 349, 359
HONG, S. J., 4, 18, 361
HOPE, A. C. A., 58, 72, 359
HORST, P., 350
HOTELLING, H., 122, 146, 359
HOUSEHOLDER, A. S., 149, 173, 359
HUBER, P. J., 349
HUNTER, J. E., 228, 359
HUNTER, T. S., 349
HUNTER, W. G., 349
HUTCHINGS, M. J., 60, 61, 73, 359

Imaginary observations, 337
Index distribution, peeled data, 15
Index of condensation, 220
Individual scaling, see Scaling
Interpolation, 5, 21–35, 46–47
  desirable properties of an interpolant, 22–23
  finite element methods, 23–24
  interpolant, 21, 22
  kriging, 24
  local coordinates property, 28
  natural neighbour interpolation, 25–35
  neighbour, 25, 26
  stiff lamma methods, 24–25
  Thiessen polyhedron, 25
  tile, 25, 26, 27
  Voronoi polyhedron, 25
  window, 21
Iron-age cemetery data, 321–323
Isoflats, 201
Isolines, 201
  three-way brush of, 202
Isoplanes, 201
Iterative scaling, generalized, 289

JARDINE, N., 350
JEFFREYS, H., 335, 336, 337, 348, 359
JENNER, W. E., 212, 213, 359
JOHNSON, E. S., 160, 173, 360
JOHNSON, M. M., 360
JÖRESKOG, K. G., 350

KAY, J. W., 343, 347, 353
KENDALL, D. G., 37, 38, 39, 40, 51, 52, 64, 72, 75–80, 77, 79, 80, 350, 354, 358, 359
KENDALL, M. G., 8, 10, 14, 18, 111, 118, 359
KENDALL, W. S., 40, 52, 77, 80, 359
KENT, J. T., 350
Kernel estimate, see Density estimate
KESTER, N., 166, 173, 360
KETTENRING, J. R., 9, 18, 85, 117, 197, 203, 212, 213, 227, 243, 274, 275, 355, 357
KLEINER, B., 85, 118, 251, 257, 275, 355, 360
Kleiner–Hartigan trees, see Pictorial display of data
KLETT, C. J., 350
Kolmogorov–Smirnov statistic, 58, 59, 60, 70

KRIGE, D., 24
Kriging, 24
KRUSKAL, J. B., 101, 118, 220, 243, 274,
  275, 329, 333, 350, 354, 360
KRUSKAL, W. H., 350, 354
KUDO, A., 9, 18, 360

LANDWEHR, J. M., 274, 275, 356, 357
LAWLEY, D. N., 350
LAWSON, C. L., 24, 36, 360
LAZARSFELD, P. F., 350
LEBART, L., 122, 126, 131, 146, 360
de LEEUW, J., 107, 118, 359, 363
LEINHARDT, S., 289, 295, 305, 306, 359
LEWIN, W. S., 279, 287, 354
LEWIS, T., 349
LINDLEY, D. V., 335, 347, 348, 360
LIPTON, S., 227, 242, 353
Location estimate, bivariate data, 15–17
LOFTSGAARDEN, D. O., 46, 52, 67, 72,
  235, 243, 360
Log-linear models,
  exchange effect, 296, 302
  for multivariate directed graphs,
    295–301
  model fitting, 298–305
  multiplexity effect, 296, 301, 302
  mutuality effect, 296, 301, 302
LOHRDING, R. K., 360
Longitudinal data, 307–319

McCULLAGH, M. J., 33, 35, 349
McGILL, R., 203, 212
McNEIL, D. R., 150, 173, 350, 360
MACWILLIAMS, F. J., 212, 213, 360
MALLOWS, C. L., 175, 185, 360
MANDEL, J., 161, 173, 360
MARDIA, K. V., 39, 52, 78, 80, 350, 360
MARLOW, S., 47, 52, 360
MARRIOTT, F. H. C., 58, 73, 350, 360
MARSDEN, P. V., 289, 292, 293, 300, 301,
  305, 357
MARUBINI, E., 319, 363
MATHERON., 9, 24, 36, 360
MAXWELL, A. E., 347, 348, 350
Means, hypotheses involving, 338–341
Measures of fit for models, display of,
  176–185
Median, bivariate, 5, 7
Medical applications, 153–155,
  178–180, 182–184, 210–211,
  279–287, 307–319, 345–347

MEISEL, W., 46, 52, 354
MELTESEN G. T., 167, 173, 354
Metal surfaces, density estimates, 40,
  49–50
Meteorology, applications in, 140–144,
  155–157, 167–171, 258
Metric scaling, see Scaling
MEYER, M. M., 289–306
Middle variables, see Pictorial display of
  data
MIELKE, P. W., 160, 173, 360
MILES, R. E., 78
MILLER, M., 256, 356
Minimum covering circle, 8
Minimum covering ellipsoid, 9, 13
Model validation or choice
  Akaike Information Criterion, 335
  Bayesian methods, 335–348
  graphical display for, 175–185
  Schwarz criterion, 335
  use of biplot, 160–171
MONKHOUSE, F. J., 254, 275, 361
MONRO, D. M., 44, 52, 361
Monte Carlo method, 324, 327
Monte Carlo test, 7, 40
  for spatial process, 57–58, 60
  simulation envelopes, 57–59
MORINEAU, A., 122, 126, 131, 146, 360
MOSTELLER, F., 196, 213, 227, 243, 247,
  275, 350
Motion, simulation of, 175, 184–185
Multidimensional scaling, see Scaling
Multidimensional unfolding, see
  Unfolding
Multimodality, 38, 42
Multivariate directed graphs, 289–306
  graphical display, 304–305
  log-linear models, 295–301
  model fitting, 298–305

NATH, G. B., 8, 18, 361
NATHANSON, J. A., 96, 101, 118, 361
Natural neighbour interpolation, 25–35
  computation, 31–32
  local coordinates property, 28
Nearest-neighbour density estimates, 46,
  194, 234
Neighbouring data sites, 25, 26
NELDER, J. A., 284, 287, 296, 306, 361
Nepalese children, convex hull peels, 4
NERLOVE, S. B., 351
NEWMAN, W. M., 350

NICHOLLS, P., 356
NISHISATO, S., 120, 146, 350, 361
Non-metric scaling, *see* Scaling
Normal distribution, multivariate, 336–344
  transformation to, 344–347
NUMATA, M., 56, 72, 361
Numerosity of data, 65, 194, 229, 268
  scales of, 194, 229

ODELL, P. L., 349
O'MUIRCHEARTAIGH, C. A., 350
Optimal scaling, *see* Scaling
ORD, J. K., 356
Ordering bivariate data, 3
  partial ordering, 3
  reduced ordering, 9
Order statistics, 3, 4–7, 11, 250
  depth of, 250
Ordination, 116
ORTON, C., 323, 333, 359
Outlier, 4, 5, 8, 15, 85, 111, 227, 238, 307, 309, 314, 316–319, 344
OVERALL, J. E., 350

Particle physics data, 208–210, 223–226, 229–232, 255–256, 263, 265–267, 269–271
PARZEN, E., 42, 43, 52, 65, 73, 361
Pattern analysis, 83
Pattern recognition, 8, 55
PAYNE, C., 350
PEARSON, K., 122, 361
PEEBLES, P. J. E., 325, 333, 361, 364
Peeling bivariate data, 3–19
  adjacency peeling, 11, 12
  convex hull peeling, 3–8, 11–14
  elliptical peeling, 9, 13
  index distribution, 15
  Tukey peeling, 10, 12, 13
PERICCHI, L. R., 347, 348, 361
Perspective view, 33, 46, 47
PHILLIPS, R. L., 361
Phosphenes, cortical electrical, 279–287
  map of, 279–280
Physics, applications in, 163–166, 208–210, 223–226, 229–232, 255–256, 263, 265–267, 269–271
Pictorial display of data, 84–85, 87, 89, 187–275
  agglomeration of data, 95, 215, 228–237, 253, 268–269

Anderson's glyphs, 256–257, 268–269
arrowhead, 262–263
back variables, 192, 195, 245
balloonogram, 235–236, 262
blunting of data, 195, 241–242
castles, 85, 257
cellulation, 230–231, 262–263, 268–269, 271
centring of data, 196
characters, 190, 246, 253–257
character scale, 246–247, 254–257
circle-based glyphs, 256–257
clottedness of data, 219, 220
colour, use of, 191, 193, 255, 262, 268–270
contours, use of, 191, 247, 248, 262, 264–267, 269–271
contrast, use of, 193
delineation, 250–253
dodecahedral (dodeca-) view, 205, 208 209
draughtsman's view, 202, 203
faces (Chernoff), 84, 190, 257, 258
front (view) variables, 192, 195, 201, 229
glyphs, 84, 190, 246, 253, 256, 257, 268–269
Kleiner–Hartigan trees, 257, 259–260
kinematic, 192
k-number fans, 260–261, 267
macrokinematic, 272
metroglyph, 256
microkinematic, 272
middle variables, 192
multiwindow display, 231–232, 262
perspective view, 202, 203
polar trace, 251
polygons, 256, 257
rootagon, 232
rootogram, 199, 207
scaling of data, 196
scatter diagram (two-view), 189, 229
shading, use of, 111–115, 191, 193, 255, 262, 263–266, 268–269
shape, use of, 193
sharpening of data, 195, 215, 237–242
ships, 85
size, use of, 193
smoothing, 245, 246–250
sphering of data, 196, 197, 226, 227
stars, 84, 256, 257, 268–269
static, 193

Pictorial display of data (*cont.*)
  summarization, 245–246
  supplemented views, 253–274
  three-way brush of isolines, 202
  trace, 250–253
  trees (Kleiner–Hartigan), 85, 257,
      268–269
  triples, 249
  wedge, 262–263
  weathervanes, 256–257
  whiskers, 254–257, 260–261
Poison data, 182–184
Poisson process
  cluster, 60, 62, 63
  complete spatial randomness, 55,
      57–60, 64–66
  Cox process, 63
  double stochastic, 63
  planar, 55
POWELL, M. J. D., 47, 52, 360
PREPARATA, F. P., 4, 18, 361
Presentation of data, 40–41, 65–67
PRESS, S. J., 339, 348, 361
PRIM-9, 272
Principal components, 46, 84, 85–91, 94,
      122, 124, 218, 223, 226, 228
  singular value decomposition, 86, 91
Principal coordinate analysis, 95–99,
      116, 226
Princos, 226
Probability density estimation, *see*
      Density estimation
Probability plot, 59, 60, 69
Probability surface, 63–68
Procrustes analysis, 108–111
  weighed generalized, 283–287
Profile, 123
  average row, 124
  row, 123
Projection index, 220
Projection pursuit algorithm, 219, 220,
      223–226, 240
Psychology, applications in, 136–139
Psychotherapy, 136
PURCELL, E., 46, 52, 354
PURI, M. L., 78, 80, 360

QUESENBERRY, C. D., 10, 46, 52, 73, 235,
      243, 360, 361

Radiation data, 163–166
Radius (and angle) plots, 198, 199
Rainmaking experiments, 140, 155–157

RALSTON, A., 350
RAMAN, S., 233, 243, 274, 275, 363
RAMSAUER, 321, 322, 327
RATCLIFF, D., 289, 299, 305, 355
RAYNAUD, H., 12, 361
Reading ability, 347
Reciprocal averaging, 119, 120, 130
REEVE, E. C. R., 157, 173, 361
REGISTER, D. T., 355
RENYI, A., 12, 19, 361
RESELE, L. F., 319, 363
Residuals, 87–89, 171–173, 176,
      180–182, 218
  plot of, 180–182
Residual sum of squares, in model fitting,
      176–177, 180–182
REYMENT, R. A., 349
RIPLEY, B. D., 55, 56, 57, 58, 59, 60, 69,
      72, 73, 354, 361
Robust estimation, 3, 14, 15
  influence curve, 14
  location estimates, 15–17
ROGERS, A., 323, 333, 361
ROGERS, W. H., 349
ROMNEY, A. K., 351
Rootagon, 232
Rootogram, 199, 207
ROSENBLATT, M., 37, 52, 361, 362
ROSS, G. J. S., 87, 117, 118, 358, 362
RUSHTON, D. N., 282, 287, 356, 362

SAGER, T. W., 5, 19, 362
SAMMON, J. R. Jr., 223, 243, 362
SANDE, G., 44, 52, 357
Scaling
  classical, 99
  dual, 119, 120
  generalized Procrustes analysis,
      108–111, 283–287
  individual, 103, 107–109
  metric, 95–99
  multidimensional, 101, 274, 329, 333
  non-metric, 99, 100, 101, 329,
      332–333
  optimal, 120
Scaling of data, 196
Scatter diagrams, *see* Pictorial display of
      data
SCHMIDT, C. F., 352
SCHMIDT, S. E., 352
SCHNEIDER, B., 37, 53, 364
SCHONEMANN, P. H., 100, 118, 362
SCHWARZ, G., 335, 348, 362

Schwarz criterion, for comparing models, 335, 336
SEAL, H. L., 157, 173, 362
Seamed quadratic element, 46
SEHEULT, A. H., 4, 15, 19, 362
Shading, 111–115, 191, 193, 255, 262, 263–266, 268–269
Shape, statistics of, 75–80
Shape-density, 76
Shape-function, 77
Shape-manifold, 75
Shape-measure, 75
Sharpening of data, 195, 215, 237–242
  by displacement, 239–241
  by excision, 238–239
  by Russian roulette, 241–242
  local sharpening, 239
SHEPARD, R. N., 274, 275, 329, 333, 351, 362
Ships, *see* Pictorial display of data
SIBSON, R., 11, 18, 21–35, 28, 31, 33, 35, 36, 47, 51, 52, 109, 118, 350, 358, 362
SIEGEL, A. F., 241
SIGEL, J. H., 256, 275, 356
Signature, of bivariate sample, 15, 16
SILVERMAN, B. W., 4, 13, 18, 19, 37–53, 39, 41, 43, 44, 45, 52, 64, 358, 362
Simcos, 227
Similarity matrix, 95, 96, 97, 111–116, 328, 332–333
  hierarchical classification, 111–116
Simplified components of data, 227
Simultaneous linear regression, 119, 120
SIOTANI, M., 9, 19, 362
SLOANE, N. J. A., 212, 213, 360
SMALL, C. G., 76, 80, 362
SMITH, A. F. M., 335–348, 335, 336, 348, 362
Smoothing of data, 245, 246–250
  by change of value, 246, 247–250
  by excision, 246
  by suppression, 246–247
  head-banging, 247
  high screen, 250
  low screen, 250
  use of triples, 249
SNEATH, P. H. A., 111, 118, 351, 362
Snowfall, density estimation, 42
Social networks, application to, 289–306
Sociology, applications in, 136–139, 289–306
SOKAL, R. R., 351

SOMMERVILLE, D. M. Y., 205, 207, 213, 362
Spanning tree, 89, 273
  minimum, 89, 90, 273
Sparse data, 68–73
SPÄTH, H., 351
Spatial data, 55–73
  analysis of, 321–333
  association in, 323–324
  sparse, 68–73
  T-square samples of, 69–71
Spatial point processes, 55–73
  Cox process, 63
  doubly stochastic Poisson process, 63
  model fitting, 60–63
  nearest-neighbour analysis, 57–58
  Poisson cluster process, 60, 62, 63
  probability surfaces, 63–68
  spectral analysis, 324–327
  test of complete spatial randomness, 55, 57–60, 69
Spatial randomness, 55, 57–60, 323–324
Spectral analysis, 321, 324–327
Spectrum, 325
  cross-, 326
  power, 325, 329–331
Spherical blackboard, 76, 78–79
Sphering of data, 196, 197, 226, 227
SPIEGELHALTER, D. J., 335–348, 335, 336, 348, 362
Splines, 23, 24, 31, 37, 38
SPRINGALL, A., 363
Squint angle, 215
Stars, *see* Pictorial display of data
Statistically equivalent blocks, 10
Steepest descent, method of, 281–282
STEFANOV, I., 37, 38, 39, 51, 64, 72, 354
STEPHENS, M. A., 39, 53, 363
Stiff lamina methods of interpolation, 24–25
STONE, M., 335, 348, 363
STRAUSS, D. J., 56, 58, 59, 60, 73, 363
SULANKE, R., 12, 19, 361
Summarization of data, 245–246
  delineations, 250–253
  polar trace, 251
  traces, 250–253

TABARD, N., 122, 126, 131, 146, 360
TAKAISHI, M., 319, 363
TAKANE, Y., 107, 118, 363
TANNER, J. M., 309, 310–313, 317, 319, 363

TANUR, J. M., 350, 354
TARTER, M., 233, 243, 274, 275, 362
363
TAŬTU, P., 350, 358
Tessellation, 24, 25, 26, 31
Dirichlet, 24, 25, 31
Thiessen polyhedron, 25
THISSEN, D., 363
THOMSON, G. D., 33, 36, 47, 51, 52, 362
Three- (or higher-) dimensional data,
display, 175–185, 187–275
Three-way data table, 106–111
THURSTONE, L. L., 228, 243, 363
Tile, 25, 26, 27
subtile, 26, 27
TITTERINGTON, D. M., 13, 14, 19, 362, 363
TORGERSON, W. S., 351
TOUSSAINT, G. T., 8, 19, 363
Tree growth, as spatial process, 55–68
Trees, *see* Pictorial display of data
Trimming,
bivariate, 3
bivariate rectangular, 8
TRYON, R. C., 351
TSIANCO, M. C., 167, 171, 173, 363
T-square sampling, spatial data, 69–71
TUKEY, J. W., 10, 19, 44, 52, 85, 150, 173,
187, 189–275, 196, 213, 220–226,
227, 236, 239, 243, 247, 251, 254,
272, 273, 274, 275, 349, 350, 351,
355, 357, 360, 363
TUKEY, P. A., 85, 89, 187, 189–275, 213,
239, 243, 273, 274, 275, 357, 363
Tukey peeling, 10, 12, 13
Turtles, probability density estimation,
39
Two-view, *see* Pictorial display of data
Two-way data table, or data-matrix,
84–95, 101–103

Unfolding, multi-dimensional, 94,
99–100, 101, 103
metric, 99
non-metric, 100, 101, 103

Vague prior information, 337
Voronoi polyhedron, 25
VRBA, E., 133

WABHA, G., 24, 25, 36, 363
WAINER, H., 363
WANG, P. C. C., 351
WARNER, J. L., 198, 213, 353
WASSERMAN, S. S., 289–306, 292, 295,
305, 306, 356
Weather modification, 140
WEBSTER, A., 325, 333, 363
WEDDERBURN, R. W., 296, 306, 361
WEGMAN, E. J., 37, 53, 364
WERTZ, W., 37, 53, 364
WHALLON, R., 323, 333, 364
WHITEHOUSE, R. H., 319, 363
WHITEMAN, D. E., 360
WILF, H. S., 350
WILK, M. B., 364
WILKINSON, H. R., 254, 361
WILLIAMS, W. T., 83, 118, 364
WISH, M., 101, 118, 274, 275, 350
WOLD, S., 24, 36, 363
WOOD, F. S., 274, 275, 349
WOODROOFE, M., 43, 53, 364

YOUNG, F. R., 107, 118, 363
YOUNG, F. W., 103, 118, 364
YOUNG, G., 91, 117, 149, 173, 356, 359
YU, J. T., 325, 333, 364

ZAMIR, S., 150, 163, 173, 357